Navies of the West

NAVIES OF THE WEST

BERNARD IRELAND

HIPPOCRENE BOOKS
New York

First published 1984

Published in the United States by
HIPPOCRENE BOOKS, Inc.,
171 Madison Avenue,
New York, N.Y. 10016

ISBN 0-88254-977-4

Printed in Great Britain

Contents

Preface

The coverage of this book extends to the major fleets of Europe and North America, the greater part of which are members of NATO. Those smaller fleets that are not composed of foreign-built tonnage tend naturally to build ships that reflect the constraints of geography and the environment in which they may be called to fight; this is particularly true of Baltic and Mediterranean navies. In ships produced by the traditional 'blue-water' fleets, these traits are less pronounced, being incorporated in hulls large enough to serve world-wide for extended periods.

It is the designing of some of these that might be open to question for, in order to be able to deal with threats perceived and projected over a 30-year lifespan, they have adopted a largely genjeral-purpose approach. In times of peace, they may appear effective and, indeed, beget generations of derivatives, successive improvements of the original. The fact that the concept of the original was in any way faulty is unlikely to be discovered until tested in a shooting war.

Conversely, specialist ships may appear to be the answer until hard economics start to dictate the overall number of hulls that can be produced on a specific budget. Exigencies of war, in addition, are no respecters of labels and an AA-orientated ship may well find herself doing battle with submarines or an AS frigate with a cruiser. Each may be found wanting.

While one must never fall into the trap of making over-hasty or over-fundamental judgements on the lessons of a limited war, it can certainly be said with conviction that the Falklands operations underlined the fact that the warship is as vulnerable as ever to aerial attack, be it by manned aircraft or missile. Further, however good a defensive system, it can be pierced by a well-coordinated saturation attack; once pierced, it will permit the ship to be hit and the question becomes one of survival.

As it can never be assumed that any warship will be operating as an element of an integrated force which, in toto, can deploy the ideal 'layered' defence beloved of planners, it follows that each should be provided with at least the minimum means of dealing alone with an aerial threat. Airborne early warning, long range aerial interception and area-defence SAM systems are luxuries applying to task groups rather than the private ship, which must think in terms of ESM and ECM/decoy systems to detect and seduce a threat, together with point-defence missiles and CIWS to deal with those threats that remain persistent. This combination must be the irreducible minimum around which any frigate-sized ship is designed. If it were vital in the South Atlantic it would be many times more so in a European

war. Regrettably, there are few Western ships that can boast such a fit.

Once hit, the survivability of a modern thin-skinned ship would not appear too good. Even if her damage control teams are of first-class calibre, it is likely that the hull will suffer catastrophic rupturing or that the ship will be consumed by fire and explosion. The object must be to keep ordnance out in the first place — the old adage that prevention is better than cure was never more demonstrably true.

Although in a period of decline in terms of total tonnage, the British merchant marine has shown that today's high-technology ships are capable of valuable auxiliary roles. An ocean container or RoRo ship will make a V/STOL or helicopter carrier, LASH and Seabee ships are ready-made LPD substitutes while today's fast ferries can act as troop transports, LSLs or even minelayers, and trawlers make excellent minesweepers. Subsidies should be freely available to owners willing to build-in features for use in an emergency — like strengthening, extra power, better sub-division, generously-dimensioned cargo access, etc.

Extrapolating from this point, could we imagine the multi-function frigate of the future built to mercantile class? A warship does not have to look like a warship and designs such as the successful MEKO work toward the designer's dream of having a basic hull capable of being rapidly outfitted with weapons and sensors to suit a ship's mission at that time. One could visualise a merchantman such as a smallish container ship, easily powered for, say, 26kts. Designed from the outset for a separate auxiliary role, she could slot-in vertical-launch missile systems for SSMs and ASROC-type rounds into the apertures of split hatchways. Space would abound for reloads, a pair of medium helicopters and containerised point-defence weapons. Electronics and decoy systems would also be 'bolt-on'. She would thus have considerable AS capacity, the ability to target surface vessels over the horizon and as much self-defence capability as any warship. All wartime equipment would normally be stowed, ready for use, at its manufacturers. With defence budgets getting even slimmer, such ships would be highly cost-effective for lower-risk duties, releasing first-line warships for other tasks and, being capable of servicing by commercial yards, would take the load off the Royal dockyards.

With regard to the book, my thanks are due, as ever, to the many people who have helped me along the way and, particularly, my wife, whose help is as unstinting as it is invaluable.

Bernard Ireland
Fareham 1983

Abbreviations and Glossary

AA	Anti-aircraft
AAW	Anti-aircraft warfare
AD	Aircraft Direction
AEW	Airborne Early Warning
AS	Anti-submarine
ASM	Air-to-surface missile
ASROC	Anti-submarine rocket
ASW	Anti-submarine warfare
BBC	Brown-Boveri Co
bhp	Brake horse power, ie Output of a diesel engine to a shaft
CIWS	Close-in-weapon system
CODOG	Combined diesel or gas (turbine)
COGOG	Combined gas or gas (turbine)
COSAG	Combined steam (turbine) and gas (turbine)
CP	Controllable pitch
DASH	Drone anti-submarine helicopter
DF	Direction-finding
Displacement	(Standard) All-up displacement less fuel and feed water
Displacement	(full load) All-up displacement
DP	Dual-purpose
ECM	Electronic countermeasures
ECCM	Electronic counter-countermeasures
EEZ	Exclusive economic zone
ER	Extended range (as in Standard ER)
ESM	Electronic support measures
FAC	Fast Attack Craft
FFO	Furnace fuel oil
FRAM	Fleet Rehabilitation and Modernisation
FY	Fiscal year
GP	General-purpose
GRP	Glass-reinforced plastic, ie fibreglass
GT	Gas turbine
HSA	Hollandse Signaalapparaten BV
HT	High tensile
IFF	identification Friend or Foe
IKL	Ingeneurkontor Lübeck
kg	Kilogramme (about 2.2 pounds)
km	Kilometre (about $\frac{5}{8}$ of a land mile)
Kt	One seamile (about 1.15 land miles) per hour

KW	Kilowatt (about $1\frac{1}{3}$ horsepower)
LAMPS	Light Airborne Multi-purpose System
LCA	Landing Craft, Assault
LCM	Landing Craft, Mechanised
LCVP	Landing Craft, Vehicle & Personnel
Length	Length of hull, overall
MCMV	Mine Countermeasures Vessel
MEKO	Mehrzwecks Kombination, ie multi-purpose
MIRV	Mobile, independently-targeted re-entry vehicles
Mk	Mark, eg Mk 32
MR	Medium Range (as in Standard MR)
MW	Megawatt, ie 1,000 kilowatts
NATO	North Atlantic Treaty Organisation
nm	Nautical mile
NTDS	Naval tactical data system
OPV	Offshore Patrol Vessel
PDMS	Point-defence Missile System
PUFFS	Passive Underwater Fire control Feasibility System
RFA	Royal Fleet Auxiliary
S-boat	Schnellboot (known as E-Boat in UK)
SALT	Strategic arms limitation talks
SAM	Surface-to-air missile
SES	Surface-effect ship (cf hovercraft)
shp	Shaft horsepower, ie power actually transmitted to propeller
SLBM	Submarine-launched Ballistic Missile
Speed	Usually service speed rather than maximum
SSM	Surface-to-surface missile
SUBROC	Submarine Rocket
TACAN	Tactical Air Naviation
TACTASS	Tactical towed-array sonar system
VDS	Variable-depth sonar
VERTREP	Vertical replenishment, ie by helicopter
VLS	Vertical-launch system
V-STOL	Vertical/Short Take-off-and Land
WW1	World War 1
WW2	World War 2

Wielingen Frigate

Belgium

	Builders	LD	L	C
F910 *Wielingen*	BT	74	76	78
F911 *Westdiep*	CH	74	75	78
F912 *Wandelaar*	BT	75	77	78
F913 *Westhinder*	CH	75	77	78

Displacement: 1,850 tons standard; 2,350 tons full load
Dimensions: 106.5m × 12.3m × 5.7m
Armament:
Four Exocet SSM launchers
One octuple Sea Sparrow SAM launcher
One 100mm DP gun
One CIWS (planned)
One six-barrelled AS rocket projector
Two torpedo launchers
Machinery:
One gas turbine, 28,000hp
Two cruising diesels, 6,000bhp
CODOG Twin shafts
Speed: 29/20kts

This individual quartette represents the first major warships both designed and built in Belgium. They are derived from an abandoned 1960s design exercise for ships to replace obsolescent war-built tonnage: these would have been mainly AS in bias and helicopter-equipped in spite of being of less than 2,000 tons displacement. A reappraisal, however, went for a more general-purpose approach, appropriate for action — and survival — in the English Channel and southern North Sea, though their cruising range of 4,500 miles would enable them to operate, without support, at some considerable distance out into the European Western Approaches.

They are of a size that can manage nearly 30kts on the output of a single Olympus gasturbine. This shares a common clutch and gearbox assembly with two cruising diesels in an adjacent compartment. The rather Dutch-looking hull runs flush almost as far as the transom, with a characteristic rise in level rear of the Sea Sparrow launcher aft. Today's 'fire-and-forget' SSMs give a frigate a formidable 'instant' firepower, though the four bulky MM38 Exocets aft obviously take more space than would a quadruple Harpoon launcher. The 100mm DP gun and six-barrelled AS rocket launcher forward are also both of French manufacture, with French L5 21in/533mm torpedoes being released from launchers rather than tubes for AS as well as anti-ship purposes. Aircraft would pose a threat in the Channel and the eight-cell Sea Sparrow will be eventually supplemented by shorter ranged CIWS selected by the Netherlands navy. Dutch influence is apparent also in the HSA radars and directors, together with their standard SEWACO automated weapons command and control system.

Westhinder, 'Wielingen' class; note position of Exocet.
Mike Lennon

Tripartite Minehunter

Belgium

For data, see under Netherlands. Ten units are planned from a building consortium called 'Polyship', starting about end-1983. Five futher vessels are projected.

MSO Minehunter

Belgium

	LD	L	C	T
M902 *J. E. van Haverbeke* (ex-MSO522)	59	59	60	60
M903 *A. F. Dufour* (ex-*Lagen* M950, ex-MSO498)	54	54	55	66
M904 *De Brouwer* (ex-*Nansen* M951, ex-MSO499)	54	54	55	66
M906 *Breydel* (ex-MSO504)	54	55	56	56
M907 *Artevelde* (ex-MSO503)	53	54	55	55
M908 *G. Truffant* (ex-MSO515)	55	55	56	56
M909 *F. Bovesse* (ex-MSO516)	54	56	56	57

Displacement: 670 tons standard, 750 tons full load
Dimensions: 52.6m × 10.7m × 4.3m
Armament: One 40mm gun when required
Machinery:
Two diesels 1,600bhp
Twin shafts
Speed: 14kts

These were built as part of the 68-strong programme of Ocean Minesweepers (MSO) put in hand by the United States as a hurried response to a widespread use of mines by the enemy during the Korean War. (The Russian aptitude for mining is well known — it just needs relearning occasionally.) Constructed with wooden hulls and non-magnetic machinery and fittings, they were originally classed as Wooden Minesweepers and carried AM numbers. Four (M906-909) were originally transferred to Belgium, with further units to other NATO fleets; two more M903-904, were trans-ferred later from Norway and the lone M902 (as MSO522) bearing the last number of the programme, was transferred new. It is noticeable that there is a careful balance of Flemish and Walloon names allocated. As constructed the ships could sweep contact, acoustic and magnetic mines but, com-mencing 1968, a modernisation programme was instituted, including the installation of an SQQ-14 mine detection and classification sonar, which can be lowered from a housing in the hull. Together with new sweep gear and communications, they emerged effectively minehunters. By the standards of today's mine technology they are not too manoeuvrable and have pronounced 'signatures'. They are now of advanc-ing years and will be replaced by the new GRP minehunters as these become available.

De Brouwer, *'MSO' class.* Mike Lennon

Nieupoort, *'MSC' class.* Mike Lennon

MSC type   Coastal minesweeper hunter   *Belgium*

M928 *Stavelot*
M930 *Rochefort*
M932 *Nieupoort*   Completed
M933 *Koksijde*   1955-56
M934 *Verviers* (ex-USS MSC259)
M935 *Veurne* (ex-USS MSC260)

For details, see under Greece. Of the six still under
Belgian colours, four are home built and two from US
yards. Only the latter pair have been connected to a
mine-hunting configuration which, interestingly,
includes a change to Voith-Schneider propulsion. This
would seem ideal from the point of view of station-

keeping and 'creeping' in strong coastal and esturial
currents but with a penalty in vulnerability and noise
when compared with, say, directional electrically-driven
thrusters. Of the original 26 of this type the Belgians
have transferred abroad no less than 16, the remainder,
beyond those named above, serving in various non-
first-line guises.

   In addition, 14 inshore-type minesweepers are still
serving in the Belgian Navy; like the MSCs they are also
elderly but, unlike them, their functions cannot be
paralleled by the new deeper-draught MCMVs, so a
new class could be expected.

Godetia/Zinnia   Support ship   *Belgium*

	Builders	Completed
A960 *Godetia*	BT	1966
A961 *Zinnia*	CH	1967

Displacement:
(G) 1,700 tons standard; 2,500 tons full load
(Z) 1,700 tons standard, 2,700 tons full load
Dimensions:
(G) 91.8m×14m×3.5m
(Z) 99.5m×15.2m×3.6m
Armament: Usually two/three 40mm guns

Machinery:
(G) Four diesels 5,400bhp
    Twin shafts 19kts
(Z) Two diesels 5,000bhp
    Single shaft 20kts
Aircraft: One light helicopter with telescopic hangar

Of a size with French and West German support ships this pair of vessels is designed primarily to back up Belgian minesweeping flotillas in command and logistic support. Though little over a year separates their completion dates and they are, in appearance, obviously sisters, they have significant differences. Not the least of these is the fact that the later ship, having a longer

Zinnia. Mike Lennon

hull and single screw, can make a better speed on lower installed power. *Zinnia* is less bulky in the superstructure and operated a helicopter from the outset, her sister acquiring one in a recent modernisation.

Iroquois Destroyer

Canada

	Builders	LD	L	C
280 *Iroquois*	MIS	69	70	72
281 *Huron*	MIS	69	71	72
282 *Athabaskan*	DSL	69	70	72
283 *Algonquin*	DSL	69	71	73

Displacement: c3,400 tons standard, 4,700 tons full load
Dimensions: 129.7m × 15.2m × 4.7m
Armament:
Two quadruple Sea Sparrow SAM launchers
One 127mm/5in gun
Two triple AS torpedo tubes
One triple AS mortar
Machinery:
Two sprint gas turbines, 50,000hp
Two cruise gas turbines, 7,500hp
COGOG Twin shafts
Speed: 29/17kts
Aircraft: Two Sea King helicopters with hangar

Known also as the 'DD280', or 'Tribal' class, these destroyers were the earliest to deploy two large AS helicopters on so small a displacement. Their rather large beam not only allows space for the wide hangar but improves stability. Indeed, the overall impression is one of an approach similar to that of the American 'Spruances', where a comparatively modest weapons

and sensor fit has been put in to a hull larger than necessary to guarantee good seakeeping. The 'Tribals' are dedicated AS ships having, outside their AS equipment, only a 127mm Oto-Melara gun and eight Sea Sparrow defensive SAMs, in two unusual retracting quadruple vertical launchers set into a magazine/deckhouse forward of the bridge, accommodating four rounds per launcher. The two hangars are angled to allow the main air downtake to the gas turbines to pass between and are placed well forward so that the flight pad, too is away from the after end, with its more violent pitching motions. Right aft is a well in the transom, housing a sizeable VDS, which is complemented both by a hull-mounted set and those in the Sea Kings. Forward of the VDS is a covered well containing a Limbo triple-barrelled mortar of the type shed — precipitately — by the Royal Navy and retained in addition to the usual two triple AS torpedo tube banks. Radars and fire control are by HSA and both pairs of gas turbines are Pratt and Whitneys. The pronounced veed funnel casings, besides being rather inelegant, would seem to be unnecessary except perhaps in a following wind.

A study for six replacement 'St Laurents' seems to be resisting the temptation to grow larger still; they are likely to be about 500 tons less than the 'Tribals' and trading one helicopter for SSMs, probably Harpoon, and a longer range SAM system.

Huron, *'Iroquois' class.* Canadian Forces Photo

St Laurent, Restigouche, Mackenzie & Annapolis
Classes Frigate

Canada

		Builders	LD	L	C	Mod			Builders	LD	L	C	Conv
206 *Saguenay*	(A)	HSL	51	53	56	65	258 *Kootenay*	(B)	BDS	52	54	59	73
207 *Skeena*	(A)	BDS	51	52	57	65	259 *Terra Nova*	(B)	VMD	52	55	59	68
229 *Ottawa*	(A)	CVM	51	53	56	64	260 *Columbia*	(C)	BDS	53	56	59	—
230 *Margaree*	(A)	HSL	51	56	57	65	261 *Mackenzie*	(D)	CVM	58	61	62	—
233 *Fraser*	(A)	BDS/YE	51	53	57	66	262 *Saskatchewan*	(D)	VMD/YE	59	61	63	—
234 *Assiniboine*	(A)	MIS	52	54	56	63	263 *Yukon*	(D)	BDS	59	61	63	—
235 *Chaudière*	(C)	HSL	53	57	59	—	264 *Qu'appelle*	(D)	DSR	60	62	63	—
236 *Gatineau*	(B)	DSR	53	57	59	72	265 *Annapolis*	(E)	HSL	60	63	64	—
256 *St Croix*	(C)	MIS	54	57	58	—	266 *Nipigon*	(E)	MIS	61	61	64	—
257 *Restigouche*	(B)	CVM	53	54	58	73							

(A) 'St Laurent' class   (C) 'Restigouche' class
(B) 'Improved Restigouche' class   (D) 'Mackenzie' class   (E) 'Annapolis' class

	(A)	(B)	(C)	(D)	(E)
Displacement:	2,250	2,400	2,370	2,380	2,400 standard
	3,050	2,900	2,880	2,900	3,000 full load
Length (oa):	111.5	113	111.5	111.5	113
Beam:	12.8	12.8	12.8	12.8	12.8
Mean Draught:	4.3	4.4	4.2	4.2	4.4
Armament:	Two 3in guns	Two 3in guns	Four 3in guns	Four 3in guns	Two 3in guns
	Two triple AS TTs	Sea Sparrow SAM	Two triple AS mortars	Two triple AS mortars	Two triple AS TTs
	One triple mortar	ASROC One tiple mortar	AS torpedo launchers	AS torpedo launchers	One triple AS mortar

Machinery:
Two sets steam turbines 30,000shp
Twin shafts
Speed: 28+kts

Aircraft: One Sea King helicopter and hangar in (A) and (E)
Disposal: 205 *St Laurent* 1975

13

Margaree, *'St Laurent' class.* Mike Lennon

Though falling into definite groupings, the 20 'St Laurents' and derivatives follow a close order of progression. Work began in the late 1940s, on the so-called '205 Program' to design a replacement for the war-built frigates with which the RCN had played so valuable a part in the Battle of the Atlantic. This replacement, more suited to Canadian needs, reflected also lessons from the war: higher freeboard forward with a characteristic 'turtle-back' to shed water rapidly, recessed and covered anchor pockets to reduce slamming shocks and wetness, fore-and-aft access below decks and a low bridge block with a minimum of other superstructure. Although highly individual in appearance they showed more than a trace of British design assistance with a passing resemblance to the Type 15 conversions. The steam turbine plant was also of British origin and survived unchanged throughout the whole series. Two twin US-pattern 3in 50s were, surprisingly, in open mountings and the high freeboard aft housed two Limbo triple-barrelled AS mortars in a covered well. These seven 'St Laurents' were rapidly followed by seven 'Restigouche' class units, very similar but with a British type 3in 70 twin gunhouse forward

and the bridge a half-level higher to give visibility over it. The bridge, previously fully enclosed, was given wings to improve 'feel' for weather conditions. Before completion of the 'Restigouche' class, the quartette of 'Mackenzies' was begun, externally virtually identical but with advances in layout that allowed a significant reduction in crew from nearly 250 to 210. Experiments with the *Ottawa* had shown the possibilities of operating a large Sea King helicopter and the final two, the *Annapolis* and *Nipigon*, were completed with a flight-pad and VDS, necessitating the suppression of the after gun mounting and one Limbo. The centreline hangar required also the division of the uptakes in a pair of casings. The arrangement proving satisfactory, the 'St Laurents' were rebuilt to an almost identical configuration. Following this, an alternative improved AS arrangement was tried in the four 'Improved Restigouche' class, which were recast to mount an American ASROC aft, together with a VDS in a transom well but, significantly, retaining one Limbo. The last three of the group were never modernised, due to the arrival of the new 'Tribals', and were placed in low category reserve.

Terra Nova, *'Improved Restigouche' class.*
Canadian Forces

Oberon   Patrol submarine

Canada

	Builders	LD	L	C
72 *Ojibwa* (ex-HMS *Onyx*)	HMC	62	64	65
73 *Onondaga*	HMC	64	65	67
74 *Okanagan*	HMC	65	66	68

For data see UK 'Oberon' class

Although being updated between 1980 and 1986, these boats will need to be retired by the early 1990s. It is to be hoped that the proposed British Type 2400 will materialise to provide a ready-made replacement otherwise, with no US interest in conventional, diesel-electric boats, the French and Germans will be given yet another market.

Protecteur   Replenishment ship

Canada

	Builders	LD	L	C
AOR509 *Protecteur*	SJD	67	68	69
AOR510 *Preserver*	SJD	67	69	70

Displacement: 8,400 tons standard; 24,700 tons full load
Dimensions: 172m×23.2m×9.2m
Armament: Two 3in 50 calibre (1×2)
Machinery:
One set steam turbines, 21,000shp
Single shaft
Speed: 21kts
Aircraft: Three Sea King helicopters, with hangar

The nearest equivalent in the Royal Navy to this pair of ships is the later 'Tide' class but the Canadians' capacity for more dry stores and a considerable quantity of ammunition sees them categorised AOR, whose closest similars are the rather larger American 'Wichitas'. Over 13,000 tons of bunker fuel oil can be carried, together with about 600 tons of diesel fuel for auxiliaries and 400 tons of aviation fuel. (With gas turbines now in use in the Canadian navy, another category will, presumably, be added.) Over 1,000 tons

of dry stores and about 1,250 tons of ammunition can be carried, all of which can be transferred underweigh at sea. Garage space below also adds the useful additional capacity for the carriage of vehicles and equipment, together with spare helicopters for the group accompanied. Three Sea Kings are also assigned to the ships' inventory, used not only for vertical replenishment but also in an AS role, the ships having also a hull-mounted SQS-505 search sonar, similar to those in the frigates.

The 'Protecteur' design was developed from the slightly smaller *Provider* (AOR508) completed by Davie Shipbuilding at Lauzon in 1963. External differences are primarily in the newer ships' divided uptakes, to increase hangar size, and a much increased freeboard.

These three ships would allow of at least two fully-supported Canadian AS groups in the event of an Atlantic war.

No minesweeping forces are at present maintained by the Canadians, their original 20 NATO-type minesweepers being reduced by sale and transfer (see French and Turkish sections) to only six, all of which are reclassified training ships. They could have sweep gear reinstated but all are now at least 25 years of age.

Peder Skram   Frigate

Denmark

	Builders	LD	L	C
F352 *Peder Skram*	HJM	64	65	66
F353 *Herluf Trolle*	HJM	64	65	67

Displacement: 2,050 tons standard; 2,750 tons full load
Dimensions: 112.4m×12m×3.7m
Armament:
Two quadruple Harpoon SSM launchers
One octuple Sea Sparrow SAM launcher
Two 5in/127mm guns (1×2)
Four 40mm guns (2×2)
Four 21in/533mm torpedo tubes (2×2)
Machinery:
Two gas turbines, 44,000hp
Two cruising diesels, 4,800bhp
CODOG Twin shafts
Speed: 30/18kts

Operating within the NATO framework, the Danish fleet has responsibility for the vital Baltic exits which, as the sea access for the Warsaw Pact fleets, would be bitterly contested in the event of hostilities. Danish warships, therefore, are biassed to anti-ship armaments, need no particular great endurance and are not encumbered with helicopters as ASW can be conducted from ashore.

Denmark's fleet requirements are too small to realise the benefits of series production but nevertheless, many of her ships are built to home-produced designs, which can be very individual in character.

For their size, the two 'Skrams' are imposing ships which possess some of the massive appearance of the larger 'Hamburg' class destroyers from neighbouring West Germany and with which they could possibly be confused. Although rather attractive-looking ships, their vast profile may prove a superb target in the shooting

match for which they were designed. Originally, they were fitted with two twin 5in gunhouses forward but B mounting was traded for eight far more effective Harpoons during their 1976-78 mid-life refits. As these SSMs are likely to be used sparingly in a shoot-out, the slow rate of fire of the 5in 38s might be crucial and they might, with advantage, also have saved topweight by exchanging them for a single 5in 54.

Peder Skram.   Mike Lennon

The quarterdeck, long an unused space after the decision not to fit the Norwegian Terne AS system, is now occupied by the Sea Sparrow launcher which, with the adjacent pair of twin 40mm guns (each with its own director) will allow for higher survivability against the heavy-aerial opposition that would be expected.

Niels Juel   Corvette

Denmark

	Builders	LD	L	C
F354 *Niels Juel*	AV	76	78	80
F355 *Olfert Fischer*	Av	77		
F356 *Peter Tordenskjold*	AV	77		

Displacement: 1,320 tons standard
Dimensions: 84m × 10.3m × 3.8m
Armament:
Two twin/quadruple Harpoon SSMs
One octuple Sea Sparrow SAM
One 76mm DP gun
One CIWS (to be fitted)
Four AS torpedo tubes (fixed)

Machinery:
One gas turbine, 18,000hp
One cruising diesel, 2,400bhp
CODOG Twin shafts
Speed: 30/20kts

Originally intended as replacements for the Italian-built 'Tritons' this trio are larger and in a different class. Designed to extremely tight limitations on total cost, displacement and draught (the Danish Baltic is very shallow) by the British Y-ARD consultancy, they have

Niels Juel.   Naval Material Command Denmark

proved very successful and an object lesson on what can be achieved on a small displacement. Due to a lack of space within the hull proper a long, full-width deckhouse has been adopted, containing living spaces and offering covered fore-and-aft access but with the penalty of siting vital areas like the operations room and ship control centre high in the ship. Where the 'Skrams' have Pratt & Whitney gas turbines, the 'Juels' have the rival General Electric LM2500, a single unit derated to about 18,000hp driving aft from the forward machinery space. Flanked by the twin shafts, an MTU cruising diesel in the after compartment drives forward into a common gearbox. The large funnel casing is flanked by the axially-located Harpoon launchers — quadruples

were planned but at least the first-of-class has had twins fitted in spite of an allowance for extra topside weight. Well aft on the quarterdeck is sited the Sea Sparrow launcher, whose two associated directors are mounted, well separated, on low towers, the forward one immediately abaft the Philips tracker over the bridge. Forward of the imposing plated-in mast is space for an as-yet unspecified CIWS. With no helicopters, the ship's AS potential is vested in a hull-mounted sonar and two AS torpedo tubes built into the hull below the quarterdeck. If, following Swedish and Norwegian practice, Denmark discards larger surface warships, an extra three 'Juels' may be built as 'Skram' replacements.

Hvidbjornen   Patrol frigate   *Denmark*

	Builders	LD	L	C
F348 *Hvidbjornen*	AF	61	61	62
F349 *Vaedderen*	AV	61	62	63
F350 *Ingolf*	SV	61	62	63
F351 *Fylla*	AV	62	62	63
F340 *Beskytteren*	AV	74	75	76

Displacement: 1,350 tons standard; 1,650 (1,970) tons full load
Dimensions: 72.5m × 11.5m × 5.0m
(74.5m × 12m × 5.1m)
Armament One 3in/76mm gun
Machinery:
Four diesels 6,400bhp (Three diesels 7,500bhp)
Single shaft
Speed: 18kts
(Figures in parentheses refer to *Beskytteren*)

Though classified as frigates, the 'Hvidbjornens' have little offensive potential being roomy and comfortable

Beskytteren. Mike Lennon

ships aimed chiefly at preserving Denmark's remaining peacetime interests in the harsh waters of the Faroes and Greenland. They can be used as survey ships and can be compared directly with the British 'Heclas', though the latter are unarmed and of considerably lower power. Built along commercial lines, they have multi-diesel machinery driving a single screw, a combination that makes for great economy and range. Space also permits a generously dimensioned hangar and flightdeck which, in time of hostilities, could easily accommodate a Lynx helicopter in place of the present French Alouette III. With the ship already fitted with the same PMS 26 sonar as the more 'regular' frigates and capable of shipping defensive AS torpedo tubes, she could prove useful. With a comparatively low speed of 18kts, however, a wartime role is rather hard to define, though room is available to take the extra staff and electronics for the defence coordination of an orthodox convoy. The fifth of the class, Beskytteren, is virtually identical in appearance with earlier ships, but differs in detail mainly around the funnel and thick mast, which acts as support and access to the upper look-out.

Willemoes   FAC (Missile/Torpedo)   *Denmark*

		Builders	Completed
P540 *Bille*		FVF	76
P541 *Bredal*		FVF	77
P542 *Hammer*		FVF	77
P543 *Huitfeld*		FVF	77
P544 *Krieger*		FVF	77
P545 *Norby*		FVF	77
P546 *Rodsteen*		FVF	78
P547 *Sehested*		FVF	78
P548 *Suenson*		FVF	78
P549 *Willemoes*		FVF	76

Displacement: 260 tons full load
Dimensions: 46m×7.5m×2.5m
Armament:
Two quadruple Harpoon SSM/No torpedo tubes
or two twin Harpoon SSM/two torpedo tubes
or No Harpoon SSM/Four torpedo tubes
One 76mm DP gun
Machinery:
Three gas turbines, 12,750hp
Two cruising diesels, 800bhp
CODOG three shafts
Speed: 38/12kts

Though larger than the 41m Swedish 'Spicas', the 'Willemoes' class bears a close resemblance, both stemming from West German Lürssen designs. Both are unusual in the long bow, with superstructure set well aft, possible because neither type carries the bulky container/launchers of the commonly-used MM38 Exocet. The American Harpoon is extremely compact, fitting-in right aft and with the possibility of eight rounds in place of the Exocet's four. As can be seen, the ratio between missile and torpedo armament may be varied, with most units opting for a mixed outfit. There could be a mistake in that most anti-ship torpedoes need to be released within the target's own SSM range and may best be delivered by a smaller and higher speed craft such as the 'Soloven' (qv) which has the agility to take rapid avoiding action. The slower 'Willemoes' has, meanwhile, lost half of its long range Harpoon advantage as a topweight penalty. Due to the bridge structure being so well aft, the boat is drier and the 76mm gun has improved firing arcs. Prominent on each side of the bridge are the rails for projecting illuminant or ECM rounds. In common with the Swedish 'Hugins' and Norwegian 'Hauks', the fire-control is a PEAB-built 9LV 200 Mk 2, capable of controlling all weapons simultaneously, even including an aerial target against which, like most FACs, this class is vulnerable. A useful feature is the inclusion of a low power cruising diesel on either wing shaft.

Soloven   FAC (Torpedo)   *Denmark*

		Builders	Completed
P510 *Soloven*		VT	65
P511 *Soridderen*		VT	65
P512 *Sobjornen*		RDK	65
P513 *Sohesten*		RDK	66
P514 *Sohunden*		RDK	66
P515 *Soulven*		RDK	67

Soulven, 'Soloven' class.
Naval Material Command Denmark

Displacement: 95 tons standard, 120 tons full load
Dimensions: 30.3m×8m×2.5m
Armament:
Four 21in/533mm torpedo tubes
Two 40mm guns
Machinery:
Three gas turbines, 12,750hp
Two cruising diesels, 600bhp
CODOG Three shafts
Speed: 54/10kts

By virtue of their flat-sectioned planing hulls, the 'Solovens' can reach 54kts in favourable conditions, making them contenders for the 'fastest conventional warship' label. Torpedo-armed craft such as these usually need to approach a target rather more closely than their SSM-armed counterparts, so that small size and considerable agility make for success. They are derived directly from the Royal Navy's 'Brave' class boats, though refined to the extent that the Proteus gas turbine on each shaft has been complemented by a low-power cruising diesel on each of the two wing shafts and the addition of controllable-pitch (CP) propellers has obviated the need for reversing gearboxes. The first two boats were built by Vospers and the remainder under licence by the Royal Dockyard at Copenhagen and it is a tribute both to the original workmanship and to subsequent maintenance that the wood on light alloy hulls has lasted so well. Under Baltic winter-ice conditions they would be placed at a disadvantage compared with the bigger steel boats such as the 'Willemoes' type. Though round-bilged displacement boats are virtually de rigueur at the moment, their advantages of weatherliness and range may be of little import in inshore waters like the Baltic islands and Norwegian leads, where small, fast boats may still retain the edge. Though the type was once fairly common, the only other operational examples are now a trio under the Libyan flag, and now of dubious status.

Narhvalen   Patrol submarine   *Denmark*

	Builders	LD	L	C
S320 *Narhvalen*	RDK	65	68	70
S321 *Nordkaperen*	RDK	66	69	70

Though Danish-built, these boats are virtually repeats of the West German Type 205 (qv) but with a smaller surface displacement. This increases the margin of safety but also increases time for submergence. Similar submarines ('Ula' class) serve under the Norwegian flag and they and the West Germans are developing a new 750ton boat at the moment — if those on order for the Norwegians prove successful, the Danes may seek to build four under licence as replacements for the 'Delfinens'.

Delfinen   Patrol submarine   *Denmark*

	Builders	LD	L	C
S326 *Delfinen*	RDK	54	56	58
S327 *Spaekhuggeren*	RDK	54	57	59
S329 *Springeren*	RDK	61	63	64

Displacement: 590 tons surfaced, 640 tons submerged
Dimensions: 54m × 4.7m × 4m
Armament:
Four 21in/533mm torpedo tubes (all forward)
Two diesels, 1,200bhp
Two electric motors, 1,200hp
Speed: 14/14kts

Designed and built in Denmark, the little 'Delfinens' were the first home-produced boats post-WW2 and will almost certainly be phased out with the eventual construction of the planned four IKL 750-tonners developed as the Type 210 for the West German and Norwegian navies. They were contemporary with the French 'Arethuse' class, of a similar size and, like them, used for inshore operation with a depth limitation. The fourth-of-class, *Springeren*, was built after the remainder as a replacement for the ex-British 'U' class boat of the same name, which was returned.
Tumleren (S328) was discarded in 1981.

Springeren, *'Delfinen' class.*
Naval Material Command Denmark

Moen.   Mike Lennon

Falster   Minelayer   *Denmark*

	Builders	LD	L	C
N80 *Falster*	NS	61	62	63
N81 *Fyn*	FVF	61	62	63
N82 *Moen*	FVF	61	63	64
N83 *Sjaelland*	NS	62	63	64

Displacement: 1,850 tons standard
Dimensions: 77m × 13m × 4m
Armament:
Sea Sparrow SAM can be fitted
Four 3in/76mm guns (2×2)
Up to 400 mines
Machinery:
Two diesels, 4,800bhp
Twin shafts
Speed: 17kts

The importance of minelaying as a means of effectively blocking the Baltic exits is reflected in the number of dedicated layers and the ability of larger units to lay as an auxiliary function. Largest by far are the four 'Falsters', whose design was closely repeated in the Turkish *Nusret*, also built by Frederikshavn Vaerft. Their hulls, with a high freeboard extending full length, are typical of their kind, allowing a mining gallery to be sited down the greater part of either side. This usable length has been increased by widening the hull at main deck level, resulting externally in a prominent knuckle fore and aft where the hull commences its transition to an acceptable hydrodynamic form. A wide transom with launching doors at either side is common, but less usual are the shell doors on either side forward and aft of the superstructure, with a hydraulic strike-down crane at either station. A now rather dated armament of four American-pattern 3in 50s is carried though provision has been made to fit a defensive Sea Sparrow SAM system in an emergency. With their spacious internal capacity, the 'Falsters' are useful in auxiliary roles in peacetime; at the time of writing, *Sjaelland* is acting as depot ship for FACs and *Moen* is employed on midshipman training. Apparently not so concerned that the mining weapon will be used *against* them, the Danes now maintain only one flotilla of eight NATO-type coastal minesweepers. These were completed in the mid-1950s and are overdue for replacement. Established designs such as the 'Hunt' or 'Tripartite' MCMVs will probably be deemed too expensive, a smaller minehunter based on a commercially available GRP hull being more appropriate.

MSC class   Coastal minesweeper   *Denmark*

M571 *Aarosund* (ex-USS *MSC127*)
M574 *Egernsund* (ex-USS *MSC129*)
M575 *Gronsund* (ex-USS *MSC256*)   Completed 1954-56
M576 *Omosund* (ex-USS *MSC257*)
M577 *Ulvsund* (ex-USS *MSC263*)
M578 *Vilsund* (ex-USS *MSC264*)

For data see under Greece. All US-built. A seventh unit, *Alssund* (M572) was discarded in 1981.

Clemenceau. Mike Lennon

Clemenceau   Aircraft carrier   *France*

	Builders	LD	L	C
R98 *Clemenceau*	BND	55	57	61
R99 *Foch*	CDA	57	60	63

Displacement: 27,300 tons standard; 32,750 tons full load
Dimensions: 265m×31.7m×8.5m (51m wide at flight-deck)
Armament: Eight 100mm DP guns (8×1)
Machinery:
Two sets geared steam turbines
Two shafts, 125,000shp
Speed: 32kts
Aircraft: 40 fixed wing (dependent upon mix)

Among the European fleets, France is now alone in operating fixed-wing carriers though, in peacetime, *Foch* ships only helicopters, an economy measure that still pays dividends in giving the fleet enhanced AS strike power. Strangely, they are still the only French carriers ever designed and built as such, earlier ships being either conversions or acquisitions and, like most Gallic major naval projects, passed through many design phases and occupied much time from conception to commissioning. Though looking rather smaller, they are much of a size with an American 'Essex', also somewhat similar in profile but with a less cluttered island and a British-style enclosed quarterdecks. Com-

pleted with eight-degree angled decks, they incorporate also a measure of armour over decks, machinery spaces and island, a degree of topweight that apparently left them a little tender for *Foch* was bulged by about a metre each side before completion, her elder sister later following suit.

When working as fixed-wing carriers, their 40-odd aircraft are divided between about 50% Super Etendard, 25% Crusader and 25% Alize, giving a self-defence, strike, interceptor, reconnaissance and AS capacity. Additionally a pair of large Super Frelon and small Alouette II helicopters are shipped, the former with a capacity for air-launching the AM39 Exocet.

Uncharacteristically, the French have retained an all-gun defensive armament where a pair of Crotale mountings would have been an appropriate addition. The very comprehensive electronics fit is geared to a SENIT2 automated Tactical Data System for close integration with other ships and aircraft.

Refits have extended the expected lives of both into the 1990s, which would seem appropriate with the seemingly endless prevarications in building their announced replacements. The 18,000ton nuclear-propelled PH75 proposed has now sunk without trace, replaced by plans for a brace of similarly-powered 32,000tonners. These, tentatively named *Bretagne* and *Provence*, are now due to be laid down in the mid-1980s.

Jeanne d'Arc; *note Exocets not fitted.*   Mike Lennon

Jeanne d'Arc   Helicopter cruiser   *France*

	Builders	LD	L	C
R97 *Jeanne d'Arc* (ex-*La Résolue*)	BND	60	61	63

Displacement: 10,000 tons standard; 12,400 tons full load
Dimensions: 182m × 24m × 7.5m
Armament:
Six MM 38 Exocet SSMs
Four 100mm guns (4 × 1)
Machinery:
Two sets geared steam turbines
Two shafts, 40,000shp
Speed: 26kts
Aircraft: Up to eight Lynx equivalents

France is one of the very few powers to operate a purpose-built training ship, the present *Jeanne d'Arc* replacing one of the same name in 1964. Her completion in the previous year anticipated the actual disposal of the earlier ship, so she carried the temporary name of *La Résolue* for a short while. Should any evidence be needed of how the character of fleets has changed since prewar days, a comparison between the big-gun cruiser-style predecessor and the present ship

will provide it. Though the Italians should take the credit for actually laying down the first modern 'helicopter cruisers' — the two 'Andrea Dorias' — in 1958, the French 'did a Dreadnought' in laying theirs down in 1960 and completing her in 1963, about eight months before the opposition. Whoever was first (and the original idea was probably launched by the Swedes in the 1920s with their Gotland) the design certainly was influential, resulting later in the Soviet 'Moskvas', the British 'Tiger' conversions, the Japanese 'Harunas' and their derivatives. All follow the same basic format of conventional warship forward and aviation aft. *Jeanne d'Arc* is a handsome ship with the forecastle rising one level to the level of the flightdeck to give drier flying conditions and adequate stowage below. Hangar space was lofty enough to stow Super Frelons but Lynxs are now carried. This flexibility can be useful in that the accommodation normally available for nearly 200 cadets can be used for short-term billeting of up to 700 commandos.

The compact superstructure carries an aircraft carrier's R pennant number and its width would seem to promote eddying (as the funnel was heightened early on), making flightdeck approaches rather bumpy.

An all-gun armament was later augmented by six MM38 Exocets, an odd choice for a ship whose role would seem to find an enhanced AA fit more useful.

Colbert. ECP Armées

Colbert   GM cruiser   *France*

	Builders	LD	L	C
C611 *Colbert*	BND	63	56	57

Displacement: 8,500 tons standard; 11,300 tons full load
Dimensions: 180.8m × 20.1m × 7.8m
Armament:
One twin Masurca SAM launcher
Two 110mm DP guns (2×1)
Twelve 57mm AA guns (6×2)
Machinery:
Two sets geared steam turbines
Two shafts, 86,000shp
Speed: 31kts

Now obsolete, Colbert continues in service by virtue of the accommodation that she offers for duties as flagship and command ship for projects such as major tests at Muraroa. Originally armed as an AA cruiser, with 16 5in and 20 57mm guns, she was a half-sister to the de Grasse, which was laid down prewar and scrapped in 1973. The later ship was designed with an eye to eventual fitting of missiles and, between 1970 and 1972 she was reconstructed to take a twin-arm Masurca SAM launcher aft. Roughly equivalent to the American 'Terrier', the Masurca is a 25-mile ranged weapon with semi-active homing, tracking radar signals emanating from a shipborne illuminating radar and bounced back from the target; 48 rounds are carried. Six of the original twin 57mm mountings have been retained but all of the US-pattern 5in guns were taken out, only two 100mm guns now being mounted forward. Space has been allocated for four MM38 Exocets which have, apparently, never been fitted. Basic helicopter facilities are provided aft but aircraft are not carried permanently.

The single funnel, with its highly individual cap, the superstructure, built out to the sides, together with the lofty foremast, give the Colbert a distinctive profile. A variety of large antennas include surface surveillance unit atop the bridge, a height finder on the foremast and an air surveillance outfit on the after side of the shorter mainmast, immediately forward of the two fire control radars associated with the Masurca. This very comprehensive outfit enables her to control aircraft and she also boasts a SENIT tactical data system so, despite her advancing years, she still operates as a useful consort to the carriers.

Suffren   GM destroyer   *France*

	Builders	LD	L	C
D602 *Suffren*	LND	62	65	67
D603 *Duquesne*	BND	64	66	70

Displacement: 5,100 tons standard; 6,100 tons full load
Dimensions: 157.5m × 15.5m × 6.1m
Armament:
Four MM38 Exocet SSMs
One twin Masurca SAM launcher
One Malafon AS weapon
Two 100mm DP guns (2×1)
Four AS torpedo launchers

Machinery:
Two sets double-reduction geared steam turbines
72,500shp Two shafts
Speed: 34kts

In spite of being crowned with an enormous and quirky radome every bit as impressive as that on the Dutch 'Tromps', this pair of destroyers have a Gallic flair of line that distinguishes them instantly. Intended to work as escorts to the French carriers, it is rather surprising that only two were built as only one can be available for a great part of the time. With the carriers lacking any real air defence outside their aircraft, the 'Suffrens' each have a Mk 2 semi-active Masurca SAM sytem aft,

23

Duquesne, 'Suffren' class. Mike Lennon

controlled by the pair of DRBR-51 directors immediately forward of the launcher and taking essential data from the three-dimensional DRBI-23 in the radome. A TACAN beacon topping the low after mast is for the purposes of aircraft control. Immediately abaft the large 'mack' which contains the boiler and auxiliary exhausts and which offers stable, low-vibration platforms for surface search and surveillance antennas, is situated a Malafon AS missile launcher. This, like *Ikara*, uses what is really a miniature, rocket-propelled aircraft which can be manoeuvred in flight to accurately place a homing torpedo near a submerged target. Lacking an organic helicopter to provide additional sonar data, the ships must be self-sufficient and, in addition to carrying a hull-mounted set, they are fitted also with a bulky VDS in a transom of highly individual configuration. Their two 100mm guns were supplemented in 1977-8 by the addition of four MM48 Exocet SSMs. Where these are non-reloadable, it is reported that some 48 rounds are carried for the Masurca and 13 for the Malafon. Both ships are fitted with the SENIT tactical data system.

Tourville   Destroyer   *France*

	Builders	LD	L	C
D610 *Tourville* (ex-F604)	LND	70	72	74
D611 *Duguay-Trouin* (ex-F605)	LND	71	73	75
D612 *de Grasse* (ex-F606)	LND	72	74	77

Displacement: 4,600 tons standard; 5,700 tons full load

Dimensions: 153m × 15.3m × 5.8m
Armament:
Six MM38 Exocet SSMs
One Malafon AS weapon
One octuple Crotale SAM launcher
Two launchers for AS torpedos
Two 100mm DP guns (2 × 1)

Tourville. Mike Lennon

Machinery:
Two sets geared steam turbines, 55,000shp
Two shafts
Speed: 32kts
Aircraft: Two helicopters with hangar

Originally classed for some strange reason as corvettes, the 'Tourville', or C67 class were reclassified frigates, yet given destroyer pennants, and this indeed is what they are. On a very moderate displacement this attractive design offers a well balanced armament and a good turn of speed. Though the concept (now known as the F67) is based on that of the one-off *Aconit*, it represented an early shift of direction, for the first of class was laid down only days after *Aconit's* launch, so the latter's somewhat low-key performance was not an influencing factor.

On an elegant hull, typical of current French practice, the superstructure is broken into two separate masses, the 'midships gap containing the carefully styled 'mack' and a Malafon AS launcher.

The bridge structure appears extra low by virtue of the stump foremast and six MM38 Exocet SSMs are set high on the after side of it. In the after house is a hangar for two Lynx helicopters, topped by a small magazine structure supporting the Crotale point-defence SAM launcher, which has replaced the original third 100mm gun. In addition to the helicopters and Malafon the 'Tourvilles' have ship-launched homing torpedoes and two sonars, one hull-mounted and one VDS. On the short foremast is the solid antenna of the DRBV-51C, a specialist low-altitude air search radar which acts also as a target designator for Exocet. Though the Crotale has a comparatively short range, the Tourvilles, like the C70s, also carry the latest long-range air search radar, the DRBV-26, whose large elliptical antenna is supported on the forward side of the mack.

What would seem in every way to be a successful type, the F67s were curtailed at three probably by the decision to adopt gas turbines and the C70s are really cut-down versions.

Georges Leygues   Frigate (AS version)   *France*

	Builders	LD	L	C
D640 *Georges Leygues* (ex-D710)	BND	74	75	79
D641 *Dupleix* (ex-D711)	BND	75	78	81
D642 *Montcalm* (ex-D712)	BND	75	80	82
D643 *Jean de Vienne*	BND	79	81	83
D644	BND	81		
D645	BND	82		

Georges Leygues.   ECP Armées

Displacement: 3,850 tons standard; 4,170 tons full load
Dimensions: 139m × 14m × 5.7m
Armament:
Four MM38 Exocet SSMs
One octuple Crotale SAM launcher
One 100mm DP gun
Two AS torpedo launchers
Machinery:
Two gas turbines, 42,000bhp
Two cruising diesels, 10,000bhp
CODOG Two shafts
Speed: 31/21kts
Aircraft: Two helicopters with hangar

Of a size with a British Type 42, the 'George Leygues' (or 'C70' class to use the official terminology) are referred to as corvettes, whilst carrying destroyers' pennants and, in reality, being CODOG frigates. As originally planned, the class would rapidly have grown to about 24 units, but financial constraints have trimmed this target so that eight of the AS version are now to be built (three completed, two building, one funded and two planned in early 1982) and an unspecified number of the AA type, treated below.

The design represents a mid-course between the unsuccessful *Aconit* prototype and the more ambitious 'Tourvilles', which were closer to destroyers and would have run to greater numbers but for the rather tardy decision to adopt the gas turbine. Except for the hull, which is typically French, the C70s general appearance is not obviously so. This is due partly to the necessary reversion to a large stack and separate lattice mast.

Of the world's major fleets, the French remains one of the most reluctant to use the gas turbine on any scale, apparently preferring the diesel where it can be used, and even the C70s, which remain the only French warships designed with GTs, use diesels for cruising.

Though primarily AS in function, they do not have room for a Malafon and rely on a pair of Lynx helicopters, which can also deploy small ASMs against minor surface targets. Four Exocets and a 100mm gun are carried for surface protection and an eight-cell Crotale, offering defence against aerial targets out to about 10 miles, is mounted in a clear position atop the hangar.

Georges Leygues   Frigate (AA version)   *France*

Four planned by 1990. Builders BND.

Displacement: 3,900 tons standard; 4,200 tons full load
Dimensions: 139m × 14m × 5.7m
Armament:
Eight MM 40 Exocet SSMs
One single-arm Standard MR SAM launcher
Two 100mm DP guns (2 × 1)
Two launchers for AS torpedoes
Machinery:
Four diesels
Two shafts, 42,400bhp
Speed: 30kts

The AA variant of the C70 frigate is built into a hull virtually identical with that of the AS (above). Should it be successful, it will be a useful exercise in showing how a basic hull can be produced and fitted out for a variety of roles which, with the ever-spiralling cost of warships, should show economies not only for the parent fleet but also for any prospective foreign purchasers with their own requirements.

With a change of function has come a change in weapon fit, the ship being virtually devoid of any AS capacity beyond a pair of launchers for homing torpedoes. The space formerly occupied by the large, double hangar and flight pad has been devoted to a launcher for an American Standard MR system and its attendant pair of SPG-51 guidance radars. These are the 51C version rather than the latest, the reason being that the whole of the system is a reconditioned hand-me-down from the Type 47 destroyers, which will be discarded on a one-for-one basis. Immediately abaft the launchers is a second 100mm gun and these are due to be supplemented by the long-awaited MM40 Exocet in two quadruple mountings.

The other major feature externally is the loss of the massive stack and air downtakes in favour of a 'mack' capped by a radome, which protects a new 3D radar, designated DRBJ-11 and manufactured by Thomson-CSF as an alternative to the American SPS-39s. The reason for the 'mack' is that, surprisingly, an all-diesel machinery fit has been specified, with economy and range obviously in mind. As four high-speed Pielsticks will radiate considerable noise when developing power for 30kts, it is perhaps not surprising that the AS content is minimal.

As there is no VDS, the upper deck is continued further aft than in the AS version, offering space to land a helicopter, though there is no hangar and only the barest facilities.

Aconit   AS frigate   *France*

	Builders	LD	L	C
D609 *Aconit* (ex-F703)	LND	66	70	71

Displacement: 3,500 tons standard; 3,800 tons full load

Dimensions: 127m × 13.4m × 5.8m

Armament:
Four MM38 Exocet SSMs
One Malafon AS weapon
One 100mm DP gun
One quadruple AS mortar
Two launchers for AS torpedoes
Machinery:
One set geared steam turbines, 29,000shp
Single shaft
Speed: 27kts

It will have been noted that French warships are almost inevitably built in state dockyards and the advantages of series production are utilised as often as possible. Lorient tends to specialise in escorts and, after a long series of increasingly specialised destroyer types, produced a multi-purpose fast frigate prototype, known as the C65 type and named *Aconit* after one of the British 'Flowers' operated with distinction in the Free French Navy during WW2. Whether she was ever intended to be more than a 'one-off' is not clear but she seems to have disappointed through falling between two ideals, that of an inexpensive single-screw vessel capable of

Aconit. Mike Lennon

being produced in quantity and that of having a comprehensive AS armament. The resulting compromise was an expensive ship with an inadequate speed. On a reasonable displacement, she deploys a well 'layered' AS fit, with an automatic mortar and torpedo launchers backed by a Malafon. Unfortunately, the modest-sized hull does not permit a helicopter to be carried, robbing her of the longest-legged means of deploying both weapons and sensors, leaving the ship with hull sonars and VDS, which may not be able to match the range of the weapons themselves in poor sonar conditions. Four lately-fitted Exocets have given a semblance of surface protection but defence against aircraft is virtually non-existent.

Electronics seem experimental, the DRBV-13 beneath the radome having a search-while track capability, yet remaining unique. Atop the mast, which grows strangely from the funnel casing, is an odd group of what look like passive detector antennas, which are repeated only in Colbert. An early DRBV-22 air surveillance antenna tops the small mainmast.

T47 type   Destroyer (GM version)   *France*

	Builders	LD	L	C
D622 *Kersaint*	LND	51	53	56
D625 *Dupetit Thouars*	BND	52	54	56
D630 *du Chayla*	BND	53	54	57

Displacement: 2,750 tons standard; 3,750 tons full load
Dimensions: 128.5m × 12.8m × 6.3m
Armament:
One single-arm Tartar SAM launcher
Six 57mm guns (3 × 2)
One six-barrelled AS rocket projector
Two triple 550mm torpedo tubes

Machinery:
Two sets geared steam turbines, 63,000shp
Two shafts
Speed: 32kts

Eleven destroyers of the Types 47, Type 53 and Type 56 (see below) are the survivors of the ultimate group of French destroyer design. Unlike their massive prewar forebears, these were to a moderate design comparable with contemporary American and British ships. The first batch, D621-632, were termed T47s and were AA-orientated. They were followed by the five T53s, D633-637, purpose-built for aircraft direction. All

27

were heavily armed with six 5in guns (American equipment was still being widely used) and six 57mm. Twelve torpedo tubes were carried by the first group and six by the second, which carried a much more comprehensive radar fit. The single T56 was D638, dealt with below. As with all 'classic' destroyers completed about this time, they were already obsolescent and have since been substantially modified. Four were rebuilt successfully in 1961-5 to incorporate a Tartar SAM system, an experiment that the Americans tried on the *Gyatt* and found to be wanting. In spite of revamping, the original ships still 'show through', the close-spaced funnels still enclosed in rather more substantial masts. The three 57mm twins have been

Dupetit Thouars *Type T47 (DDG)*. Mike Lennon

retained but the 5in gunhouse in A position has been replaced by a multi-barrelled 375mm AS rocket projector and both those aft by the Tartar launcher, its 40-round magazine and its two prominent SPG-51B directors. An American SPS-39 tops the mainmast. A SENIT tactical data system allows the ships to work with the carriers. In spite of their advanced years, each has a way yet to go as it has been announced that the Tartar systems will be used again for the new AA C70s, the first of which is not due to commission until 1987. A further unit, *Bouvet* (D624) was discarded in 1982.

T47 type   Destroyer (AS version)   *France*

	Builders	LD	L	C
D627 *Maille Brézé*	LND	53	54	57
D628 *Vauquelin*	LND	53	54	56
D629 *d'Estrées*	BND	53	54	57
D631 *Casabianca*	ACG	53	54	57
D632 *Guépratte*	ACB	53	54	57

Casabianca, Type T47 (ASW). Mike Lennon

Displacement: 2,750 tons standard; 3,900 tons full load
Dimensions: 132.5m × 12.8m × 6.3m
Armament:
One Malafon AS weapon
Two 100mm DP guns (2 × 1)
Two triple 550mm torpedo tubes
Machinery/Speed: As T47 GM version

As modified for ASW between 1968 and 1971, this group was quite extensively remodelled. The foremast was changed and the mainmast removed, the bridge being extended aft and built out to extend accommodation. All gun armament was landed and two 100mm DP weapons installed in A position and atop the long, low after deckhouse, the after end of which forms the magazine for the Malafon launcher at the old Y position. This weapon is somewhat squeezed between the house and the large VDS, the DUBV-43

common to several French classes. Lacking the means to ship a helicopter even temporarily, the ships are dependent upon their VDS and the hull-mounted DUBV-23. In spite of the age of these ships, the sonars are identical to those fitted in currently completing classes. In the forward superfiring position is a sextuple 375mm AS rocket projector, similar to that in the GM version of the T47. A triple bank of 550mm torpedo tubes on either side of the waist can fire weapons for either AS or anti-ship use, self-homing or wire-guided.

T53 type   Destroyer   *France*

	Builders	LD	L	C
D633 *Duperré*	LND	54	56	57

Displacement: 2,800 tons standard; 3,900 tons full load
Dimensions: As T47 (ASW)
Armament:
Four MM38 Exocet SSMs
One 100mm DP gun
Launchers for AS torpedoes
Machinery/Speed: As T47 (GM/ASW)
Aircraft: One helicopter

A one-off conversion which, while retaining an AS bias, has traded gun and armament for four SSMs, sited between the funnels. Originally of the AD group (see under T47 [GM version]) she is alone in providing pad and hangar for a Lynx helicopter which, together with the VDS, consume the entire after end from the funnels aft. Increased topweight has led to the torpedo tubes being landed in favour of launchers and only one 100mm gun being carried; this is sited forward, without a forward-firing AS rocket projector. That the French still value these ships is apparent from the fact that, after incurring heavy damage from stranding in 1978, *Duperré* was given new machinery and electrics at the age of over 20 years.

T56 type   Destroyer   *France*

	Builders	LD	L	C
D638 *la Galissonnière*	LND	58	60	62

Displacement: 2,750 tons standard; 3,900 tons full load
Dimensions: AS T47 (ASW)
Armament:
One Malafon AS weapon
Two 100mm DP guns (2 × 1)
Two triple 550mm torpedo tubes
Machinery/Speed: As T47 (GM)
Aircraft: One helicopter

Though originally very similar to the remainder of the group, *la Galissonnière* was modified to act as trials ship for Malafon, which accounts for her later completion. Her layout was an apparently successful compromise between the T47 (ASW) type and the single T53, *Duperré*, and carried Malafon, a helicopter and two guns, at the cost of the multi-barrelled AS rocket projector in B position. The helicopter hangar is atop the 13-round Malafon magazine and has sides that fold downwards and outboard to provide a flight pad.

La Galissonnière, *'T56' class.*   ECP Armées

d'Estienne d'Orves   Corvette   *France*

	Builders	LD	L	C
F781 *D'Estienne d'Orves*	LND	72	73	76
F782 *Amyot d'Inville*	LND	73	74	76
F783 *Drogou*	LND	73	74	76
F784 *Detroyat*	LND	74	76	77
F785 *Jean Moulin*	LND	75	76	77
F786 *Quartier Maître Anquetil*	LND	75	76	78
F787 *Commandant de Pimodan*	LND	75	76	78
F788 *Second Maître le Bihan*	LND	76	77	79
F789 *Lt de Vaisseau le Henaff*	LND	77	78	80
F790 *Lt de Vaisseau Lavallée*	LND	77	79	80
F791 *Commandant l'Herminier*	LND	79	80	82
F792 *Premier Maître l'Her*	LND	78	80	81
F793 *Commandant Blaison*	LND	79	80	82
F794 *Enseigne de Vaisseau Jacoubet*	LND	80	81	82
F795 *Commandant Ducuing*	LND	80	81	82
F796	LND	81	82	83
F797	LND	82	83	84

Displacement: 950 tons standard; 1,200 tons full load
Dimensions: 80m × 10.5m × 5.5m
Armament:
Two Exocet MM38 (2 × 1) can be fitted to each but normally carried only by F781, F783, F786 and F787
One 100mm DP gun
One sextuple 375mm AS rocket launcher
Four fixed AS torpedo tubes
Machinery:
Two diesels, 11,000bhp
Twin shafts
Speed: 24kts

Known usually as the 'A69s', these little ships represent an almost hull-for-hull replacement for the larger and more capable A50/A52 'Le Normand' class frigates. They feature careful design, which enables series production in a special under-cover facility, with each unit being assembled in a dock from 15 prefabricated modules and 'flooded-out' in an advanced state of completion. They are unusual in concept for a Western navy at the present time, being paralleled most closely by the Italian 'de Cristofaros' of over a decade earlier. Designed for inshore ASW, they have also a similar function, neither class needing to be built around a space-absorbing helicopter as each can operate under shore-based protection. Nevertheless, with experience of generations of colonial 'avisos', the French have produced here an attractive and weatherly little escort which can and, no doubt, will proceed worldwide powered economically by two medium speed diesels. All AS weaponry is sited, unusually, aft, a multi-barrelled Creusot-Loire rocket projector with a wide firing arc atop a deckhouse containing four fixed tubes for firing a variety of homing torpedoes. Forward is a 100mm gun, looking somewhat oversized and stability reserves permit a brace of Exocets to be carried abaft the mast-diesel uptake assembly.

Bereft of friendly aircraft cover, the A69s would be vulnerable to air attack. These are handy little 'peacetime' warships and have already shown their capabilities for general use within the state's EEZ. F789 and 791 are replacement hulls for two, ordered by South Africa but blocked and then bought by Argentina, which later ordered a third.

D'Estienne d'Orves, *'A69'*.   Mike Lennon

Commandant Rivière Frigate   *France*

	Builders	LD	L	C
F725 *Victor Schoelcher*	LND	57	58	62
F726 *Commandant Bory*	LND	58	58	64
F727 *Admiral Charner*	LDN	58	60	62
F728 *Doudart de Lagrée*	LND	60	61	63
F729 *Balny*	LND	60	62	70
F733 *Commandant Rivière*	LND	57	58	62
F740 *Commandant Bourdais*	LND	59	61	63
F748 *Protet*	LND	61	62	64
F749 *Enseigne de Vaisseau Henry*	LND	62	63	65

Displacement: 1,750 tons standard; 2,250 tons full load
Dimensions: 103.7m × 11.7m × 4.8m
Armament:
Four MM38 Exocet SSMs
Two 100mm DP guns (2 × 1)
One quadruple 305mm AS mortar
Two triple 550mm topedo tubes
Machinery:
Four medium speed diesels 16,000bhp
Two shafts
Speed: 25kts

These useful little ships were derived directly from the E50/52 classes, the last pair of which, *l'Alsacien* and *le Vendéen*, have recently been deleted from the active fleet. They differ fundamentally in adopting all-diesel propulsion and in having single 100mm guns in place of the twinned 57mm of the earlier ships. The rearrangement of the machinery spaces is visible externally in the fatter funnel, sited further aft. With a four-diesel outfit, only one per shaft would normally be run for economy. Much use has been made of these ships for trials purposes. *Bory* was completed with all gas-turbine propulsion by Turbomeca, but has since been re-engined with SEMT-Pielsticks, similar to the remainder except *Balny*. This unit is a single-screw ship with an experimental CODAG outfit, unusual in the SNECMA gas turbine providing about 75% of the power. With the diesels providing so small a remaining proportion of the power, it would hardly seem to justify the extra complication of gearing to run both types of engine together, though 25% diesel power would suffice for cruising.

As completed, the ships had two guns aft and one forward, the latter superfired by a quadruple 305mm AS mortar. An automatically-loaded weapon, it normally fires a 225kg AS projectile but can be used for shore-bombardment purposes in conjunction with a modified 100kg projectile.

Several were modified aft to take a helicopter platform but these have all been replaced by four MM38 Exocet SSMs in X position and a 100mm gun in Y (*Balny* retains three guns). An interesting feature, in keeping with the class's 'serve-anywhere' aviso role, is the ability to carry temporarily some 80 troops and two small landing craft.

Commandant Rivière. Mike Lennon

Le Foudroyant. ECP Armées

Le Foudroyant Ballistic missile nuclear submarine *France*

	Builders	LD	L	C
S610 *le Foudroyant*	CND	69	71	73
S611 *le Rédoutable*	CND	64	67	69
S612 *le Terrible*	CND	67	69	71
S613 *l'Indomptable*	CND	71	74	75
S614 *le Tonnant*	CND	74	77	79
S615 *l'Inflexible*	CND	80	82	84

Displacement: 8,050 tons surfaced, 8,950 tons submerged
Dimensions: 128.7m × 10.6m × 10m
Armament:
Sixteen ICBM launch tubes
Four 533mm/21-inch torpedo tubes
Machinery:
One WC reactor powering two turbo-alternators
One electric motor on single shaft 18,000hp
Two diesels (auxiliary) each of 1,300bhp
Speed: 21/25kts

Remaining outside the NATO alliance, France had to develop her own nuclear deterrent force, the successful outcome of which has occasioned much national pride. Subsequent to its trials in the one-off research submarine *Gymnote*, the M1 system first went to sea in *le Rédoutable* in 1971, its performance roughly equivalent to the then 10-year old, 1,300 mile ranged Polaris A2, a time-lag that has remained a feature of further updates. The third of class, *le Foudroyant*, took the M2 of 1,600 miles range in 1974, followed by *le Rédoutable*, after modification. With double the explosive power at one megaton, the M20 was fitted in the last two of the first quintet (and will be retro-fitted in the first three) but this, in turn, will be superseded by the M4, currently being developed. Reportedly carrying six or seven MIRV warheads out to 3,000 miles, it will be equal to the American Poseidon C3. The new *l'Inflexible* should be the first to acquire the system, which will then go into the remainder, except for the oldest unit. Built to roughly the same parameters as the early Polaris boats, it is not surprising that they are very similar in size to both the American 'Lafayettes' and the British 'Resolutions'. In appearance, they have a less pronounced hump aft than the Americans but share the fin-mounted planes. The upper casing has a distinct discontinuity forward and the rudders are hung on skegs, neither feature helping the cause of quietness. A defensive armament of four torpedo tubes is also fitted, though the purchase of Subroc has apparently been cancelled in favour of the long-awaited SM39, encapsulated version of the Exocet.

Interesting features of the propulsion system include non-pressurised reactor water-cooling which obviates the need for noisy pumps, and a pair of small auxiliary get-you-home diesels which can drive the main shaft in an emergency for about 5,000 miles.

Rubis Fleet submarine *France*

	Builders	LD	L	C
S601 *Rubis* (ex-*Provence*)	CND	76	79	82
S602 *Saphir* (ex-*Bretagne*)	CND		81	
S603 (ex-*Bourgogne*)	CND			
S604	CND			
S605	CND			

Displacement: 2,400 tons surfaced; 2,700 tons submerged

Dimensions: 72m × 7.5m × 6.5m
Armament: Four 533m/21-inch torpedo tubes (all forward)
Machinery:
One reactor developing 48MW powering to two turbo alternators
One drive motor on single shaft
Emergency electric motor
Speed: 25kts

Completion of *Rubis* was a milestone in French naval progress and one that had been particularly hard to achieve. Construction began back in 1957 on what was known as Q244, which would have been the first nuclear submarine outside the United States but, unfortunately, the project was cancelled in 1959 and the incomplete hull was eventually finished as the conventionally-powered trials submarine *Gymnote*.

Possibly the most notable statistics of the class are the small overall dimensions, nearly 11m shorter, for instance, than a British 'Swiftsure'. This must have resulted from tight design discipline following the intention of building two squadrons of the type, one for Atlantic and one for the more restricted waters of the Mediterranean. One obvious factor has been the production of a small reactor, whose published output is 48MW. It should be remembered that this is power at the reactor stage and, but the time that the efficiencies of steam plant and transmission are taken into account, the propeller will see possibly only about a quarter, representing about 16,000hp. The single shaft can also be driven by a small auxiliary electric motor (in contrast to the SSBN's diesels); if a battery is fitted, this motor would also give a useful 'creep' facility for silent manoeuvring.

This class continues also the move to the more universally used 533mm torpedo tube, allowing interchangeability of weapons with other Western navies. With the forward bulkhead of the reactor compartment

Rubis. ECP Armées

almost exactly amidships, the whole of the after end is devoted to machinery. From the reactor bulkhead forward to about the leading edge of the fin is a section three decks deep, the remaining forward end being devoted to weaponry and sonars.

Agosta   Patrol submarine   *France*

	Builders	LD	L	C
S620 *Agosta*	CND	72	74	77
S621 *Bévéziers*	CND	73	75	77
S622 *La Praya*	CND	74	76	78
S623 *Ouessant*	CND	74	76	78

Displacement: 1,450 tons surfaced; 1,725 tons submerged

Dimensions: 67.5m × 6.8m × 5.5m
Armament: Four 533mm/21-inch torpedo tubes (all forward)
Machinery:
Two diesel-generators powering one propulsion motor, 4,500shp. Single shaft
Small electric manoeuvring motor
Speed: 12/20kts

Agosta. ECP Armées

France's largest conventional, or patrol, submarines, the 'Agostas' have proved attractive also for those navies that operate the earlier 'Daphnés', with two (originally ordered by South Africa) being built for Pakistan and a further four being constructed under licence by Spain. Great efforts to reduce noise have resulted externally in a very clean hull, even to the extent of enabling external fittings to retract into the casing. They would seem to be the last French class to mount their forward hydroplanes at the bows rather than the fin while being the first to adopt the single large diameter propeller with cruciform control surfaces, though without an extreme 'high-speed' hull. French designers cling to the skeg-mounted rudder but, whilst undoubtedly more robust, this arrangement reduces effective rudder area while increasing noise and resistance. Unusually in boats designed for upwards of six weeks' endurance, only four torpedo tubes are carried, all forward. Four reloads are carried for each, a mixture of anti-submarine and anti-surface ship weapons capable of rapid reload and 'swim-out' launch down to a reported 300m depth. Another 'Agosta' 'first' was the adoption of the 533mm/21in tube, with the attendant advantages of interchangeability with foreign weapons and an eye to home-produced items being more saleable abroad.

A particularly comprehensive sonar fit is carried, comprising a large passive unit in a conformal array around the bows, long-range and attack active sets, and the home-built equivalent of a PUFFs passive ranging arrangement.

Machinery has been resiliently mounted to reduce noise and includes a very low power electric 'creep' motor for ultra-silent manoeuvring.

Daphné   Patrol submarine

France

	Builders	LD	L	C
S641 *Daphné*	DN	58	59	64
S642 *Diane*	DN	58	60	64
S643 *Doris*	CND	58	60	64
S645 *Flore*	CND	58	60	64
S646 *Galateé*	CND	58	61	64
S648 *Junon*	CND	61	64	66
S649 *Venus*	CND	61	64	66
S650 *Psyché*	BND	65	67	69
S651 *Sirène*	BND	65	67	70

Displacement: 870 tons surfaced; 1,045 tons submerged
Dimensions: 57.8m × 6.8m × 4.5m
Armament: Twelve 550mm torpedo tubes (eight forward, four aft)
Machinery:
Two diesel-generators powering two propulsion motors
Two shafts, 1,600shp
Speed: 13/16kts

Externally the 'Daphnes' strongly resemble the small 'Aréthuse' class from which they reportedly were developed, but there the resemblance ends for they are designed with an eye more to work in the open sea rather than within the confines of the Mediterranean. Most unusually, they carry eight torpedo tubes forward and four aft. With today's highly sophisticated torpedoes, only one or two shots per target would be expected, with large 'spreads' a thing of the past so beyond having a range of torpedoes 'up the spout' ready to counter any type of target at a moment's notice, it is hard to see the merit in such a battery for, even with recently updated electronics, the boat's fire control would not be up to multiple instantaneous runners. Nevertheless, the overall specification has been well accepted abroad, with a total of 14 under the flags of Pakistan, Portugal, South Africa and Spain, the last-named having built its own under licence. Although the earlier 'Aréthuse' design had featured a single screw, this ran in a closed aperture (unlike today's arrangement) which limited propeller diameter, obliging the more powerful 'Daphnes' to revert to twin-screw propulsion. Though now not in the first flush of youth, this class, reputed to be very quiet in operation, is equipped with up-to-date electronics, similar to that in the later 'Agostas'.

A feature of existing French boats, up to the 'Daphnés', has been one or two WT aerials strung from the trailing edge of the fin to the after casing. These would tend to 'strum' if not de-rigged before diving, causing a low-frequency noise that would carry far, and it is noteworthy that the 'Agostas' have discontinued them.

Junon, *'Daphné' class.*   Mike Lennon

Amazone, 'Aréthuse' class.   Mike Lennon

Aréthuse   Patrol submarine

France

	Builders	LD	L	C
S636 *Argonaute*	CND	55	57	59
S639 *Amazone*	CND	55	58	59
S640 *Ariane*	CND	55	58	60

Displacement: 545 tons surface; 750 tons submerged
Dimensions: 49.5m × 5.8m × 4m
Armament: Four 550mm torpedo tubes
Machinery:
Two diesels 1,050bhp surfaced
Two electric motors 1,300bhp submerged
Speed: 12.5/16kts

The four 'Aréthuse' class boats are, by far, the smallest in the French fleet and geared to operations in the more confined areas of the Mediterranean. As their endurance is not great, what must be very cramped conditions for the (by modern standards) large crew of 40 men was acceptable. They lack the dumpy proportions of current practice, their finer lines forward giving space for only four torpedo tubes (with but one spare round inboard for each) and the conformal passive sonar array. Though single-screwed boats, they predated the 'Albacore' type hull and the propeller ran in an aperture, its small area being able to absorb the low propulsive power. This arrangement made the fitting of the larger, and slower-revving (ie quieter) propeller impossible without major modification and may have contributed to their early demise, even before the old 'Narvals'. The leadship of the class was disposed of in 1979 and both *Amazone* and *Ariane* reduced to low category reserve.

Narval   Patrol submarine

France

	Builders	LD	L	C
S631 *Narval*	CND	51	54	57
S632 *Marsouin*	CND	51	55	57
S633 *Dauphin*	CND	52	55	58
S634 *Requin*	CND	52	55	58
S637 *Espadon*	N	55	58	60
S638 *Morse*	SM	56	58	60

Displacement: 1,635 tons surfaced; 1,910 tons submerged
Dimensions: 77.5m × 7.8m × 5.4m
Armament: Six 550mm torpedo tubes (all forward)
Machinery:
Three diesels. Two propulsion motors of 2,400bhp
Two shafts
Speed: 15/18kts

Dauphin, 'Narval' class.   Mike Lennon

Immediate postwar submarine designs were much influenced by the successful German Type XXI, the French running one of these until the 1960s as the *Roland Morillot*. It was no coincidence when the four (later six) units of the 1949 'Narval' programme paralleled the German craft in dimensions, strength and endurance. This strength has stood them in good stead for all were extensively modernised in about 1966-70 and, despite most having seen 25 years of service, they still soldier on as France's largest 'conventional' on

Atlantic patrols out of Brest, their 45 days' endurance limited by their largish crew of 63 men.

During their refits, two casing-mounted torpedo tubes were removed and updated sonars and fire-control fitted. The old-style direct-drive diesels and electric motors were exchanged for an unusual arrangement where three medium-speed Pielstick power alternators, feeding power via rectifiers to the two drive motors which are directly coupled to the shafts.

Eridan   Minehunter   *France*

	Builders	LD	L	C
M641 *Eridan*	LND	77	79	81
M642 *Cassiopée*	LND	79	81	82
M643 —			81	82
M644 —			82	83
M645 —			83	84
M				
M				
M				
M				
M				

For particulars of this class, see under Netherlands 'Alkmaar' class. France plans to build 10 of these, so-called, 'Tripartite' class minehunters.

Eridan — *an example of the 'Tripartite' minesweepers — fitting out; note A69s also fitting out.*
Jean Biangeumol

Circé   Minehunter

France

	Builders	Completed
M712 *Cybèle*	CMN	72
M713 *Calliope*	CMN	72
M714 *Clio*	CMN	72
M715 *Circé*	CMN	72
M716 *Ceres*	CMN	73

Displacement: 460 tons standard; 510 tons full load
Dimensions: 51m×8.9m×3.4m
Armament: One 20mm gun
Machinery:
One diesel 1,800bhp
Two active rudders for manoeuvring
Two shafts
Speed: 15kts

Distinctive little ships, the 'Circés' are slightly stretched versions of the standard NATO design, based on the British coastals. Some $4\frac{1}{2}$m longer, they have their forecastle carried well back, leaving only a short handling deck aft which, lacking bulwarks, looks as though it could be very wet. Superstructure consists of a single, long deckhouse with a very low bridge set within it at half height. An advantage of the greater volume of enclosed space above the main deck is that, during sweeping operations, no personnel need be below this level, the machinery being arranged for unmanned operation.

Designed as minehunters, the class carries no sweeping gear and is equipped with comprehensive detection and classification gear, and plotting facilities. Divers and PAP self-propelled destructor vehicles are carried, with a comparatively large complement of 48 men. Almost certainly, the 'Circés' will be the last wooden-built French minehunters or sweepers.

Making up French minesweeping forces at the moment are 10 MSOs (see under Belgium for details), five NATO coastals (see under UK, 'Ton' class) and 12 MSCs (see under Denmark). Some of the larger vessels will probably be decommissioned as the new 'Eridans' enter service.

Ouragan   Landing ship (Dock)

France

	Builders	LD	L	C
L9021 *Ouragan*	BND	62	63	65
L9022 *Orage*	BND	66	67	68

Displacement: 5,800 tons standard; 8,500 tons full load
Dimensions: 149m×23m×5.5m; Draught 8.7m aft when flooded down
Armament:
Two 120mm mortars (2×1)
Four 40mm guns (4×1)
Machinery:
Two diesels 8,600bhp
Two shafts
Speed: 17kts
Aircraft: Four heavy or 14 light helicopters

These very austere vessels are similar in concept to both American and British LSDs but smaller and slower. They differ in being diesel driven, the low-profile engines permitting the machinery space to be placed largely beneath the docking area, which can therefore be made longer. Another innovation is to offset the small island superstructure to starboard, allowing the ship to function as a utility aircraft carrier. The main helicopter deck is that covering a through garage space, which can be used for stowing either transport or the aircraft themselves, which would be transferred upward by the portside 35ton crane. A portable platform spanning the docking well is also capable of being used for either stowage or flying operations. The dock itself can accommodate a pair of the 59m LCTs known as EDICs or up to 18 small LCMs, all of which can be preloaded. A small number of troops can be carried, with LCAs, transport, heavy helicopters and the necessary command facilities to oversee a small-scale operation. That *Ouragan* carries a sonar suggests that the AS capabilities of embarked helicopters are intended to be exploited.

Champlain, 'Batral' class.   Marine Nationale

Batral   Light transport   *France*

	Builders	Completed
L9030 *Champlain*	BND	74
L9031 *Francis Garnier*	BND	74

Displacement: 750 tons standard; 1,400 tons full load
Dimensions: 80m × 13m × 2.4m
Armament:
One 40mm gun
One 81mm mortar
Machinery:
Two diesels, 3,600bhp
Two shafts
Speed: 16kts

These rather stylish vessels show that amphibious craft need not necessarily be box-like. In size they lie between an LCT and an LST, and pains have been taken to fair the bow doors into the fine entry, permitting a useful speed of 16kts. With a capacity for heavy vehicles below and lighter transport topside, they would have considerable commercial potential in the Pacific. They can transport up to about 140 troops whose passage ashore can, as an alternative to taking the beach, be effected by means of a couple of small landing craft handled by the 10ton self-slewing derrick heeled on the bridge front. The monoblock superstructure is continued aft as a helicopter platform and, somewhat surprisingly, the ships are reported to be sonar fitted. Two more units are on order for delivery in 1983/4 and a further two planned.

Five 102m LSTs also serve in the French fleet, namely *Argens* (L9003), *Bidassoa* (L9004), *Trieux* (L9007), *Dives* (L9008) and *Blavet* (L9009).

Trident   FAC (Patrol)   *France*

	Builders	Completed
P670 *Trident*	AA	76
P671 *Glaive*	AA	77
P672 *Epée*	CMN	76
P673 *Pertuisane*	CMN	77

Glaive, 'Trident' class; note SS12 launch frames abaft wheelhouse.   Mike Lennon

Displacement: 115 tons standard; 130 tons full load
Dimensions: 37m×5.5m×1.6m
Armament:
Six SS12 SSMs
One 40mm gun
Machinery:
Two diesels, 4,000bhp
Two shafts
Speed: 26kts

Though France has been a successful exporter of FACs, she operates few of her own in peacetime. In addition, those built to foreign account are mainly 'Lürssen'-derived designs produced under licence. This home-produced design hardly merits the classification of Fast Attack Craft as it is very modestly powered for a lowish speed (although the diesels could certainly be increased in size or, even possibly be augmented by an extra centreline or two wing shafts) and its attack capability is limited to a half-dozen small Nord Aviation SS12s, which can take a 30kg warhead out to about three miles. This combination of limitations makes one wonder just what their role is supposed to be and they are probably best viewed as patrol craft. Only four were built out of a planned 30 but the first two of a derived 50m class are at present under construction.

Eight larger FACs, the 40m, 320ton 'Rapier' class have been ordered, the nameship (P674) being launched in 1981.

Rhin   Depot ship   *France*

	Builders	LD	L	C
A615 *Loire*	LND	65	66	67
A617 *Garonne*	LND	63	64	65
A618 *Rance*	LND	64	65	66
A621 *Rhin*	LND	61	62	64
A622 *Rhône*	LND	62	62	64

Displacement: 2,075 tons standard (A615 and 617 2,325 tons standard); 2,450/2,700 tons full load
Dimensions: 101m×13m×3.7m
Armament: None to three 40mm guns
Machinery:
Two diesels, 3,300bhp
One shaft
Speed: 16.5kts
Aircraft: See below

Spread over naval programmes from 1959 to 1963, this interesting group of ships was completed piece-meal to a variety of configurations, none of which are necessarily permanent. Their profiles differ considerably, *Rance* and *Garonne* having a long forecastle deck extending three-quarters aft and the remainder having a forecastle of half the length, leaving a well before the bridge.

Loire is used as a minesweeper support ship, carrying no helicopter. *Garonne* has a bulkier superstructure and greater workshop capacity for use as a repair ship for detached forces; no helicopter. *Rance* is an experimental support ship with a large hangar and pad for the operation of three Alouettes; the large antenna of a DRVB-23 long range air search radar is prominent amidships. *Rhin* is a mobile electronic maintenance ship and carries one helicopter. *Rhône* is a submarine depot ship but sometimes used as a fisheries support ship. Carrying cranes and small landing craft in addition, these are useful vessels and obviously highly versatile.

Durance   Underway replenishment tanker   *France*

	Builders	LD	L	C
A607 *Meuse*	BND	77	78	80
A629 *Durance*	BND	73	75	76
A608 *Var*	BND	79	81	82
— —	BND			86

Displacement: 17,800 tons full load
Dimensions: 157.3m×21.2m×8.8m
Armament: Usually two 40mm guns (2×1)
Machinery:
Two diesels, 20,000bhp
Two shafts
Speed: 19kts
Aircraft: One Lynx helicopter

Bearing more than a passing resemblance to the larger Canadian 'Protecteur', this pair are, somewhat surprisingly, the only purpose-built ships of their type under French colours.

With France's policy of maintaining naval forces in the Indian Ocean, Pacific and West Indies it is, perhaps, timely that two further units have been funded. Their useful deadweight is about 10,000 tons which, in the *Meuse*, is divided between 50% bunker fuel oil, 32% diesel fuel, 18% aviation spirit and the remaining 10% between foodstuffs, munitions, distilled water and dry stores. There are two transfer stations on either side, the after on each nominally for fuel and the forward for other gear, which can be of considerable bulk. In common with other French oilers, a stern manifold is also provided. Up to 45 passengers can be given passage.

Lütjens, 'Adams' class.   Mike Lennon

Adams   Guided-missile destroyer

West Germany

	Builders	LD	L	C
D185 *Lütjens* (ex-DDG28)	BIW	66	67	69
D186 *Mölders* (ex-DDG29)	BIW	66	68	69
D187 *Rommel* (ex-DDG30)	BIW	67	69	70

For data, see US 'Adams' class

Early staff requirements were for eight 6,000ton derivatives of the 'Hamburgs', propelled by Olympus gas turbines and armed with a Tartar SAM system. They were even provisionally allocated the traditional light cruiser names of *Bremen, Düsseldorf, Kiel, Mainz, München, Saarbrücken, Stuttgart* and *Wiesbaden*. It was then decided that the American 'Adams' design would be adequate, saving design costs; three were to be US-built and the remainder constructed in German yards under licence. In the event the final five were cancelled in 1968.

Owing to the more steeply-raked bow to carry the stem-anchor clear of the SQS 23 sonar bulb, they are marginally longer than the earlier ships of the US group. Externally they differ in having their funnels plated square at the top, with the exhaust ducts protruding obliquely. On the after funnel is stepped a mast which, supporting (visibly) only a DF loop and communications whip, would seem to be rather a luxury in terms of the interference it must cause to the neighbouring SPS-52 3D air search antenna, which is vital to the SAM system. Now undergoing mid-life modernisation, they will emerge with the Standard MR in place of the Tartars, together with a new digital fire control. In addition, the after 5in gun will be surrendered in favour of two Harpoon SSM mountings. If these are only twins, as reported, there can be little margin for extra topweight in this design.

Hamburg   Destroyer

West Germany

	Builders	LD	L	C
D181 *Hamburg*	HCS	59	60	64
D182 *Schleswig-Holstein*	HCS	59	60	64
D183 *Bayern*	HCS	60	62	65
D184 *Hessen*	HCS	61	63	68

Displacement: 3,350 tons standard; 4,650 tons full load
Dimensions: 133.8m × 13.5m × 6.4m

Armament:
Four MM38 Exocet SSMs
Three 100mm DP guns (3 × 1)
Eight 40mm guns (4 × 2)
Two four-barrelled AS mortars
Four AS torpedo tubes (2 × 2)
Machinery:
Two sets steam turbines, 68,000shp
Twin shafts
Speed: 34kts

Hamburg. Mike Lennon

Though almost identical in dimensions and displacement with the 'Adams' class, DDGs, the 'Hamburgs' look larger by virtue of their massive top-hamper, seemingly out of proportion with the low-freeboard hull, with its graceful sheerline. As all-gun 'super-destroyers' they were obsolete even on completion, the design probably seeking to impress while underlying the then essentially defensive nature of the Bundesmarine. Latterly improved by the replacement of X-gun by four Exocets, the 'Hamburgs' still have little more to offer — except speed and seakeeping qualities — than the French 'Commandant Rivière' class frigates of half the displacement. That the Exocets themselves were only an interim choice is indicated by the installation of Harpoons on the new Type 122s. Sadly deficient in AA protection, the 'Hamburgs' would best be employed deepsea and it would seem, in retrospect, short-sighted that the hull was not configured for a

later installation of an area SAM system. As it is, they are essentially anti-ship orientated and could complement the 'Adams'. A hull-mounted sonar is carried, but only short-range AS weaponry. All electronics are of Dutch HSA origin. As with many German surface ships, the 'Hamburgs' are equipped with mine-laying rails on the weatherdeck. With the new Type 122s slated to replace both the American 'Fletchers' and the 'Köln' class frigates, some shortfall in numbers of hulls will result and, if more new frigates are not ordered, the 'Hamburgs' may need to soldier on to the end of the decade. Two flotillas, each of six Type 122s, directly replacing the earlier three classes, would be more effective and significantly, reduce the total manpower requirements from over 3,500 to less than 1,200.

Bremen Frigate   *West Germany*

	Builders	LD	L	C
F207 *Bremen*	BVV	79	79	82
F208 *Niedersachsen*	AGW	79	80	82
F209 *Rheinland-Pfalz*	BVH	80	80	83
F210 *Emden*	TNE	80	80	83
F211 *Köln*	BVH	80	81	84
F212 *Karlsruhe*	HDW	81	82	84

Displacement: 3,420 tons full load
Dimensions: 130m × 14.6m × 4.5m
Armament:
Two quadruple Harpoon SSM launchers

One eight-cell Sea Sparrow point defence SAM launcher
One 76mm gun
Two twin AS torpedo tubes
Machinery:
Two gas turbines, 52,000hp
Two diesels, 10,600bhp
Twin shafts
Speed: 30/20kts

Though basically similar to the Dutch 'Kortenaers', the six 'Bremens' are distinctive visually by virtue of an

Bremen, *Type 122.*
Marineamt, Bildstelle

amidships-set mainmast that seems modelled on the Eiffel Tower in place of the clean-cut pole of the Dutchman. Further, where the latter have the radome of the WM25 fire control set on a solid pyramoidal structure, that of the West Germans has an openwork lattice base. Eventually the 'Kortenaers' will get a CIWS mounting on the hangar roof, to underpin the Sea Sparrow point defence system, but where the 'Bremens' have the latter in the same position forward, superfiring the undersized 76mm gun, they will complement it by two short-ranged RAM (Rolling Airframe Missile) mountings, each containing 24 rounds and sited at the corners of the hangar roof. This type of missile will also be shipped aboard the 143A class FACs. The hangar, again housing two Lynx helicopters,

is carried to the sides of the ship to increase capacity.

Perhaps the major difference is below for, where the Dutch selected a COGOG, two Olympus/two Tyne machinery arrangement, the Germans have CODOG, two American LM2500s for high speeds and a pair of home-built MTU diesels for cruising. Besides acting as lead builder, Bremer Vulkan also fit the major part of the weapons and electronics systems. The nomenclature is also confusing; Bremen, a semi-autonomous Hanseatic city, followed by two Länder, together with three city names still borne by the 'Köln' class frigates. As the latter are due to revert to a training role rather than for disposal, more new names will be required. A further class of six Type 122s is highly probable.

Köln   Frigate

West Germany

	Builders	LD	L	C
F220 *Köln*	HCS	57	58	61
F221 *Emden*	HCS	58	59	61
F222 *Augsburg*	HCS	58	59	62
F223 *Karlsruhe*	HCS	58	59	62
F224 *Lübeck*	HCS	59	60	63
F225 *Braunschweig*	HCS	60	62	64

Displacement: 2,100 tons standard; 2,650 tons full load
Dimensions: 110m × 11m × 5.2m
Armament:
Two 100mm DP guns (2 × 1)
Six 40mm guns (2 × 2) + (2 × 1)
Two four-barrelled AS mortars
Four 21in/533mm torpedo tubes (4 × 1)
Machinery:
Two gas turbines, 24,000hp
Four cruising diesels, 12,000bhp
CODAG Twin shafts
Speed: 28/18kts

As the Bundesmarine's first major postwar class, the 'Kölns' were designed in the austerity of the early 1950s and their equipment reflects something of what was available at the time. Their great innovation was the inclusion of a pair of BBC gas turbines to boost the four cruising diesels. The arrangement is in the now-unusual CODAG configuration and, by current standards, there is an awful lot of engines and gear-boxes to produce 36,000shp, although the system is extremely flexible. Further, the official maximum speed of 28kts would seem low for this power. Coming from the same builders as the larger 'Hamburgs', the two classes have a close resemblance in the hull, though the low freeboard and sharp flare in the 'Kölns' would suggest wetness forward and extremely lively pitch motions. This particular hull was 'stretched' from the T37-51 class of small destroyer still building at Elbing at the war's end. No missiles have been fitted, the gun armament including a single 100mm DP weapon at either end, each superfired by a twin 40mm with a further single 40mm on either beam. A hull-mounted

Braunschweig, 'Köln' class. Mike Lennon

sonar is used in conjunction with two four-barrelled Bofors 375mm AS mortars, firing ahead from a rather constricted space by the bridge front, and four short 533mm torpedo tubes mounted singly in the waist. Fire controls and radars are all supplied by the Dutch HSA company. Rails for up to 80 mines run the length of the after end on either side, discharging over the transom. Though rather cramped and complex, the Kölns have given good service over a couple of decades and, when replaced by the Type 122s, will see further service as training ships, renamed as the T122s commission.

Type 205   Patrol submarine

West Germany

	Builders	L	Completed
S180 *U1*	HWK	67	67
S181 *U2*	HWK	66	66
S188 *U9*	HWK	66	67
S189 *U10*	HWK	67	67
S190 *U11*	HWK	68	68
S191 *U12*	HWK	68	69

U2, *Type 205*. Marineamt, Bildstelle

Displacement: 420 tons surfaced; 450tons submerged
Dimensions: 44m × 4.5m × 4.3m
Armament: Eight 533m/21in torpedo tubes (all forward)
Machinery:
Two diesel generators
One propulsion motor, 1,200shp
Single shaft
Speed: 10/17kts

Even more than the Mediterranean, the Baltic and North Sea are bad submarine country and those Western fleets who need to operate in both have tended to develop the short, tubby submarine with the best characteristics to meet the natural conditions of the area. The shape offers the best usable volume and least wetted area for a given displacement and exhibits a small target for active sonars. With resiliently mounted machinery and a large diameter slow-turning propeller, she is also very quiet; this not only reduces her chances of being detected by a target but give her own passive sonars the opportunity to work in an environment not swamped by self-generated noise. Careful design also means a degree of automation that requires only a small crew (22 in this case), necessitating in turn, a smaller proportion of available space needing to be devoted to accommodation and an improved endurance.

West Germany pioneered the idea in the Type 205s

mainly because, at that time, they were still bound by treaty restrictions to an upper limit of 450 tons displacement. Such inflexibilities refine the design process to take ruthless account of priorities and a true Baltic-sized boat resulted.

The forward battery of eight tubes is loaded through the bow caps to save space, no spares being carried. An innovation was the employment of amagnetic steels for the hull, to reduce the boat's magnetic signature. Unfortunately, the steels had inferior metallurgical properties, resulting in the rebuild of *U1* and *U2*, and the early scrapping of *U3-U8*. *U9-U12* were constructed from more conventional materials. Two improved Type 205s were built by Denmark as the 'Narhvalens' and the Norwegian 'Ulas' are a derivative.

Mention should be made of the *Wilhelm Bauer* which, as the *U2540*, was one of the last of the revolutionary Type XXIs. Scuttled, salvaged and refitted, she still serves as a trials submarine.

Type 206   Patrol submarine   *West Germany*

	Builders	L	Completed
S192 *U13*	HWK	71	73
S193 *U14*	RNE	72	73
S194 *U15*	HWK	72	74
S195 *U16*	RNE	72	73
S196 *U17*	HWK	72	73
S197 *U18*	RNE	72	73
S198 *U19*	HWK	72	73
S199 *U20*	RNE	73	74
S170 *U21*	HWK	73	74
S171 *U22*	RNE	73	74
S172 *U23*	RNE	73	74
S173 *U24*	RNE	73	74
S174 *U25*	HWK	73	74
S175 *U26*	RNE	73	75
S176 *U27*	HWK	73	74
S177 *U28*	RNE	74	74
S178 *U29*	HWK	73	74
S179 *U30*	RNE	74	75

Displacement: 450 tons surfaced; 500 tons submerged
Dimensions: 48.5m×4.5m×4.5m
Armament: Eight 533m/21in torpedo tubes (all forward)
Machinery: Two diesel generator sets. One propulsion motor 1,800shp single shaft
Speed: 10/17kts

Though the Type 206 represents an improvement on the basic 205, it has been at the expense of an extra 5m in length. Visually they differ in the 206's more bulky fin profile and an added bow fairing. The latter allows more space for the large passive sonar array, together with providing more buoyancy forward to improve seakeeping when underweigh on the surface. In the enlarged fin fairing are escape hatches, active intercept sonar and an element of a passive ranging set similar in function to the American PUFFS. Again, all eight tubes are concentrated forward and, again, probably without reloads. A variety of self-homing or wire-guided torpedoes can be used and it has been reported that to improve utilisation an external pack can be added to transport and lay mines, the carriage of which would, otherwise be at the expense of the torpedo complement.

Both the 205 and 206 designs came from IKL, responsible also for the very successful export submarine, the Type 209. Experience from all these is being put into a new 750 ton design which will suffice for the next generation of Norwegian boats and also for the West German navy, whose area of responsibilities was, in 1980, enlarged from a nominal 24-hour steaming-distance from base to a more realistic zone including northern Norwegian and Icelandic waters.

Thetis   Corvette   *West Germany*

	Builders	Completed
P6052 *Thetis*	RWB	61
P6053 *Hermes*	RWB	61
P6054 *Najade*	RWB	62
P6055 *Triton*	RWB	62
P6056 *Theseus*	RWB	63

Displacement: 640 tons standard; 530 full load
Dimensions: 70m×8.5m×4.3m
Armament:
Two 40mm guns (1×2)
One four-barrelled AS mortar
Four 21in/533mm torpedo tubes (4×1)

Najade, 'Thetis' class. Marineamt, Bildstelle

Machinery:
Two diesels 6,800shp

In essence, these little ships are first cousins to the enormous number of PCEs built mainly under WW2 programmes to tackle submarines in inshore waters. They were funded originally in the late-1950s as torpedo recovery vessels, for which purpose they were so obviously oversize that this was probably a stratagem to get them approved. As AS corvettes, however, they carry a fair punch in the shape of the 375mm rocket launcher and four single torpedo tubes common also to the contemporary 'Köln' class frigates together with a small, hull-mounted sonar. The twin 40mm gun mounting aft is now inadequate for survival and mention has been made for an exchange with a 76mm Oto-Melara, used extensively in the Bundesmarine; as the class has now seen 20 years of service this would seem unlikely. Nevertheless, capability against submarines in the shallow and difficult waters of the Western Baltic is a distinct requirement, for which modern frigates are over-large and over-complex. There is a real place for such unsophisticated small ships to work in conjunction with shore-based helicopters to counter such a threat. Oddly enough, in the two decades since the 'Thetis' class were built, the steel-hulled FAC has evolved and developed to the degree where a 70m corvette-type 'leader' would seem a distinct possibility. Though slow for the job, the 'Thetis' represents a surprisingly similar aspect to that of such leaders.

A single, stretched version of the design also exists in the *Hans Bürkner* and, in peacetime, the whole group acts as the Fleet Service Flotilla, a 'maids-of-all-work' function.

Type 143   FAC (Missile)   *West Germany*

	Builders	Completed
P6111 *Albatross* (ex-S61)	LV	76
P6112 *Falke* (ex-S62)	LV	76
P6113 *Geier* (ex-S63)	LV	76
P6114 *Bussard* (ex-S64)	LV	76
P6115 *Sperber* (ex-S65)	KR	76
P6116 *Greif* (ex-S66)	LV	76
P6117 *Kondor* (ex-S67)	KR	76
P6118 *Seeadler* (ex-S68)	LV	77
P6119 *Habicht* (ex-S69)	KR	77
P6120 *Kormoran* (ex-S70)	LV	77

Displacement: 310 tons standard, 390 tons full load
Dimensions: 57.5m × 7.5m × 2.5m
Armament:
Four Exocet MM38 SSMs
Two 76mm DP guns (2 × 1)
Two 533m/21in torpedo tubes
Machinery:
Four diesels, 16,000bhp
Four shafts
Speed: 38kts

Far removed from the last of the 'Jaguars' that they replaced, the Type 143s are developed logically from the preceeding 148s. The most significant difference is an increase in hull length of over 10m, permitting a one-third increase in power (the MTU diesels, nominally rated at 4,000bhp, can be overrun to 4,500bhp output for up to two hours), doubling of bunker space, the installation of automated command facilities for the coordination of flotilla operations by smaller FACs not

Geier, *Type 143 FAC.* Marineamt, Bildstelle

so equipped and the substitution of a second 76mm in place of the after 40mm in earlier boats. A bonus with the larger hull is an improvement in ability to keep the sea and capitalise on the extended range. Like most FACs the 143s are essentially offensive in character with four MM38 Exocets set well aft. (With the longer-ranged Harpoon now in service in the Bundesmarine, and the 40m PHMs demonstrating the ability to carry two quadruple canister/launchers there is an acute need for the more compact MM40 version in place of the bulky but trusted MM38.)

On either quarter are long-full-calibre torpedo tubes for launching large, wire-guided torpedoes, but no mining capacity is apparent. While the forward 76mm gun is usual the after one is not and has proved an over-large luxury; each boat is due to lose it in favour of the RAM rolling-airframe PDMS when the latter enters

service shortly. This will be a great step forward as the greater majority of FACs are highly vulnerable to air attack by aircraft or SSM. The conspicuous radome contains a gyro-stabilised platform upon which are mounted antennas for the search and fire-control/tracker components of the WM27 system by Hollandse Signaal Apparaten, capable of controlling guns, missiles and torpedoes simultaneously.

With the West Germans abandoning plans for the Type 162 version of the PHM (qv), 10 modified 143s, known as 143As, have been ordered. Interestingly, these have reverted to steel hulls in place of the 143s wood-on-light alloy which, while having a lower magnetic signature and being more habitable, are probably limited by the abrasive effects of Baltic ice and by the diminishing number of boatyards able to build and repair in wood.

Type 143A   FAC (Missile)   *West Germany*

	Builders	Completed	
P6121 *Gepard* (ex-S71)	LV	82	**Displacement:** 395 tons full load
P6122 *Puma* (ex-S72)	LV	82	*Dimensions:* 57.6m × 7.8m × 2.2m
P6123 *Hermelin* (ex-S73)	KR	83	*Armament:*
P6124 *Nerz* (ex-S74)	LV	83	Four Exocet MM38 SSMs
P6125 *Zobel* (ex-S75)	LV	83	One multi-cell RAM launcher (planned)
P6126 *Frettchen* (ex-S76)	LV	83	One 76mm gun
P6127 *Dachs* (ex-S77)	LV	84	*Machinery:*
P6128 *Ozelot* (ex-S78)	LV	84	Four diesels, 16,000bhp
P6129 *Wiesel* (ex-S79)	KR	84	Four shafts
P6130 *Hyäne* (ex-S80)	KR	84	*Speed:* 38kts (max)

This class is essentially a repeat of the Type 143 but will be armed with only one 76mm gun, forward. Acknowledging the grave threat posed to FACs from the air, a point-defence SAM launcher will be mounted aft. Whether this will be a smaller version of the 24-round unit shipped on the Type 122s is not known. Interestingly, the 76mm guns for the class will be removed from the after ends of the Type 143s which, when similarly fitted with RAM (rolling air frame) missiles, will be known as Type 143Bs.

Type 148   FAC (Missile)   *West Germany*

	Builders	Completed
P6141 *Tiger* (ex-S41)	CMN	72
P6142 *Iltis* (ex-S42)	CMN	73
P6143 *Luchs* (ex-S43)	CMN	73
P6144 *Marder* (ex-S44)	CMN	73
P6145 *Leopard* (ex-S45)	CMN	73
P6146 *Fuchs* (ex-S46)	CMN	73
P6147 *Jaguar* (ex-S47)	CMN	73
P6148 *Löwe* (ex-S48)	CMN	74
P6149 *Wolf* (ex-S49)	CMN	74
P6150 *Panther* (ex-S50)	CMN	74
P6151 *Häher* (ex-S51)	CMN	74
P6152 *Storch* (ex-S52)	CMN	74
P6153 *Pelikan* (ex-S53)	CMN	74
P6154 *Elster* (ex-S54)	CMN	74
P6155 *Elk* (ex-S55)	CMN	75
P6156 *Dommel* (ex-S56)	CMN	75
P6157 *Weih* (ex-S57)	CMN	75
P6158 *Pinguin* (ex-S58)	CMN	75
P6159 *Reiher* (ex-S59)	CMN	75
P6160 *Kranich* (ex-S60)	CMN	75

Displacement: 235 tons standard; 265 tons full load
Dimensions: 47m × 7m × 21m
Armament:
Four MM38 Exocet SSMs
One 76mm DP gun
One 40mm gun

Marder, *Type 148 FAC.*   Marineamt, Bildstelle

Machinery:
Four diesels 12,000bhp
Four shafts
Speed: 37kts

Though, like the Type 143, the 148 is Lürssen-designed, it is of steel-hulled construction, French-built and marketed as the 'Combattante II' (or Greek 'Konidis' class), the German variant being known as an A4L. The Cherbourg CMN yard has done very well exporting these German-designed boats and, in fact, built this group of 20, although even-numbered hulls from S46 onwards were subcontracted to Lürssen's Bremen yard for fitting-out in France. In appearance they differ considerably from the later boats, lacking the tall tripod mainmast, having instead a lattice structure which, with small tower atop the wheelroom, bear the component parts of the Thomson CSF Vega/Pollux fire control system which includes opto-electronic sensors for 'quiet' use. This is not surprising bearing in mind the boats' French ancestry but, with a near-identical armament to the 143s, logistics must be complicated. Though topweight allowances permit a pair of torpedo tubes to be shipped, this is not usually the case. Mining rails are not believed to be fitted, although the removal of the 40mm gun aft would release space for about eight.

The 148s were built as hull-for-hull replacements for the first 20 'Jaguars' to be deleted.

Zobel/Type 142 FAC (Torpedo) *West Germany*

	Builders	Completed
P6092 *Zobel*	LV	61
P6093 *Wiesel*	LV	62
P6094 *Dachs*	LV	62
P6095 *Hermelin*	KR	62
P6096 *Nerz*	LV	63
P6097 *Puma*	KR	62
P6098 *Gepard*	LV	63
P6099 *Hyäne*	KR	63
P6100 *Frettchen*	LV	63
P6101 *Ozelot*	LV	63

Displacement: 190 tons standard; 225 tons full load
Dimensions: 42.5×7m×3.0m
Armament:
Two 40mm guns (2×1)
Two 533mm/21in torpedo tubes
Machinery:
Four diesels 12,000bhp
Four shafts
Speed: 37kts

Production of the 'Jaguar'/Type 141 class of FAC ceased in 1960 (see under Greece for details) and an improved class, designated Type 142, commenced on the same-sized hull. With improvements and additions came an inevitable loss in speed, originally only from 42 to 40kts but now reduced still further by age. They are the last class whose ancestry can be traced from the WW2 S-boat and, though not small, now contrast unfavourably with other torpedo-armed FACs, such as the similarly-sized Swedish 'Spica'. There is still a definite role for the torpedo boat operating alongside missile boats, modern long-range weapons being highly accurate, with self-homing and/or wire guidance, and difficult for the target to detect and counter. Confidence in the excellence of their large weapons is manifested by the designers putting only two tubes on each boat, firing aft over the transom. Intended to operate by darkness or in thick weather, the 142s are poorly armed by contemporary standards and would fare badly against surface or aerial attack; stealthy attack and rapid disengagement would be vital. The radome houses an HSA-built M20 fire-control, capable of firing solutions for both guns and torpedoes. Construction is of wood on light alloy. It is anticipated that the class will be progressively 'sold out' on the completion of units of the new Type 143A class, a belief underlined by their names being re-allocated to the newbuildings.

Nerz, 'Zobel' class, Type 142. Marineamt, Bildstelle

Perseus, 'Schütze' class minesweeper.
L. & L. van Ginderen

Schütze   Coastal minesweeper

West Germany

	Builders	Completed
M1051 *Castor*	ARL	62
M1054 *Pollux*	ARL	61
M1055 *Sirius*	ARL	61
M1056 *Rigel*	ARL	62
M1057 *Regulus*	ARL	62
M1058 *Mars*	ARL	60
M1059 *Spica*	ARL	61
M1060 *Skorpion*	ARL	63
M1062 *Schütze*	ARL	59
M1063 *Waage*	ARL	62
M1064 *Deneb*	GSW	61
M1065 *Jupiter*	GSW	61
M1067 *Altair*	SWT	61
M1069 *Wega*	ARL	63
M1090 *Perseus*	SWT	61
M1092 *Pluto*	GSW	60
M1093 *Neptun*	SWT	60
M1094 *Widder*	GSW	60
M1095 *Herkules*	SWT	60
M1096 *Fische*	ARL	60
M1097 *Gemma*	ARL	60
Y849 (ex-M1061) *Stier*	ARL	61

Displacement: 305 tons full load
Dimensions: 47.5m × 7m × 2.3m
Armament: One 40mm gun

Machinery:
Two diesels 4,500bhp
Two shafts
Speed: 15.5kts (free running)

Running in parallel with the 'Lindau' class building programme was that of the 30 'Shütze' class (Type 340/341). Originally classified as 'inshore' minesweepers, as opposed to the NATO type's 'coastal' classification, they were again wooden-built but with shallower draught. In spite of the lack of freeboard for offshore work, they are as long as the 'Lindaus' and, being finer in the beam, compensate by lower displacement. An apparent inconsistency is that they have a higher installed power, yet a lower speed on a slimmer hull. All are fitted as straightforward 'sweepers except *Stier*, fitted with a re-compression chamber for use in clearance diving. *Algol, Capella, Krebs, Mira, Orion, Pegasus, Steinbock* and *Uranus* have already been sold out to various, mainly training, organisations and it is planned to dispose of the remainder as Troika enters service.

The Bundesmarine, faced with much shallow water ideal for mining, operates also ten 245 ton 'Frauenlob' class inshore 'sweepers (Type 394), dating from 1966-9 and eight 250 ton 'Ariadne' type (Type 393) from which they were evolved. Like the 'Schützes', their draught has been limited to a bare 2m, enabling them to work in any channel that could be of interest to shipping.

Schleswig, *'Lindau' class CMS.* Marineamt, Bildstelle

Lindau   Coastal minesweeper/minehunter

West Germany

	Builders	Completed
M1070 *Göttingen**	BSB	58
M1071 *Koblenz**	BSB	58
M1072 *Lindau**	BSB	58
M1073 *Schleswig*	BSB	58
M1074 *Tübingen**	BSB	58
M1075 *Wetzlar**	BSB	558
M1076 *Paderborn*	BSB	58
M1077 *Weilheim**	BSB	59
M1078 *Cuxhaven**	BSB	59
M1079 *Düren*	BSB	59
M1080 *Marburg**	BSB	59
M1081 *Konstanz*	BSB	59
M1082 *Wolfsburg*	BSB	59
M1083 *Ulm*	BSB	59
M1084 *Flensburg**	BSB	59
M1085 *Minden**	BSB	60
M1086 *Fulda**	BSB	60
M1087 *Völkingen**	BSB	60

* Minehunter conversions

Displacement: 465 tons full load
Dimensions: 47m × 8.3m × 2.9m
Armament: One 40mm gun
Machinery:
Two diesels 4,000bhp
Two shafts
Speed: 15.6kts (free-running)

Variations of the standard NATO wooden minesweeper, the 18 'Lindaus' were each lengthened by something over 2m shortly after completion — no mean feat on wood-plank construction. Twelve were subsequently converted to minehunters (Type 331) with high definition and classification sonars together with the French-built PAP remote disposal vehicles. The remaining six, perhaps surprisingly in view of their age, are being modified as control ships for the RMC351 (Troika) remotely-controlled mine sweeping system. Their classification will be changed from the standard Type 320 to Type 351. Each control ship and three slaves will form a unit, the whole fleet replacing the 'Schütze' class inshore sweepers.

Troika sweepers are of 24.8m overall length and draw only 1.8m of water. They consist of a highly survivable hull design built around a closed steel cylinder which contains a 360° Schottel propulsion unit, an electrical compartment and a diesel which turn a generator and hydraulic pump, the propulsor being hydraulically-driven. The steel hull cylinder is wound with two coils of copper wire for magnetic minesweeping and, to cater for acoustics, a deep-tone generator can be towed, backed up at four hull points by medium-tone emittors. Control of the unmanned slaves is over a coded radio link, with information being returned to the controller automatically by the same means.

Each control ship has a large-diameter radar display upon which the channels to be swept can be electronically superimposed and progress monitored continually with reference to a fixed point such as a buoy on a taut mooring. Though a safe method of sweeping, it is limited to dealing only with magnetic and acoustic mines and these, it would appear, are detonated perilously close to the slaves.

Rhein Depot ship

West Germany

	Builders	Completed
A54 *Isar*	BVH	64
A55 *Lahn*	FWL	64
A56 *Lech*	FWL	64
A58 *Rhein*	SWH	61
A61 *Elbe*	SWH	62
A63 *Main*	PLK	63
A65 *Saar*	NWH	63
A66 *Neckar*	LV	63
A67 *Mosel*	SWH	63
A68 *Werra*	PLK	64
A69 *Donau*	SWT	64

Displacement: 2,950 tons full load
Dimensions: 98.3m × 11.8m × 4.5m
Armament:
Two 100mm guns (2 × 1)
Four 40mm guns (2 × 2)
Machinery:
Six diesels, 14,400bhp
Two shafts
Diesel driven in A58, 61, 63, 66, 68 and 69
Diesel-electric drive in remainder
Speed: 20kts

Though differing in appearance, this group of ships parallels closely the overall size and functions of the French 'Rhin' class and may well have acted as models for the latter. Similarly, they act as depot ships for MCM, submarine and FAC squadrons for use in advance areas remote from base facilities. They differ in having a more powerful armament, necessitating search radar and fire control, both provided by HSA. Interestingly, they have also a hull-mounted sonar set, whose purpose is obscure as neither AS weapons nor helicopter is carried. *Weser* has been transferred to Greece and *Ruhr* to Turkey. In addition to the *Rheins*, which are used in an essentially static mode, the Bundesmarine has support ships for the same squadrons, capable of underweigh transfer as well as maintenance of missile-armed vessels. These are the eight 'Lüneburg' class ships of about 3,500 tons displacement. Though ammunition transports and mine transport/layers are also operated, fleet replenishment ships are limited to three small and comparatively slow tankers.

Deutschland Training ship

West Germany

	Builders	Completed
A59 *Deutschland*	NR	63

Displacement: 5,700 tons full load
Dimensions: 138.2m × 16m × 5.8m
Armament:
Four 100mm guns (4 × 1)
Six 40mm guns (2 × 2) and (2 × 1)
Two quadruple 375mm AS rocket launchers
Six 533mm/21in torpedo tubes (6 × 1)
Machinery:
Geared steam turbine, 8,400shp on centreline shaft
Four diesels, 8,000bhp, paired on wing shafts
Three shafts
Speed: 22kts max, 17kts diesel, 14kts steam turbine

Though sharing the imposing looks of her 'Hamburg' class contemporaries, the *Deutschland* is a purpose-designed training ship with much of her bulk resulting from accommodation and facilities for up to 250 cadets who can work the ship in all departments and who are carried in addition to the normal crew of about 240. Her weapons, sensors and machinery fit were chosen to give across-the-board practical experience and are, as a result, complex.

She must, for instance, be unique in having a three-shaft arrangement, with the centreline propeller driven by a steam plant and the wing shafts by pairs of diesels. Gun armament comprises four single 100mm pieces and six 40mm weapons in pairs and singles. Ahead-firing Bofors AS rocket launchers are fitted abaft B gun and six torpedo tubes are carried, two of which are for anti-ship torpedoes only. All radars and directors are by the Dutch HSA company. Mines can also be carried and launched.

The problem with such an original concept is that it dates badly. Most of the ship's gear is aimed at training crews for the 'Hamburgs' and 'Kolns' and, very soon, the main forces in the fleet will be the new 'Bremens' and the three 'Adams' with entirely different fits in all departments. Even her two types of diesel — Daimler Benz and Maybach — are now marketed under the common MTU banner. In the event of hostilities, her accommodation would open up possibilities for use in operations control but her very modest speed would pose problems.

Gearing (FRAM I and FRAM II) Destroyer

Greece

	Builders	LD	L	C
FRAM I				
D212 *Kanaris* (ex-USS *Stickell*, DD888)	CSC	45	45	45
D213 *Kountouriotis* (ex-USS *Rupertus*, DD851)	BSQ	45	45	46

FRAM 1 — continued	Builders	LD	L	C
D214 *Sachtouris* (ex-USS *Arnold J. Isbell*, DD869)	BSS	45	45	46
D215 *Tompazis* (ex-USS *Gurke*, DD783)	TPS	44	45	45
D216 *Apostolis* (ex-USS *Charles P. Cecil*, DD835)	BIW	44	45	45
D217 *Kriezis* (ex-USS *Corry*, DD817)	CSC	45	45	46
FRAM II				
DD210 *Themistocles* (ex-USS Frank Knox, DD742)	BIW	44	44	44

(Note — For illustration of FRAM I 'Gearing', see under Spain)

Displacement: 2,425 tons standard; 3,500 tons full load
Dimensions: 119m × 12.6m × 6.0m
Armament:
FRAM I
Four 5in (127mm) guns (2×2)
One 76mm gun
One ASROC launcher
Two triple AS torpedo tubes
FRAM II
Six 5in (127mm) guns (3×2)
Two triple AS torpedo tubes
Two Hedgehog AS spigot mortars
Machinery:
Two sets geared steam turbines, 60,000shp
Two shafts
Speed: 32kts
Aircraft: One light helicopter in FRAM II only

Third and last of the major US WW2 destroyer series were the 'Gearings', which were little more than 'Sumners' stretched by the insertion of an extra section amidships and a miniscule increase in beam. As a result the funnels are more widely spaced than in the very similar earlier class; the machinery installation was identical, allowing for extra bunker capacity and electronics space.

Ninety-nine 'Gearings' were completed, five dismantled before completion and a further 49 cancelled. Like their forebears, those equipped with torpedo tubes either landed them or reduced their number, the final half of the series never receiving them. Despite this they still have a reputation as heavy rollers and are liable to bury their bows in a head sea.

The FRAM I programme of the early 1960s aimed to get the newly-developed ASROC to sea in significant numbers while purpose-built tonnage was still in the piepeline, incidentally up-rating the destroyer's qualities and appointments, to give a further eight years of useful life. Most surrendered B mounting, gained an ASROC launcher amidships and an after superstructure modified for the abortive DASH (Drone AS Helicopter) system.

FRAM II conversions were less thorough, retaining the full original gun armament, gaining the DASH installation but no ASROC. Both types acquired a new electronics fit, resulting in a sturdy tripod foremast and an inelegant lattice structure atop the DASH hangar.

Sumner (FRAM II) Destroyer *Greece*

	Builders	LD	L	C
D211 *Miaoulis* (ex-USS Ingraham, DD694)	FSB	43	44	44

Displacement: 2,200 tons standard; 3,300 tons full load
Dimensions: 114.8m × 12.5m × 5.8m
Armament:
Six 5in (127m) (3×2)
Two triple AS torpedo tubes
Two Hedgehog AS spigot mortars
Machinery:
Two sets geared steam turbines, 60,000shp
Two shafts
Speed: 34kts
Aircraft: One light helicopter

Over 70 'Sumners' were completed for the US fleet, most in 1944. They were descended directly from the 'Fletchers' and, by adopting the twin 5in 38 gunhouse, mounted a six-gun armament on a hull of similar length, though nearly 0.5m needed to be added to the beam to compensate for the added topweight. Even so, they were really over-gunned, a situation aggravated by a continuous superstructure with two quintuple banks of torpedo tubes mounted high up. Their general unhandiness in heavy weather resulted in these TTs being landed early in most.

Originally the class was divided into 58 conventionally equipped units and 12 fitted for minelaying (Turkey still operates one of the latter), but, near the end of the 1950s, 43 were given a FRAM II conversion. Surprisingly, and unlike the larger 'Gearings' they retained their full gun armament but had the after superstructure enlarged to accommodate a DASH helicopter. This project proved abortive, although the resulting space has proved just sufficient to operate a French-built Alouette III.

Still trim despite her years, *Miaoulis* has a reasonable AS potential with a hull-mounted sonar and a VDS (visible right aft) though, beside the helicopter, only AS torpedo tubes (01 level amidships) and two Hedgehogs (flanking the bridge) are carried by way of weapons.

Considering her operating area, she must be vulner-

able to airborne attack, relying only on ECM (in mainmast-mounted pods) to act as a counter. Transferred from the USN in 1971.

Miaoulis, 'Sumner' FRAM II.   Hellenic Naval Official

Fletcher Destroyer

Greece

	Builders	LD	L	C
D06 *Aspis* (ex-USS *Conner*, DD582)	BNY	42	42	43
D16 *Velos* (ex-USS *Charette*, DD581)	BNY	41	42	43
D28 *Thyella* (ex-USS *Bradford*, DD545)	BSP	42	42	43
D56 *Lonchi* (ex-USS *Hall*, DD583)	BNV	42	42	43
D63 *Navarinon* (ex-USS *Brown*, DD546)	BSP	42	43	43
D85 *Sfendoni* (ex-USS *Aulick*, DD569)	CSC	41	42	42
D42 *Kimon* (ex-Z3) (ex-USS *Wadsworth*, DD516)	BIW	42	43	43
D65 *Nearchos* (ex-Z4) (ex-USS *Claxton*, DD571)	CSC	41	42	42

Displacement: 2,050 tons standard; 3,050 tons full load
Dimensions: 114.7m × 12m × 5.5m
Armament:
Four/five 5in (127mm) guns (4/5 × 1)
Six 3in (76mm) guns in some (3 × 2)
Two Hedghog AS spigot mortars
Five 21in (533mm) torpedo tubes in some (1 × 5)
Launching gear for AS torpedoes
Machinery:
Two sets geared steam turbine, 60,000shp

Two sets
Speed: 32kts

No fewer than 171 'Fletcher' class destroyers had been built for the US Navy when the programme was terminated in 1944 in favour of the 'Sumners' and 'Gearings'. Developed from the preceding 'Benson'/'Gleaves' class, the 'Fletchers' dropped the raised forecastle and reverted to the flush deck used in earlier types. They were also over nine metres longer to allow for a fifth gun, in Q position, and more generous bunker capacity.

The 'Fletchers' did not undergo FRAM modifications but were modernised, visible externally by the substitution of a widely-braced tripod for the original pole foremast in order to support the heavy SPS-6 (air search) and SPS-10 (surface search) antennas. Q gun and the forward torpedo tube bank were also landed and replaced by six 3in guns. A Hedgehog AS mortar was placed in a forward-firing position on either side of the bridge.

Kimon, 'Fletcher' class (seen as West German Z3). Marineamt, Bildstelle

Greece acquired six of the type between 1959 and 1962. West Germany had five, of which one (Z1) was used as a target and sold to the Greeks in 1979 for spares. Z3 and Z4 were transferred in 1980/1 and the remaining pair are reported also to be following as the new Type 122's commission.

Kortenaer Frigate   *Greece*

	Builders	LD	L	C
F450 *Elli* (ex-*Pieter Florisz*)	KMdeS	77	79	81
F451 *Limnos* (ex-*Witte de With*)	KMdeS	78	80	82

For data see under Netherlands

Both above units have been purchased from out of the Dutch 'Kortenaer' production line and it is the intention of the Greeks to build further of the class at their own Skaramanga facility under licence and, presumably, with Dutch assistance. They are identical with Netherlands-flag ships except that they will reportedly carry a twin Breda L/70 mounting on either side of the hangar structure. In place of the intended brace of Lynx helicopters, a reported Italian AB212 is to be carried.

Where the comparatively large Greek destroyer force is now over-aged and obsolete, the choice of the 'Kortenaer' as replacement would seem less than ideal, it being designed for a long-range Atlantic war and on the large side for Eastern Mediterranean use. An influence was obviously ready availability at the right price but the improved 'Descubierta' (qv) from Spain at under 2,000 tons full load would seem adequate. As things are, the proposed Dutch 'M' frigate may also prove attractive.

Cannon Destroyer escort   *Greece*

	Builders	LD	L	C
D01 *Aetos* (ex-USS *Slater*, DE766)	TSC	43	44	44
D31 *Ierax* (ex-USS *Elbert*, DE768)	TSC	43	44	44
D54 *Leon* (ex-USS *Eldridge*, DE173)	FSB	43	43	43
D67 *Panthir* (ex-USS *Garfield Thomas*, DE193)	FSB	43	43	44

Displacement: 1,250 tons standard; 1,900 tons full load
Dimensions: 93.3m × 11.3m × 4.3m
Armament:
Three 3in (76mm) guns (3 × 1)
Six 40mm guns
Two triple AS torpedo tubes
Hedgehog
Machinery:
Diesel electric with four diesel generators 6,000shp
Two shafts
Speed: 19kts

American destroyer escorts were closer to light destroyers rather than to frigates and, as such, are comparable with, say, the British 'Hunts' or German 'torpedo boats' though larger. Critically short of escorts on entering WW2, the USN instituted vast construction programmes, that governing DEs eventually resulting in 565 ships with a further 450 being cancelled at the cessation of hostilities. Where equivalent British designs favoured simple reciprocating machinery for reliability, ease of production and personnel training, the Americans put speed as a higher priority. In conjunction with other demands, this over-stretched industrial capabilities, so the basic DE type evolved into sub-groups propelled by steam turbines, by diesels, by turbo-electric plant, or, in the case of the 'Cannons', by diesel-electric installations. In these, the four diesels can each drive generators, the output of which is rectified to feed dc propulsion motors coupled directly to the two shafts. The arrangement allows for very fine shaft speed control, no gearing and simple reversing together with short shafts as the motor room can be sited well aft. Even so, the heavy electrical gear resulted in a 40ton penalty compared with diesel-driven equivalents.

Very much in their original condition, the four Greek units were acquired in 1951 and, like a large number of ex-American ships under the Greek flag, must soon be replaced.

Combattante III   FAC (Missile)   *Greece*

	Builders	Completed
P20 *Antiploiarhos Laskos*	CMN	77
P21 *Plotarhis Blessas*	CMN	77
P22 *Ipoploiarhos Mikonios*	CMN	78
P23 *Ipoploiarhos Troupakis*	CMN	77
P24 *Simeoforos Kavaloudis*	HSS	80
P25 *Antiploiarhos Kostakos*	HSS	80
P26 *Ipoploiarhos Deyiannis*	HSS	80
P27 *Simeoforos Zenos*	HSS	81
P28 *Simeoforos Simitzopoulos*	HSS	81
P29 *Simeoforos Starakis*	HSS	81

Displacement:
(P20-P23) 360 tons standard; 425 tons full load
(P24-P29) 330 tons standard; 430 tons full load
Dimensions: 56.2m × 8m × 2.2m
Armament:
(P20-P23) Four MM38 Exocet SSMs
(P24-P29) Six Penguin II SSMs
All: Two 76mm DP guns (2 × 1)
Four 30mm guns (2 × 2)
Two 533mm (21in) torpedo tubes (2 × 1)

Machinery:
Four diesels, 18,000bhp
Four shafts
Speed: 36kts

This type is really a 'Combattante II', stretched by something over 9m, placing it in the largest current category of FACs beyond which, in terms of size, lie corvettes. Why the earlier, 47m boats were terminated at only four is not clear; from the point of view of size, they were already larger than other varities of FAC under the Greek flag. The extra length certainly confers extra seakindliness and has enabled the armament to be uprated to a brace of 76mm guns and, possibly more importantly, to add a couple of paired Emerlec 30mm mountings on the bridge structure to meet the threat from the air. In the first four, French-built craft four MM38 Exocets are fitted but in the half-dozen, home-built follow-ons the smaller Penguin II has been adopted, allowing a battery of six to be shipped. A tube for the launching of anti-ship wire-guided torpedoes is set on either quarter.

Ipoploiarhos Troupakis, *'Combattante III'*.
Mike Lennon

At least in the French-built examples, a modified SATIN automated combat system allows for the Type IIIs to coordinate operations and a 50% increase in diesel output power has been necessary to achieve a similar speed. The general impression is one of a very ambitious weapon fit on the displacement but which will not be able to replace the obsolete destroyer force.

However, taking into account the short ranges involved in operations in their island-studded coastal waters, FACs would prove eminently suitable for the likely 'now-you-see-me, now-you-don't' type of warfare. Like the Swedish navy the Greeks could dispense with larger ships but would be unwilling to do so if the Turks still operated them.

Combattante II   FAC (Missile)   *Greece*

	Builders	Completed
P14 *Antiploiarhos Anninos* (ex-*Navsithoi*)	CMN	72
P15 *Ipoploiarhos Arliotis* (ex-*Evniki*)	CMN	72
P16 *Ipoploiarhos Kondis* (ex-*Kymothoi*)	CMN	72
P17 *Ipoploiarhos Batsis* (ex-*Kalypso*)	CMN	71

Displacement: 235 tons standard; 255 tons full load
Dimensions: 47m × 7.1m × 2.5m
Armament:
Four MM38 Exocet SSMs
Four 35mm guns (2 × 2)
Two 533mm/21in torpedo tubes (2 × 1)
Machinery:
Four diesels 12,000bhp
Four shafts
Speed: 36kts

Closely similar to the West German navy's Type 148s, the 'Combattante IIs' share with them a common ancestry in the TNC45, a Lürssen 45m design built under licence by CMN, having been stretched by 2m. With a round-bilged steel hull and aluminium superstructure, the basic design has proved very successful and exported to several countries in different configurations of weaponry and sensors. All, being SSM orientated, have the monoblock superstructure set well forward to allow the large, canister-launcher Exocets to be placed in pairs angled at 45 degrees off the centreline. This, inevitably, reduces the effective firing arc of the forward gun mounting. (Compare with layout of, say, a Swedish 'Spica' with a gun/torpedo fit and no SSMs.) Where most examples mount a 76mm gun forward and pair of smaller calibre automatic AA weapons aft, the Greeks have, unusually, opted for paired 35mm Oerlikon/Buhrle guns forward and aft. This may well be to conserve topweight to allow for the fitting of two aft-facing anti-ship torpedo tubes. As with the German equivalents, radars are largely from the French Thomson-CSF company but an interesting addition is the Plessy IFF antenna offset from the Triton surveillance and target indication scanner.

Jaguar   FAC (Torpedo)   *Greece*

	Builders	Completed
P50 *Hesperos* (ex-Seeadler, P6068)	LV/KR	58/64
P51 *Kataigis* (ex-Falke, P6072)	LV/KR	58/64
P52 *Kentauros* (ex-Habicht, P6075)	LV/KR	58/64
P53 *Kyklon* (ex-Greif, P6071)	LV/KR	58/64
P54 *Lelaps* (ex-Kondor, P6070)	LV/KR	58/64
P55 *Skorpios* (ex-Kormoran, P6077)	LV/KR	58/64
P56 *Tyfon* (ex-Geier, P6073)	LV/KR	58/64

Displacement: 160 tons standard; 190 tons full load
Dimensions: 42.5m × 7.3m × 2.5m
Armament:
Two 40mm guns (2 × 1)
Four 533mm/21in torpedo tubes (4 × 1)
Machinery:
Four diesels 12,000bhp
Four shafts
Speed: 42kts

The sleek, racy profile of the 'Jaguar' typifies the German S-boat of the pre-missile age. Derived from the E-boats of WW2, via the 'Silbermöwe' class, the 'Jaguars' went to a class of 40, the final 10 being completed as the 'Zobel' group, now being retired from the Bundesmarine. Of these, 32 were built by the designers, Lürssen, and the remaining eight by Krogerwerft at Rendsburg.

With its raised forecastle, this 'traditional' type of boat has an enviable reputation for dryness forward but the permanent dodgers suggest quantities of free water aft. Unlike earlier boats, the 'Jaguars' forward pair of tubes do not fire through doors in the sides of the forecastle, the latter being appropriately inset to allow flank

launching. The after pair of tubes can be removed to permit the carriage of four mines. The forward gun is set down to maindeck level to allow bridge personnel better visibility forward and to lower its centre of gravity. Construction is of wood on steel frames, with light alloy superstructure and continued the German preference for a displacement type hull as opposed to the flat-sectioned, planing hulls often built elsewhere. Built before the formation of the MTU combine, the

Kentauros, 'Jaguar' class. Hellenic Navy Official

majority of the 'Jaguars' had 20-cylinder Daimler-Benz diesels and the remainder 16-cylinder Maybachs. With strict fairness reminiscent of American transfers to South American fleets, West Germany passed seven 'Jaguars' each to the rival Greek and Turkish navies, each receiving in addition three older hulls for disposal as spares.

Tjeld FAC (Torpedo) *Greece*

	Builders	Completed
P196 *Andromeda*	BM	67
P197 *Kastor*	BM	67
P198 *Kyknos*	BM	67
P199 *Pigassos*	BM	67
P200 *Toxotis*	BM	67

For data see under Norway.

Five survivors of a class of six built by Batservis to Greek account. They are to the same design as the Norwegian boats and the sixth unit, *Iniohos*, was deleted after damage in 1972.

Glavkos Patrol submarine *Greece*

	Builders	Completed
S110 *Glavkos*	HWK	71
S111 *Nereus*	HWK	72
S112 *Triton*	HWK	72
S113 *Proteus*	HWK	72
S116 *Poseidon*	HWK	79
S117 *Amphitrite*	HWK	79
S118 *Okeanos*	HWK	79
S119 *Pontos*	HWK	80

Displacement:
(S110-113) — 1,100 tons surfaced, 1,210 tons submerged
(S116-119) — 1,140 tons surfaced, 1,285 tons submerged
Dimensions:
(S110-113) — 54.4m × 6.2m × 5.5m
(S116-119) — 55.9m × 6.2m × 5.7m
Armament: Eight 533mm torpedo tubes (all forward)
Machinery: Four diesel generators powering one propulsion motor, 4,900shp. Single shaft
Speed: 11/23kts

A typical product of the West German IKL stable, the Type 209 has enjoyed enhanced sales from 'knock-on' effects among rival fleets. This has happened in South America as well as in Greece and Turkey. Each of the latter was equipped solely with ageing ex-American submarine tonnage, not really suitable for confined Mediterranean use and, when Greece acquired four 209s, Turkey replied likewise and embarked on building her own under licence. Greece, thereupon, purchased four more. All very good for German exports, of course, but, though probably demonstrating disunity in NATO rather than accord, serving to strengthen the West's submarine arm with suitable craft at a sensitive spot. Capable of a 50-day endurance, these boats have a single hull and can dive to at least 250m. The relatively large fin houses up to eight telescopic masts: from forward these are — anti-helicopter missiles (if fitted), search periscope, 'snort' induction mast,UHF/HF communications antennas, ECM gear, attack periscope and radar antenna. Unusually, four diesel generators are used, being sited two-thirds aft. A double-armature propulsion motor is sited well aft, driving a large-

diameter, slow-turning propeller through a tunnel in the after ballast and trim tanks. Batteries account for about 20% of the boat's displacement and can be force-cooled to meet high demands. The eight torpedo tubes

Amphitrite, *Glavkos Type 209*.   Hellenic Navy Official

Guppy type   Patrol submarine

Greece

	Builders	LD	L	C
S114 *Papanikolis* (ex-USS *Hardhead*, SS365)	MSB	43	43	44
S115 *Katsonis* (ex-USS *Remora*, SS487)	PNY	45	45	46

Displacement	*S114*	*S115*
Surfaced	1,850	1,975
Submerged	2,450	2,450

Dimensions: 93.2m×8.2m×5.3m   99.5m×8.2m×5.2m
Armament: (Both) Ten 533mm (21in) torpedo tubes (six forward, four aft)
Machinery:
S114: Three diesels, 4,800bhp
S115: Four diesels, 6,400bhp
Both: Two electric motors 5,400shp
Two shafts
Speed:
S114, 17/15kts
S115, 20/15kts

Two of the diminishing number of survivors from the extensive American WW2 submarine programme. *S114* is one of the 124 'Balao' class boats and S115 from the 23-strong follow-on 'Tench' class, very similar but deeper-diving. Though designed for 600ft submergence, age has probably reduced this. Benefiting from the lessons of the German Type XXI, the Americans embarked postwar on a long-term reconstruction project to improve the performance of this large force of nearly new but already obsolescent submarines. This was known as the 'Guppy' (Greater Underwater Propulsive Performance) programme, under which 47 boats were rebuilt in varying degrees.

The 'Guppy IIIs', of which *Katsonis* is an example, kept their four original diesels for a high surface speed of 20kts, in addition having their two electric propulsion motors replaced by others of twice the power. Better electronics and uprated batteries resulted in the need for a new hull section to be added, increasing length by over 6m. *Papanikolis* is a 'Guppy IIA', the major differences in which is that improved electronics have been fitted at the expense of one diesel. The comparatively low submerged speed of each betrays her wartime ancestry. In spite of their heavy battery of torpedo tubes, they are large for Mediterranean work and would prove vulnerable to detection, particularly as this type of boat is very noisy by modern standards. Externally they differ by *Katsonis* having the three prominent fins of a PUFFS sonar installation spaced along her hull. Transferred in 1972/3, they cannot be retained much longer.

Navkratoussa   Landing ship (Dock)

Greece

	Builders	Completed
L153 *Navkratoussa* (ex-USS *Fort Mandan*, LSD 21)	BNY	45

For data see under *Galicia*, Spain.

Transferred in 1971 to take the place of earlier ship of the same name. Greek amphibious forces include also two ex-US 117m 'County'-type LSTs, five 100m LSTs, two LCTs, five LSMs and a variety of minor craft.

MSC type   Coastal minesweeper

Greece

	Completed
M202 *Atalante*(ex-*St Truiden*, ex-USS MSC169)	54
M205 *Antiopi* (ex-*Herve*, ex-USS MSC153)	54
M206 *Faedra* (ex-*Malmedy*, ex-USS MSC154)	54
M210 *Thalia* (ex-*Blankenberge*, ex-USS MSC170)	54
M211 *Alkyon* (ex-USS MSC319	68
M213 *Klio* (ex-USS MSC317)	68
M214 *Avra* (ex-USS MSC318)	68
M240 *Pleias* (ex-USS MSC314)	67
M241 *Kichli* (ex-USS MSC308)	64
M242 *Kissa* (ex-USS MSC309)	64
M246 *Aigli* (ex-USS MSC299)	65
M247 *Dafni* (ex-USS MSC307)	64
M248 *Aedon* (ex-USS MSC310)	64
M254 *Niovi* (ex-*Laroche*, ex-USS MSC171)	54

Displacement:
(M202-210, M254) 330 tons standard; 400 tons full load
(M211-248) 320 tons standard; 370 tons full load
Dimensions: 44m×8.5m×2.5m
Armament: Two 20mm guns (1×2)
Machinery:
Two diesels, 900bhp
Two shafts
Speed: 13kts (running free)

This type of 'sweeper' represents a postwar improvement of the war-built AMS (Auxiliary Minesweeper), both types being reclassified as MSC (Minesweeper, Coastal) in the 1950s. The postwar programme was part of the upsurge in Western interest in mine counter-measures after the Korean War. Besides building for their own use, the Americans built also for other NATO navies which, in some cases, also constructed to the same design in home yards. Belgium was one such, with 18 US-built units and eight from Belgian yards.

Five of these were transferred to the Greek flag in 1969, to serve together with nine further vessels built to Greek account in the USA during the mid-1960s. They are little smaller than the standard NATO coastals (represented by the British 'Tons') and, like them, are of wood-on-non-ferrous-framed construction, with maximum attention paid to reducing magnetic signature. None of the Greeks has been converted to a minehunting role. Externally the ex-Belgian vessels can be identified by the close similarity to the Danish 'Sunds' (qv).

P31   Offshore patrol vessel

Ireland

	Builders	Completed
P31 —	VCD	1984

Displacement: 1,900 tons full load
Dimensions: 81m×12m×4.3m
Armament:
One 57mm gun
Two 20mm guns (2×1)
Machinery:
Two diesels, 6,600bhp

Twin shafts
Speed: 19kts
Aircraft: One helicopter with hangar

Planned to be eventually a four-ship class, the P31s are meant to operate patrols of up to 19 days duration, primarily in those areas of the Irish continental shelf off the exposed west and south coasts. A major difference, compared with the earlier P22s, is the adoption of helicopter facilities, with a Lynx-sized aircraft being accommodated aboard, with a pad large enough to

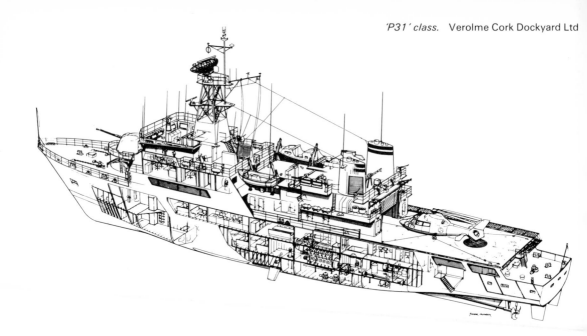

accept a larger unit in Vertrep mode. Being centreline, the hangar has split the uptakes from the two Ruston diesels, the handsomely-proportioned funnels of the earlier ships giving way to a rather poor pair of sided casings that do nothing for the looks of the ship. Superstructure in way of the bridge has been carried to the sides with forward screen doors for higher security; no bow bulwarks are fitted to allow the quicker passage overboard of loose water. Anchors are set in pockets to reduce slamming and forward flare seems to be more moderate, reducing pitch accelerations.

Armament specification has been enhanced to a Bofors-built 75mm gun set on a forward extension of

the bridge front and laid by a HSA-built fire control system. Surveillance radars are also by HSA, with Decca navigation units. Interestingly, a small Plessey sonar is fitted, suggesting a basic AS capability on the part of the helicopter.

Another interesting development over the P22 is the adoption of twin cp screws and twin rudders. As greater manoeuvrability is hardly of interest to an OPV, this may be a measure to absorb the 40% increase in power, without increasing the draught, whilst giving an ability to up-rate power further without additional major modifications.

Deirdre and Emer Offshore patrol vessel *Ireland*

	Builders	Completed
P20 *Deirdre*	VCD	72

Displacement: 975 tons full load
Dimensions: 56.2m × 10.4m × 4.4m
Armament: One 40mm gun
Machinery:
Two diesels 4,200bhp
Single shaft
Speed: 18kts

	Builders	Completed
P21 *Emer*	VCD	78
P22 *Aoife*	VCD	79
P23 *Aisling*	VCD	80

Displacement: 1,020 tons full load
Dimensions: 65.2m × 10.5m × 4.4m
Armament: One 40mm and smaller

Machinery:
Two diesels, 4,800bhp
Single shaft
Speed: 18kts

The Irish Naval Service was one of the last to operate the splendid old 'Flower' class corvettes. A trio of these were replaced in 1971 by three 'Ton' class minesweepers, acquired also from the Royal Navy. Though these proved satisfactory interim fishery protection vessels, they lacked the range and weatherliness necessary for work in deeper water particularly on the Atlantic coasts, so a larger vessel was ordered from the Cork Yard of the Dutch Verolme group. This ship, *Deirdre*, had considerable style with more than a hint of her Dutch origins. The hull had adequate freeboard, with a bulwark forward and a full cruiser stern. No helicopter facilities incorporated in the

design, the quarterdeck being kept clear for a towing winch with associated bitts and a horse. No rigid inflatables were provided so, in view of the number of times that the motor boat could expect to be launched in a seaway, the lack of hull sheathing in way of the davits is surprising.

Three years of evaluation followed before the ordering, in 1975, of the *Emer*, the first of three. Experience pointed to the need for a longer hull, with extra power to compensate, together with better subdivision and attention to crew comfort in conditions of heavy

Deirdre. Verolme Cork Dockyard Ltd

weather and with respect to machinery-induced noise and vibration. With the acquisition of a ratified EEZ, the Eire government then ordered two more.

The later units carry one boat less (having a Gemini under a single arm davit) have a pair of Oerlikon 20mm guns abaft the bridge, no forward bulwarks (but have a half-height forecastle) and no specialised towing gear. Diesels in the first three were changed from British built Polars to French Pielstick medium-speed units.

Giuseppe Garibaldi   Light aircraft carrier   *Italy*

	Builders	LD	L	C
C551 *Giuseppe Garibaldi*	IM	81	83	85

Displacement: 10,100 tons standard; 13,370 tons full load
Dimensions: 180m×30.5m (width over flight deck) ×6.8m
Armament:
Four Otomat SSM launchers
Two octuple Aspide SAM
Two triple AS torpedo tubes
Three twin 40mm guns
Machinery:
Four gas turbines, 80,000shp
Twin shafts
Speed: 30kts+
Aircraft: 12 Sea King helicopter equivalents

In the event of full hostilities the Soviets will need to control the Turkish Black Sea exit if their southern fleet is to have any hope of functioning. Yet, even if Turkish soil is occupied for this purpose, the West's submarines will dispute this access. In addition, older SSBNs of both persuasions with shorter-ranged missiles will also need to use the Mediterranean to cover their targets. To support and counter these various activities, many highly-capable fleet submarines will be deployed and the Italian Navy will have an important role in neutralising those of the enemy. Thus, after years of land-based airpower to support the fleet, a carrier is at last being built. *Giuseppe Garibaldi* will be one of a growing number of ASW-biassed 'aviation-capable' ships that are being loosely grouped under the title of 'light aircraft carriers', and is directly comparable with the British *Invincible*, the Soviet *Moskva*, the Spanish *Dedalo* and the French *Jeanne d'Arc* which, between them, offer a wide range of opinion as to the preferred form of this new breed.

Garibaldi has an air of Italian dash and will be a nicely balanced ship when completed, well capable of leading an AS group. Her usually-quoted 18 Sea King capacity includes six that would need to be stowed

Giuseppe Garibaldi. Italian Official

topsides, and any V/STOL aircraft embarked would reduce the number of helicopters further. Two Aspide systems will give AA coverage out to about 10 miles but these are not sufficiently agile to cope with SSMs and the chosen Vanessa system is still under development. Four Otomat launchers, with reloads, give long-range anti-ship coverage but if any enemy submarine gets close enough to be successfully attacked by the ship's own AS torpedoes, the ship herself would indeed be at hazard, although the large hull-mounted sonar suggests an active part for her in any hunt. *Garibaldi* is a true carrier, with starboard-set island but, lacking angled deck, arrestor gear or catapults, could not deploy fixed-wing aircraft.

Like the *Invincible*, she is propelled by four large gas turbines on twin shafts, in this case Fiat-built General Electric LM2500s, apparently derated to 20,000hp apiece. As efficiency demands that these be run at high speed the arrangement would not appear to be ideal for cruising.

The design has passed through many castings and the protracted building period suggests that the size of the ship may be causing unforeseen construction difficulties.

Vittorio Veneto   Helicopter cruiser

Italy

	Builders	LD	L	C
C550 *Vittorio Veneto*	IC	65	67	69

Displacement: 7,500 tons standard; 8,750 tons full load
Dimensions: 179.5m × 19.5m × 6m
Armament:
One Terrier SAM system
Eight 76mm DP guns
Two triple AS torpedo tubes
Machinery:
Twin sets steam turbines, 73,000shp
Twin shafts
Speed: 32kts max
Aircraft: Nine medium helicopters with hangar

This 'one-off' is a combination of the watered-down approach to a much more ambitious vessel and operational experience from the pair of 'Andrea Dorias' (qv). To be named *Italia* (suggesting a flagship), the original ship would have carried a large flight of helicopters and a capacity for amphibious assault. This scheme proved beyond available budgets, so the design was recast and renamed *Trieste* (suggesting a downgrading), then shelved until 1968 before being abandoned. *Vittorio Veneto* herself was produced in parallel with the latter being laid down in 1965 and suffering herself from several re-castings during the construction, which, surprisingly, lasted a bare four years. She has much in common also with the influential French *Jeanne d'Arc*, completed shortly before though, where both have a flight deck one level higher than the forecastle to improve stowage below and dryness on top, the Italian's far higher installed power has demanded two widely-spread machinery spaces, the uptakes from which have, in turn, dictated the superstructure layout.

She is an AS ship with the capacity to command a group. Beneath the flightdeck is stowage for up to nine Agusta Bell 212ASWs, helicopters equivalent in size and performance to the Anglo-French Lynx. For defensive purposes while she pursues her calling, *Veneto* has

a US Terrier area defence SAM system forward and, by today's standards, the comparatively large gun armament of eight 76mm in the older single 'Brescia' mountings. Two substantial 'macks' serve as machinery exhausts and supports for the surveillance and 3D tracker antennas, and two American SPG-55B Terrier controls are sited on the bridge structure. A long-range hull-mounted sonar is also fitted. Due soon for a mid-

Vittorio *Veneto*   Italian Official

life modernisation, Veneto probably has the space to acquire a Mark 10 launcher capable of handling both Standard ER and ASROC rounds. This would enhance her performance in both areas and be fully compatible with sonar and directors already fitted.

Andrea Doria   Helicopter cruiser   *Italy*

	Builders	LD	L	C
C553 *Andrea Doria*				
(ex-*Enrico Dandalo*)	CNR	58	63	64
C554 *Caio Duilio*	IC	58	62	64

Displacement: 5,000 tons standard; 6,500 tons full load
Dimensions: 149.5m × 17.2m × 5m

Caio Duilio, *'Andrea Doria' class.*   Mike Lennon

Armament:
One Standard ER SAM system
Eight 76mm DP guns
Two triple AS torpedo tubes
Machinery:
Two sets steam turbines, 60,000shp
Twin shafts
Speed: 32kts
Aircraft: Four medium helicopters with hangar

This handsome pair represented considerable innovation on their completion in 1964 and may well be contrasted with the contemporary British 'County' class destroyers of much the same size. The latter's area-defence SAM was the ungainly Sea Slug whose massive support facilities dictated the ship's parameters and, allowing, almost as an afterthought, the inclusion of a large Wessex AS helicopter.

On the other hand, the American Terrier system was far more compact, the loading arrangements allowing a forward siting. With the after end completely free, sufficient space was available for four small helicopters, since replaced by Agusta Bell 212ASWs, stowed in the boxy after end of the superstructure. During their construction, the veteran cruiser Garibaldi was fitted with a further Terrier system for training purposes. Both the 'Dorias' and the later Veneto have flattish runs aft which allow of retangular flightdecks without excessive flare though the earlier ships have a flush deck, not having the need to strike the helicopters below. Eight 76mm automatic DP guns are still carried by Doria but only six in the Duilio, and only the former has been modernised to exchange her Terriers for the later Standard ERs. Duilio has taken the place of venerable San Giorgio as training ship and, in view of this, it seems unlikely that she would be extensively modernised before both ships are due to be replaced by the new light carrier Garibaldi in the second half of the decade.

Impavido Destroyer   *Italy*

	Builders	LD	L	C
D570 *Impavido*	CNR	57	62	63
D571 *Intrepido*	IC	59	62	64

Displacement: 3,200 tons standard; 3,850 tons full load
Dimensions: 135m × 13.5m × 4.5m
Armament:
One Standard MR launcher
Two 5in (217mm) guns (1 × 2)
Four 76mm guns
Two triple AS torpedo tubes
Machinery:
Two sets steam turbines, 70,000shp
Twin shafts
Speed: 33kts

This pair of ships are interesting in being contemporary with both the West German 'Hamburg' class and the American 'Adams'. All are much of a size and the Italians represent a link between the large, 'heavy destroyer' approach of the former and the new wave GM destroyers of the Americans, who had discovered that conversions of conventional destroyer tonnage to GM escorts could not be effected economically. Compared with the more logical approach of the 'Adams', the armament seems rather unbalanced; the single Standard MR system is again complemented by a pair of 5in guns (albeit of an older 38-calibre pattern) but, if the SAM was held to be effective, why were four 76mm weapons shipped? The topweight could have been better utilised in the form of the Menon AS mortar for which space had been left in B position. As it is, with no helicopter, they depend upon AS torpedo tubes for protection against submarine attack and these are likely to pose little threat to a fast modern boat. Now approaching 20 years of age, both have had a degree of modernisation, but this has been confined mainly to improving fire control of both missile and gun armament rather than changing the armament itself. By the time that the new Garibaldi enters service about 1985, they will be distinctly elderly to be viewed as alternatives to the 'Audaces' as her escorts but may need to soldier on until the brace of 'improved Audaces' enter service, at a date yet unspecified.

Impavido. Mike Lennon

Indomito. Mike Lennon

Impetuoso Destroyer

Italy

	Builders	LD	L	C
D558 *Impetuoso*	CNR	52	56	58
D559 *Indomito*	AL	52	55	58

Displacement: 2,750 tons standard; 3,800 tons full load
Dimensions: 127.5m × 13.3m × 4.6m
Armament:
Four 5in (127mm) guns (2 × 2)
Sixteen 40mm guns (2 × 4) and (4 × 2)
Two triple AS torpedo tubes
One triple-barrelled AS mortar
Machinery:
Two sets steam turbines, 65,000shp
Twin shafts
Speed: 34kts

As Italy's first postwar destroyers, the 'Impetuosos' not only have an American outfit of armament and electronics but also show a strong Transatlantic influence in general design. Earlier Italian destroyers had considerable dash but little substance, speed without seakindliness and 'presence' without punch.

The raised forecastle was dropped in favour of a flush-decked hull with pronounced sheer and the bridge built on to a full-width deckhouse, an arrangement which became common to several Italian classes. Trunked funnels exhausting earlier concentrated and vulnerable machinery spaces were abandoned in favour of a pair of funnels of distinctly American aspect above more widely-spaced boiler rooms. The more modest top speed is also more likely to be sustained in a seaway. In keeping with postwar thinking, no large calibre torpedo tubes were fitted for antiship purposes, the original pair of AS tubes being exchanged for the more-common American triple Mark 32s at a later date. In the superfiring position forward is an Italian-built Menon mortar, a triple-barrelled AS weapon that fires at a fixed 45° elevation to put a pattern of 160kg projectiles out to about 1,000m. What is surprising is that the ships have retained their full dated outfit of 16 40mm guns and a mainmast with no apparent function. Together with some of the older frigates, they are now paying-off-into reserve, largely to provide crews for the new 'Maestrales' and, short of an emergency, they are unlikely to see further service.

Audace Destroyer

Italy

	Builders	LD	L	C
D550 *Ardito*	IC	68	71	73
D551 *Audace*	CNR	68	71	72

Displacement: 3,600 tons standard; 4,400 tons full load
Dimensions: 136.5m × 14.2m × 4.5m
Armament:
One Standard MR launcher
Two 127mm guns (2 × 1)
Four 76mm guns (4 × 1)
Two triple AS torpedo tubes
Machinery:
Two sets steam turbines 73,000shp
Twin shafts
Speed: 33kts
Aircraft: Two AB212 or one Sea King helicopter, with hangar

Though rated as 'Improved Impavidos' and carrying a similar scale of armament, the 'Audaces' are very different in appearance, and comparison is instructive in demonstrating the impact of the helicopter on ship design. Firstly, the length has been increased (though this may be to reduce vertical accelerations, it seems also an inescapable result of 'improvements') and the after run flattened out to give greater beam for the flight deck. Then, the after freeboard has been increased to reduce wetness aft. Next, the addition of the boxy hangar has resulted in the missile launcher moving upwards, followed by directors. This general upward movement was accentuated by the exchange of the old American-pattern twin 5in 38 gunhouse for the more capable OTO-Melara weapons, which required a superimposed B gun, resulting in a higher bridge and funnels. They were also the first Italian class to ship the new Compatto pattern 76mm guns; four of

65

these are carried, a combination of the general Italian tendency to carry a large number of guns by current standards and necessity because of poor firing arcs. In the course of the mid-life refit due shortly, it would make sense to land the 127mm gun in the superimposed position in favour of an Albatros/Aspide PDMS. The 'Audaces' were among the earliest escorts to provide facilities for a pair of helicopters, being laid down even before the Canadian 'Tribals'. They are likely to be the last steam turbine ships in the Italian Navy and full use has been made of the two funnel casings

Ardito, 'Audace' class.   Mike Lennon

for rigid supports for mast and antennas. On the after funnel is the tilted rectangular antenna of the American SPS-52, 3D air search unit for the Standard, whose pair of characteristic SPG-51 directors are adjacent. Beside AS torpedo tubes, these ships were equipped with four fixed tubes firing large weapons through the transom but, with the obsolescence of the G2B Kangaroo, these may have been removed.

Maestrale   Frigate

Italy

	Builders	LD	L	C
F570 *Maestrale*	CNR	78	81	81
F571 *Grecale*	CNR	79	81	82
F572 *Libeccio*	CNR	80	81	82
F573 *Scirocco*	CNR	80	82	82
F574 *Aliseo*	CNR	81	82	83
F575 *Euro*	CNR	81	83	83
F576 *Espero*	CNR	82	83	83
F577 *Zefiro*	CNR	82	84	84

Displacement: 2,530 tons standard; 2,040 tons full load
Dimensions: 122.7m × 12.9m × 5.9m max
Armament:
Four Otomat SSM
One octuple Aspide SAM
One 127mm gun
Two twin 40mm guns
Two 533mm torpedo tubes
Two triple 324mm torpedo tubes
Machinery:
Two sprint gas turbines, 50,000shp
Two cruise diesels, 11,000shp
CODOG Twin shafts
Speed: 33kts max, 21kts cruise
Aircraft: Two AB 212 or one Sea King helicopter, with hangar

With their strong 'family' resemblance to the 'Lupos', the 'Maestrales' are inevitably viewed as a necessary enlargement to an originally over-ambitious design. While there is probably an element of truth in this, the official line is that they are larger in order to improve their AS potential without reducing by too great a degree the powerful surface armament of the earlier vessel. The overall length has been increased by about 9.5m and the beam by nearly a metre which, while increasing the full load displacement by over 20% has greatly improved capacity, habitability and, almost certainly, seakeeping. Four of the eight Otomats have been landed in favour of facilities for a second helicopter. An enlarged hangar and flight pad has called for fuller lines aft, which have also allowed for a VDS installation and two aft-firing 533mm (21in) tubes for the Whitehead A184 wire-guided torpedo (or, presumably, the Mark 48 if required) for use against submarine or surface targets. Two twin 40mm mountings are combined in the eight-cell Aspide launcher with in aerial defence, the latter with a useful 15,000m range. The 127mm gun forward is a larger weapon than usual in this size of ship. This powerful armament package is bought at the expense of a fire-prone aluminium superstructure, but sufficient deadweight is left to add extra fuel if required to give a range of better than 6,000nm cruising at 15kts. Propulsion is by the same means as

he 'Lupos', two Fiat-built General Electric LM2500 gas turbines of 50,000shp in a space forward of the cruising diesel room, which houses two GMT engines.

Because of financial stringencies, only the first six were ordered in 1977, the remaining two following in 1980.

Lupo   Frigate

	Builders	LD	L	C
F564 *Lupo*	CNR	74	76	77
F565 *Sagittario*	CNR	76	77	78
F566 *Perseo*	CNR	77	78	79
F567 *Orsa*	CNR	77	79	80

Displacement: 2,210 tons standard; 2,525 tons full load
Dimensions: 113.2m × 12m × 3.7m
Armament:
Eight Otomat SSM
One octuple NATO Sea Sparrow PDMS
One 127mm gun
Two twin 40mm guns
Two triple AS torpedo tubes
Machinery:
Two sprint gas turbines, 50,000shp
Two cruising diesels, 7,800hp
CODOG Twin shafts
Speed: 35kts max, 20.5kts cruising
Aircraft: One AB 212 helicopter with telescopic hangar
Lupo' class:
One of the most successful 'export' designs of recent times, the 'Lupos' offer a remarkable package for their size. On a hull marginally smaller than that of a 'Leander', for instance, they have twice the number of SSMs and of greater range, without sacrifice of either gun or helicopter; they have a longer range PDMS (even so, due to be replaced by an Albatros/ Aspide system in time); they have nearly twice the installed power; including economic cruising diesels. Above all, they manage on only 185 crew, compared with 223 of the, admittedly, steam-powered Exocet 'Leander'. The uncharitable would say that they have so much armament that there is no room for more crew but even more modern British designs compare unfavourably in crew strength, and the through-life costs of a warship are largely a function of manpower. All this, plus a readiness on the part of the Italian Government to part with ships already under construction has led to 14 export sales to Venezuela, Peru and Iraq.

Though the CNR yards are by no means large, their

Sagittario, note Otomats not yet fitted. Italian Official

construction methods are well planned, the 'Lupos' having hulls of 13 prefabricated sections, only two of which are actually built on the open slip, and superstructure of a further six. All can be wired and fitted to an advanced degree before main assembly, allowing launches about 75% complete.

The early weakness in helicopter facilities has been remedied by raising the flightdeck level and the electronics fit reflects the ships' all-round capability. Unusually, the forward bulb is purely for performance reasons rather than to house a sonar. Whether or not these ships are, indeed, over-ambitious will be seen only in time.

Alpino   Frigate

	Builders	LD	L	C
F580 *Alpino* (ex-*Circe*)	CNR	63	67	68
F581 *Carabiniere* (ex-*Climene*)	CNR	65	67	68

Displacement: 2,000 tons standard; 2,700 tons full load
Dimensions: 113.3m × 13.3m × 4m
Armament:
Six 76mm guns (6 × 1)

Two triple AS torpedo tubes
One single-barrelled AS mortar
Machinery:
Two gas turbines, 15,000hp
Four diesels, 17,000hp
COSAG Twin shafts
Speed: Diesel only — 22kts, Combined 29kts
Aircraft: Two AB-212 helicopters

The original names of this handsome pair suggest that they were viewed as improved 'Centauros' though, in reality, they are more truly frigates, having more in common with the 'Bergaminis' (qv). Alpino was more than four years from keel-laying to launch, so it would seem that the design was recast. A clue to the reason for this may lay in the rather unusual COSAG machinery which obviously follows the influences of the British 'Tribals' and 'Counties', then coming into service. In both these classes the low-power gas turbines supply no more than half of the combined machinery power and the same Metrovick pattern was built under licence by Tosi for trial also in the 'Lampo' class FACs of the time. The hull has retained the long sheerline and low freeboard of earlier classes and the addition of a pair of medium helicopters has necessitated the continuing aft of the 01 level, stopping

Carabiniere, 'Alpino' class.   Mike Lennon

short of the transom for the accommodation of a bulky VDS. Though the single, well-proportioned stack is large in cross-section as demanded by GT machinery, it is also quite high to clear the top of the bulky hangar. It makes a carefully-modelled grouping with the mast which, though braced at funneltop level, looks vibration prone. As with the majority of Italian warships, there is no shortage of guns, in this case six 76mm with a Menon AS mortar immediately forward of the bridge. These ships still have enough mileage left to swap a pair of their guns for an Albatros/Aspide PDMS. They are certainly very capable AS frigates and it is a pity that a planned second pair — to have been named Perseo and Polluce — were never built.

Bergamini   Frigate

Italy

	Builders	LD	L	C
F593 *Carlo Bergamini*	IM	59	60	62
F594 *Virgilio Fasan*	IC	60	60	62
F595 *Carlo Margottini*	IC	59	60	62
F596 *Luigi Rizzo*	IC	57	60	61

Displacement: 1,400 tons standard; 1,650 tons full load
Dimensions: 95m × 11.5m × 3.2m
Armament:
Two 76mm guns (2 × 1)
Two triple AS torpedo tubes
Single-barrelled AS mortar
Machinery:
Four diesels, 16,000shp
Twin shafts

Speed: 25kts
Aircraft: One AB204B helicopter

Following shortly after the 'Centauros', the ancestry is plain in the very similar, but smaller, hull. Where the 'Centauros' were really cut-down destroyers, the 'Bergaminis' have been built to a reduced specification. By the adoption of diesel power of considerably lower output, a large saving in length was possible, with the exhausts contained in an odd 'mack' structure slightly aft of amidships. Immediately abaft this was a minute pad, atop the after deckhouse, to allow basic facilities for a small helicopter with the Italian designers, ambitious as ever, also squeezing in the same armament as on the larger preceding class. In modifications between 1968 and 1971, the single after 76mm gun

was removed to allow the flightpad to be extended further aft and a telescopic hangar to be added. By these means, an AB204B helicopter can be carried permanently although the movement of so small a hull must severely inhibit its use. Though having some remaining value as mercantile escorts, they would prove vulnerable to air attack, especially from astern. *Rizzo* has already paid off to low-category reserve or disposal and the remainder may be expected to follow to release trained crews for newer tonnage.

Centauro Frigate

Italy

	Builders	LD	L	C
F551 (ex-D570) *Canopo*	CNT	52	55	58
F553 (ex-D573) *Castore*	CNT	55	56	57
F554 (ex-D571) *Centauro*	AL	52	54	57
F555 (ex-D572) *Cigno*	CNT	54	55	57

Displacement: 1,810 tons standard, 2,250 tons full load
Dimensions: 103m × 12m × 3.8m
Armament:
Three 76mm guns (3 × 1)
Two triple AS torpedo tubes
One triple-barrelled AS motor
Machinery:
Two sets steam turbines, 22,000shp
Twin shafts
Speed: 25kts

Funded by the American offshore programme, these ships still have much equipment of US origin. They are unusual in themselves, being neither true frigate nor destroyer; as hulls, they temporarily carried a 'D' pennant number and the Americans themselves categorised them as 'destroyer escorts' which, with their limited speed and lack of anti-ship torpedo tubes, described them fairly accurately. As completed, they each carried two twin 76mm mountings of 'Ansaldo' design. These were in A and Y positions and were unusual in having the guns mounted one above the other. In spite of being very compact and having an advertised firing rate of 80 rounds per minute per barrel, the weapons must have possessed severe shortcomings as, between 1966 and 1973, the whole class was rearmed with the newer, single Brescia model, an extra mounting being added in the superfiring X position in place of the earlier pair of twin 40mm guns. The AS escort's usual triple-barrelled Menon mortar is mounted hard by the bridgefront and supplemented by two triple Mark 32 AS torpedo tubes, probably firing the Italian pattern A244 torpedo. Some of the electronics have been updated with indigenous gear but search radars and sonars remain American. Pretty little ships with a characteristic 'boat' bow and well-modelled stern, they are , nevertheless, outdated in all departments, with a steam plant demanding a large crew by current standards. They cannot last much longer.

Centauro.   Italian Official

De Cristofaro. Italian Official

F 540

de Cristofaro   Corvette   *Italy*

	Builders	LD	L	C
F540 *Pietro de Cristofaro*	CNR	63	65	65
F541 *Umberto Grosso*	AL	62	64	66
F546 *Licio Visintini*	IM	63	65	66
F550 *Salvatore Tadaro*	AL	62	64	66

Displacement: 870 tons standard; 1,020 tons full load
Dimensions: 80.3m × 10.3m × 2.7m
Armament:
Two 76mm guns (2 × 1)
Two triple AS torpedo tubes
One single-barrelled AS mortar
Machinery:
Two diesels 8,400bhp
Twin shafts
Speed: 23kts

With only a small increase in dimensions, this class represents a great improvement on the preceding 'Albatros' (qv). Better seakeeping is given by the re-adopted raised forecastle and the armament has been greatly augmented. The basic 40mm guns have been up-rated to two of the newly-introduced 76mm Brescias and space found abaft the diminutive stack for an AS projector. Coastal escorts such as these face great problems in detecting submarines, with inshore waters prone to temperature and salinity 'layering'. For this reason the medium range, hull-mounted SQS-36 was augmented by an SQS-35 VDS, also of American origin and handled by the prominent hydraulic crane on the quarterdeck. Detection ranges in shallow waters are likely to be unreliable and low, and the range of both mortar and AS tubes are adequate. There is neither space nor need for the helicopter which so inflates the size of too many current classes, as the ships will normally work within the range of shore-based air support. Two medium-speed diesels each drive a shaft; one might have expected a single screw in so small a ship but two certainly improve survivability as well as manoeuvrability. Such is the economy of diesels that the 'de Cristofaros' are credited with a 4,000-mile range at 18kts, yet this type of drive is still rarely used in warships, largely because of noise problems. Much of this has to be prejudice as modern machinery mountings are well capable of de-coupling vibration from the hull. A replacement class of about 1,000 tons displacement has long been spoken of but obviously commands low priority.

Albatros   Corvette   *Italy*

	Builders	LD	L	C
F542 (ex-PCE 1626) *Aquila* (ex-HNMS *Lynx*)	BMM	54	54	56
F543 (ex-PCE 1919) *Albatros*	IC	53	54	55
F544 (ex-PCE 1920) *Alcione*	IC	53	54	55
F545 (ex-PCE 1921) *Airone*	IC	53	54	55

Displacement: 800 tons standard; 950 tons full load
Dimensions: 76.5m × 9.5m × 2.8m
Armament:
Two 40mm guns
Two triple AS torpedo tubes
Two Hedgehog AS mortars
Machinery:
Two diesels, 5,200bhp
Twin shafts
Speed: 19kts

In the constricted and shallow waters bordering her coasts Italy was able to use corvette-type escorts with some success against the submarines of WW2 and the 'Albatros' class ships are derived from the 'Apes' of that period. As with several fleets rebuilding after the war, the Italians received some American funding, which accounts for the early PCE categorisation of these modest little vessels which really still reflect the state-of-the-art of ASW in 1955. Eight were built in Italian yards, four for Danish account and a surprising one-off

for the Dutch. Of these, the Danes have long since scrapped two and decommissioned the others and the Dutch transferred theirs back to the Italian flag after only five years service, which suggests that the class did not suit Northern waters — probably too light and too wet. Nevertheless, where the basic design was stretched to become the 'Bergamini' (qv) and modified (with improved freeboard) to the 'de Cristofaros' (qv), the originals still soldier on where later ships have passed on. Probably, this is because like others, eg the Dutch 'Wolf' class, also US-funded, they are simple and

Alcione, *'Albatros' class.*   Italian Official

economical to run and therefore, useful for multifarious 'odd-jobs' — fishery protection, training, and keeping a 'presence' — that fall to the lot of every fleet. They can be run with a deal less than their rated complement of 100 men and either of their two low-power diesels can be idled or stopped whilst cruising. With their original armament of two 76mm guns and a twin 40mm (as the Danes carry) they were, perhaps, a trifle ambitious.

Sparviero   Hydrofoil

Italy

	Builders	Completed
P420 *Sparviero*	AS	74
P421 *Nibbio*	CNR	80
P422 *Falcone*	CNR	81
P423 *Astore*	CNR	81
P424 *Grifone*	CNR	82
P425 *Gheppio*	CNR	82
P426 *Condor*	CNR	82

Displacement: 63 tons
Dimensions:
24.5m × 12.1m × 4.5m (Max over extended foils, hullborne)
23m × 7m × 15m (Hull dimensions)
Armament:
Two Otomat SSM launcher/containers
One 76mm DP gun
Machinery:
Foilborne 4,500hp gas turbine and waterjet

Hullborne 160bhp diesel and propeller
Speed: 50kts max; 8kts hullborne

Hydrofoils, like hovercraft, exhibit a potential that seems to be hard to translate into terms of an actual role though inevitably, their 'dash' appeals greatly to the Italian character. Italy, together with West Germany, had been partners with the United States in the so-called 'NATO Hydrofoil' but due to high cost over-runs and delays, the European partners pulled out leaving the Americans to develop what became the 'Pegasus' class PHM (qv). The Italian navy, meanwhile, may well have to counter hostile FACs as well as larger surface warships in its major NATO role controlling the east-west Mediterranean axis and there is need for fast, agile units not only to act as a rapid interdiction force but also to train other larger friendly warships in anti-FAC procedures. For these functions the hydrofoil would seem to have promise, though a smaller and

cheaper option was made in the 'Sparviero'. The name ship was delivered in 1974 as a prototype for evaluation, having been built by Alinavi at La Spezia, a partnership between the experienced home-based firm of Rodriquez and Boeing of Seattle. When six further craft were ordered, however, the American connection was cut by placing the contract with CNR at Muggiano — a strange choice, perhaps, with the latter already deeply committed with the 'Maestrale' programme and with export work.

In spite of its modest size the 'Sparvieros' carry a

Sparviero. Italian Official

76mm OTO-Melara, looking disproportionately large. Right aft are squeezed-in a brace of Otomat SSM canister-launchers, whose 50-60 mile ranged weapons would require a mid-course correction from a third party. The craft are reported to have met their design requirements but their 400-odd mile range whilst foilborne is a severe limitation compared with the more orthodox FAC which, while slower, can keep the sea for extended periods.

Sauro   Patrol submarine

Italy

Nazario Sauro. Italian Official

	Builders	LD	L	C
S518 *Nazario Sauro*	IM	74	76	80
S519 *Fecia di Cossato*	IM	75	77	80
S520 *Leonardo da Vinci*	IM	78	79	81
S521 *Guglielmo Marconi*	IM	79	80	82

Displacement: 1,455 tons surfaced; 1,630 tons submerged
Dimensions: 64m × 6.8m × 5.8m
Armament: Six 533mm/21in torpedo tubes (all forward)
Machinery:
Three diesel-generators powering one propulsion motor 3,650bhp
Single shaft
Speed: 11kts surfaced, 20kts submerged

All current Italian submarines are built by the Monfalcone yard of Italcantieri, which has designs for

three basic types, of 1,700, 1,450 and 500 tons surface displacement. The four Sauros, officially termed the Type 1081, are of the second group and, while quite large by current European standards, are much smaller and handier than the elderly ex-American boats that they are designed to replace. Even so, they are on the big side for Mediterranean operations and are probably built with an eye to near-Atlantic work, if required, having a published maximum range of over 17,000 miles at low speed. They are of a size with the French Agostas and boast a similar endurance of 45 days but a puzzling discrepancy lies in the French boat's four tubes with 20 reloads and the Italian's six tubes with only one reload per tube — scarcely sufficient for an extended patrol. Attention has been paid to noise reduction with the clean hull having sonars within the casing. The single, large diameter propeller has seven blades which are heavily skewed to reduce tip vortices caused by high loading, a common factor in noise. It also revolves slowly, driven by a motor with a double-wound armature placed right aft and separated by a switch-room from the space two thirds aft which houses the three diesel generators. Submerged, the maximum speed of 20kts can be sustained only for 20 minutes and commissioning of the first pair was delayed considerably because of battery problems. They are reported to be capable of diving to 300m.

Two more vessels are to be ordered.

Toti   Patrol submarine   *Italy*

	Builders	LD	L	C
S505 *Attilio Bagnolini*	IM	65	67	68
S506 *Enrico Toti*	IM	65	67	68
S513 *Enrico Dandalo*	IM	67	67	68
S514 *Lazzaro Mocenigo*	IM	67	68	69

Displacement: 525 tons surfaced; 580 tons submerged
Dimensions: 46.2m × 4.7m × 4.1m
Armament: Four 533m/21-in torpedo tubes (all forward)
Machinery:
Two diesel-generators powering one propulsion motor 2,200shp
Single shaft
Speed: 14kts submerged, 15kts submerged

These little boats were Italy's first postwar submarines and were contemporary with the German Type 205s (qv). The latter have gone for an eight-tube battery forward with no reloads; the 'Totis', on the other hand, have only four tubes and, being barely 2m longer, scarcely have room for re-loading. Being a 'pre-Albacore' design the Italians' single screws are sited in an aperture forward of the control surfaces, resulting in a comparatively low submerged speed. Known officially as Type 1075s, their external appearance is dominated by sonar housings. Right forward is the active sonar dome, used sparingly in practice to add more precise range data to that gained by the passive set, whose transducer elements are wrapped 'conformally' around the front end of the pressure hull. Three pairs of small fins, equispaced along the hull, contain the sensors for the PUFFS-type passive rangefinder sonar, which uses the submarine's own hull as a baseline from which to measure the range of a sound source by time-lapse techniques. Such small boats are not capable of long patrols in spite of their 3,000-mile range on the surface at low speeds, the crew of 26 being very confined. For coastal work, their 200m diving limit would be adequate.

Lazzaro Mocenigo, *'Toti' class*.   Italian Official

Guppy Type   Patrol submarine

Italy

	Builders	LD	L	C
S502 *Gianfranco Gazzana Priaroggia* (ex-USS *Pickerel* SS514)	BNY	44	44	49
S515 *Livio Piomarta* (ex-USS *Trigger* SS564)	GDE	49	51	52
S516 *Romeo Romei* (ex-USS *Harder* SS568)	GDE	50	51	52

Details under USA.

S502 is a 'Tench' class boat, of an improved 'Balao' type, later modernised to 'Guppy III' standard and

transferred in 1972. S515 and 516 are 'Tang' class boats transferred in 1973 and 1974 respectively. S516 differs in having diagonally-disposed stabilisers aft. All three are due for disposal in 1984.

Lerici   Minesweeper

Italy

	Builders	Completed
M5550 *Lerici*	IMS	82
M5551 *Sapri*	IMS	83
M5552 *Milazzo*	IMS	84
M5553 *Vieste*	IMS	84
M *Gaeta*	IMS	
M *Termoli*	IMS	
M *Alghero*	IMS	
M *Numana*	IMS	
M *Crotone*	IMS	
M *Viareggio*	IMS	

Displacement: 470 tons standard; 500 tons full load
Dimensions: 50m × 9.6m × 2.6m
Armament: One 20mm gun

Machinery:
(Passage) One diesel 1,850bhp. Single shaft
(Manoeuvring) Waterjets
Speed: 15/17kts

Of a size almost identical with the 'Tripartite' MCMVs, the 'Lericis', as a national project, typify the lack of uniformity in NATO thinking. The fact that the builders have landed a useful order for the Malaysians also demonstrates that to go it alone often pays, although NATO will be the weaker by the slowing down in the home programme to meet it. With a GRP hull and an outfit nearly identical with the 'Tripartites', the main difference lies in the 'creep' propulsion units, which are low-power water jets. Electronics are home-produced, some under licence.

MSO   Minesweeper

Italy

	Completed
M5430 *Salmone* (ex-MSO507)	56
M5431 *Storione* (ex-MSO506)	56
M5432 *Sgombro* (ex-MSO517)	57
M5433 *Squalo* (ex-MSO518)	57

Four standard MSOs, built in the US, with Offshore Funds, to Italian account.

MSC   Minesweeper/hunter

Italy

M5504 *Castagno*	M5524 *Mogano*
M5505 *Cedro* *	M5525 *Palma*
M5508 *Frassino*	M5527 *Sandalo*
M5509 *Gelso*	M5531 *Agave*
M5510 *Larice*	M5532 *Alloro*
M5511 *Noce*	M5533 *Edera*
M5512 *Olmo*	M5535 *Gelsomino*
M5516 *Platano* *	M5536 *Giaggiolo*
M5517 *Quercia*	M5538 *Loto* *
M5519 *Mandorlo* *	M5540 *Timo*
M5521 *Bambu*	M5541 *Trifoglio*
M5522 *Ebano*	M5542 *Vischio*
M5523 *Mango*	

First 10 US built between 1953 and 1954. Remainder from Italian yards 1956-7. Despite their age (four have already been discarded) there is a continuing pro-gramme to update them from sweepers to hunters. Those marked * already converted.

Stromboli Fleet tanker   *Italy*

	Builders	LD	L	C
A5327 *Stromboli*	CNR	73	75	75
S5329 *Vesuvio*	CNR	76	77	78

Displacement: 3,560 tons standard; 8,700 tons full load
Dimensions: 129m × 18m × 6.5m
Armament:
One 76mm gun
Two 40mm guns
Machinery:
Two diesels 11,400bhp
Single shaft
Speed: 20kts

This pair of recent tankers are the only ones under the Italian flag capable of refuelling at sea, as the fleet usually operates within the confines of the Mediterranean. They are rather similar to the British 'Rovers', but smaller and, predictably, armed, though for the purpose of creating a 'fierce face' rather than anything serious. A useful deadweight of some 4,700 tons is carried; of this about two thirds is FFO bunker fuel for the navy's major units, still steam powered. In addition, about 1,000 tons of diesel oil is carried for auxiliary machinery use and the few motor frigates. Some 400 tons of distillate fuel for gas turbine units is shipped but this proportion would be expected to increase as the 1975 Fleet Programme bears fruit. Some dry stores are also carried, a large helicopter pad being provided for 'vertical replenishment'. No hangar is provided for the permanent attachment of a helicopter and the pronounced slab of superstructure probably produces enough eddying to provide any pilot with a few bad moments.

Tromp Destroyer   *Netherlands*

	Builders	LD	L	C
F801 *Tromp*	KM de S	71	73	75
F806 *de Ruyter* (ex-*Heemskerck*)	KM de S	71	74	76

Displacement: 4,300 tons standard; 5,400 tons full load
Dimensions: 138.5m × 14.8m × 4.6m

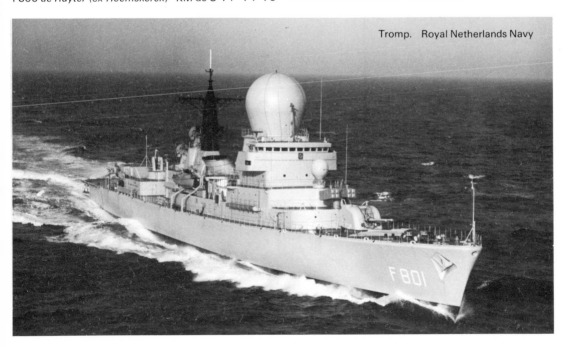

Tromp. Royal Netherlands Navy

Armament:
Sixteen Harpoon SSM
One Tartar SAM launcher
One Octuple Sea Sparrow PDMS
One twin 120mm gun
Two triple AS torpedo tubes
Machinery:
Two sprint gas turbines, 50,000shp
Two cruise gas turbines, 8,000shp
COGOG Twin shafts
Speed: 30kts
Aircraft: Only Lynx helicopter with hangar

Known, inevitably, as 'Kojaks', this pair have functional topsides growing from what would appear to be a stretched version of the hull of the aborted Frigate 75 (later the 'Standaard'/'Kortenaer'). While little larger than a 'Kortenaer', they are classed as destroyers, customary with single-ended area SAM-armed ships, although they still carry an 'F' flag superior. Both ships have the accommodation and communications of flagships, being designed to lead Atlantic A/S groups including up to four 'Kortenaers' and a supply ship. The 'Tromps' present SAM system is the American Tartar with a single arm Mark 13 launcher and a pair of SPG-51 directors, 3D information being supplied by an HSA antenna housed under the radome. While the Mark 13 can also handle the later Standard MR, the ships' mid-term refit may logically see them rearmed with one of the Mark 26 series, able to handle the standard and ASROC rounds. A further useful modification would be to extend the hangar further to either beam to give accommodation for a second Lynx. The Sea Sparrow PDMS in 'B' position will probably be retained but the heavy twin 120mm gun mounting forward (bequeathed from the old destroyer *Gelderland*) will make way for 76 or 127mm OTO-Melara.

In appearance the ships could be possibly confused only with the French 'Suffrens' by virtue of the enormous radomes, though the resemblance really ends there. The massive fort-like bridge structure and squat veed funnel casings are highly distinctive.

Kortenaer Frigate   *Netherlands*

	Builders	LD	L	C
F807 *Kortenaer*	KM de S	75	76	78
F808 *Callenburgh*	KM de S	75	77	79
F809 *van Kinsbergen*	KM de S	75	77	80
F810 *Banckert*	KM de S	76	78	80
F811 *Piet Heyn*	KM de S	77	78	81
F816 *Abraham Crijnssen*	KM de S	78	81	82
F823 *Philips van Almonde*	WF	77	79	81
F824 *Bloys van Treslong*	WF	78	80	82
F825 *Jan van Brakel*	KM de S	79	81	83
F826 *Willem van der Zaan*	KM de S	79	82	83

Displacement: 3,500 tons standard; 3,790 tons full load
Dimensions: 130m × 14.6m × 4.5m
Armament:
Two quadruple Harpoon SSM
One octuple NATO SeaSparrow PDMS
One/two 76mm DP guns
One CIWS planned
Four AS torpedo tubes
Machinery:
Two gas turbines, 52,000shp

Van Kinsbergen, *'Kortenaer' class.* Mike Lennon

Two cruise turbines, 8,000shp
COGOG Twin shafts
Speed: 30/16kts
Aircraft: One/two Lynx helicopters with hangar

In seeking a replacement for their ageing 'Holland' and 'Friesland' class destroyers, the Dutch looked at Britain and American equivalents, considered a modified 'broad-beam Leander' and failed to agree with the British on a joint project. Finally they produced the 'Standaard' frigate design, known now as the 'Kortenaer' class, with ship parameters decided largely by the choice of propulsion system and the decision to accommodate two helicopters. The result is a handsome ship, a little unusual in modern frigate practice in the superstructures not extending over the full beam.

Emphasis is on AS qualities, the roomy hangar being dimensioned for two Lynx helicopters, though only one is carried in peacetime. Four tubes for launching Mk 46 (and later, presumably ALWT) torpedoes are situated in the after structure where loading and servicing can be carried out under protected conditions. A 76mm DP gun and a NATO Sea Sparrow PDMS are mounted forward; on the hangar roof a CIWS is due but, owing to difficulties in selection, a second 76mm has been added in earlier ships of the class and a 40mm in others. Two quadruple Harpoon SSMs round off a powerful armament.

The large LW08 air surveillance radar aft has advanced ECCM facilities and the ZW06 is sited high to detect low-level threats. An American SQS-505 sonar is mounted in a large bow dome, supplemented by helicopter sensors as required. COGOG propulsion is by two Olympus and two Tynes, driving twin shafts. Only one, centreline rudder is fitted.

Two of the class *Pieter Florisz* (F812) and *Witte de With* (F813) have been sold to Greece whilst under construction and others of the same name are being built as replacements. The replacements are to be armed as air defence frigates. They are:

	LD	L	C
F812 *Jacob van Heemskerck*	81	83	84
F813 *Witte de With*	81	84	85

Armament:
Two quadruple Harpoon SSMs
Tartar SM system
Sea Sparrow paint defence SAM
Goalkeeper CIWS
Four ASW torpedo tubes
No guns or helicopters are to be carried

The 'Kortenaer' design was used also as a baseline for West Germany's Type 122's (qv). By careful design, the complement has been kept down to a very creditable 176 men.

van Speijk   Frigate   *Netherlands*

	Builders	LD	L	C
F802 *van Speijk*	NSM	63	65	67
F803 *van Galen*	KM de S	63	65	67
F804 *Tjerk Hiddes*	NSM	64	65	67
F805 *van Nes*	KM de S	63	66	67
F814 *Isaac Sweers*	NSM	65	67	68
F815 *Evertsen*	KM de S	65	66	67

Displacement: 2,200 tons standard; 2,850 tons full load
Dimensions: 113.4m × 12.5m × 5.8m
Armament:
Two quadruple Harpoon SSMs
Two quadruple Seacat PDMSs
One 76mm DP guns
Two triple A/S torpedo tubes
Machinery:
Two sets DR steam turbines, 30,000shp
Twin shafts
Speed: 30kts
Aircraft: One Lynx helicopter with hangar

As built these were repeats of the British 'Leander' class (qv) but modified to use Dutch equipment. By late 1982 all will have undergone an extensive mid-life modernisation which, in many respects, compares more than favourably with the British equivalents in that the ships have retained their all-round capability as well as receiving an up-grading in potential. The twin 4.5in gunhouse has been replaced by the almost inevitable 76mm OTO-Melara, perched on a pedestal to clear the forecastle. This has effected a great saving in topweight, aided further by the substitution of AS torpedo tubes for the earlier Limbo mortar. As a result, two quadruple Harpoons can be shipped: compared with the RN MM38 'Exocet Leanders', this represents twice

Van Nes, *'van Speijk' class.*   Royal Netherlands Navy

the number of missiles, with twice the range and heavier warheads — and still without the surrender of the gun armament. A more capable Lynx will prove useful in capitalisation on the over-the-horizon capabilities of the SSMs as well as exercising its abilities in carrying ASMs and AS hardware. New HSA directors have been fitted for the 76mm and each of the Sea Cats, together with a compact VDS for deep-water use.

C3 equipment has also been completely up-dated and all modifications have been carried out with an eye to reducing complement. Thus, where the RN Exocet conversions need 223 men, the van Speijks require 185 — a saving of 17%.

'M' class Frigate   *Netherlands*

	Builders	LD	L	C
F				
F				

Displacement: 2,500 tons standard
Dimensions: 107.5m × 13m × 4m
Armament:
Two quadruple Harpoon SSMs
One octuple NATO Sea Sparrow PDMSs
One 76mm DP gun
One CIWS
Four AS torpedo tubes
Machinery:
One sprint gas turbine, 28,000shp
Two cruise diesels, 4,250shp each
CODOG Single shaft
Speed: 28kts on GT, 19.5kts on diesels
Aircraft: One Lynx with hangar

The 'M' class frigates are designed to replace the old American-built PCEs of the 'Wolf' class, though far exceeding them in capability, as their tasks will be infinitely more demanding. Replacement has been late as resources have been concentrated on ships for the three Atlantic groups committed to NATO. Aimed specifically at North Sea operations, the M's will, never-theless, have a full deep-sea potential and, except in speed, their specification compares interestingly with the ambitious Italian 'Lupos'.

Very much diminutives of the 'Kortenaers', they were designed with as many interchangeable features as possible to ease logistics. For their size, they pack tremendous firepower, a necessity to survive aerial attack in the confines of the North Sea. To meet this threat they have a long range air surveillance radar, a Sea Sparrow on the hangar roof and an Oto-Melara 76mm DP gun which share the HSA-built WM25 fire control radar in the masthead dome. The CIWS in B position looks like being a 'Shortstop' combination of the HSA Flycatcher radar and General Electric GAU-8 30mm Gatling, favoured also for the 'Kortenaers'. Main AS potential resides in the single Lynx helicopter, the ship-borne sonar being in a bow dome and surprisingly large for shallow water use. Four AS torpedo tubes fire from inside the long deckhouse. The large stack and downtakes are typical of gas turbine practice; not so common is the single screw, driven either by the Olympus for sprint use or by one or two diesels for cruising. A high degree of automation assists in keeping the crew below 90.

It is unlikely that funds for the M's will be committed until the mid-1980s.

Wolf Corvette   *Netherlands*

	Builders	LD	L	C
F817 *Wolf* (ex-PCE 1607)	AMW	52	54	54
F818 *Fret* (ex-PCE 1604)	GSE	52	53	54
F819 *Hermelijn* (ex-PCE 1605)	GSE	53	54	54
F820 *Vos* (ex-PCE 1606)	GSE	53	54	54
F821 *Panter* (ex-PCE 1608)	AMW	52	54	54
F822 *Jaguar* (ex-PCE 1609)	AMW	52	54	54

Panter, 'Wolf' class.
Mike Lennon

Displacement: 850 tons standard; 970 tons full load
Dimensions: 56.3m × 10.3m × 3.0m
Armament:
One 3in (76mm) gun
Four/six 40mm guns (4 × 1) or (2 × 1) and (2 × 2)
One Hedgehog AS mortar
Machinery:
Two diesels, 1,800bhp
Twin shafts
Speed: 15kts

Due to be replaced by the projected 'M' class frigates, the six 'Wolfs' have been surprisingly durable. They were supplied by and built in the United States under the wide-ranging 'offshore agreement'; what was surprising was that they were built new to the basic wartime PCE design at a time when many of the original craft were still available for transfer. Near-identical in appearance with the warbuilt units, these lack the former's diminutive funnel and carry a larger

boat under davits on the port side. Now very dated, they carry a Hedgehog AS spigot mortar, a 3in gun and automatic weapons, and can manage 15kts on two General Motors diesels. For North Sea work under peacetime conditions, they have proved very useful and versatile although, at 78, their crew is nearly as numerous as that of the far larger and immensely more capable M's, a measure of the changes in warship design inside three decades.

Walrus   Patrol submarine   *Netherlands*

	Builders	LD	L	C
S802 *Walrus*	RDM	79	84	86
S803 *Zeeleeuw*	RDM	81	85	87

Displacement: 2,220 surfaced, 2,500 tons submerged
Dimensions: 67m×8.5m×7m
Armament: Six 533mm/21in torpedo tubes (all forward)
Machinery:
Three diesel-generators powering one propulsion motor
Single shaft
Speed: Not announced

Although heavily based on the preceding 'Zwaardvis' class, the 'Walrus' design is sufficiently different to be looked upon as a separate class. As they are to replace the four 'Potvis' class boats, it may well be that a further pair will eventually be ordered. Generally similar in dimensions, the form is less extreme, the teardrop hull being more parallel in section and fitted with diagonal control surfaces. Each surface is part-hydroplane, part-rudder and the arrangement has the advantage of narrower beam and reduced draught,

together with freedom from the 'locked-plane' bogey, but at the expense of complex response, capable of being handled effectively only by computer. The deep-diving characteristics of earlier classes are retained and probably well exceeded by the use of specially-made HT steel of French origin. As is usual with conventional attack submarines the hull is single-skinned and very deep in section, with two full decks amidships over the batteries. It is likely that the same six-tube battery has been fitted forward as in the 'Zwaardvis' type, but fire control is vested in the newer HSA Gipsy system which will digest imputs from up to three separate sonars, ship's attitudes and movements, radars and position finding gear, together with information from ESM and noise analysis before computing a firing solution. Perhaps the most surprising innovation, considering the similarity in size to the preceding class, is the reduction in crew strength from 65 to only 49; this requires a firm hand during the design stage with automation and agreement on multi-function crew grades but pays great dividends with through-life costs and in limiting the size of the boat itself. One aspect, common in mercantile practice, is the adoption of normally unmanned machinery spaces.

Zwaardvis   Patrol submarine   *Netherlands*

	Builders	LD	L	C
S806 *Zwaardvis*	RDM	66	70	72
S807 *Tijgerhaai*	RDM	66	71	72

Displacement: 2,350 tons surfaced; 2,650 tons submerged
Dimensions: 66.2m×10.3m×7m
Armament: Six 533mm/21in torpedo tubes (all forward)

Zwaardvis. Royal Netherlands Navy

Machinery:
Three diesel generators powering one propulsion motor
5,200bhp
Single shaft
Speed: 14kts surfaced, 20kts submerged

Where West German and Danish submarines are dimensioned for North Sea and Baltic operations, Dutch boats are larger, the 'Zwaardvis' pair being of a size with the French 'Agostas'. Their lines are closely similar to those of the American 'Barbel' class, which was the first to fully incorporate the lessons of the high-speed

'Albacore', the deep, humpbacked hull having a roomy two-deck interior. The large fin is mounted well forward and supports the forward hydroplanes; the fairing in the trailing edge housing sonar and ECM gear. Following contemporary practice, all tubes are carried forward, some if not all, having a water ejection or 'swim-out' facility for firing. Weapons carried are reported to be a mix of British-built heavyweight torpedoes and American Mark 37s though this can be expected to change to the large US Mark 48 and the new ALWT

when available, together with the encapsulated Harpoon. A computerised HSA M8 fire control, coordinates sensors and weapons and can deal with three simultaneous targets.

Three diesel generators power the single propulsion motor for surface and 'snort' running and for recharging the double bank of batteries. These are water-cooled to cope with rapid discharge conditions when short bursts of high submerged speed are required. One five-bladed propeller is fitted.

Potvis Patrol submarine

Netherlands

	Builders	LD	L	C
S804 *Potvis*	WF	62	65	65
S805 *Tonijn*	WF	62	65	66
S808 *Dolfijn*	RDM	54	59	60
S809 *Zeehond*	RDM	54	60	61

Displacement: 1,495 tons surfaced; 1,825 tons submerged

Dimensions: 79.5m × 7.8m × 5m
Armament: Eight 533mm/21in torpedo tubes (four forward, four aft)
Machinery:
Two diesels, 3,100bhp total
Two electric motors, 4,200hp total
Twin shafts
Speed: 15kts surfaced, 17kts submerged

Potvis. Royal Netherlands Navy

This class of boat is typical of the innovative approach of Dutch submarine design. In place of the usual pressure hull, there are three parallel tubes, a central one flanked by two shorter which are set lower; for given scantlings, these smaller diameter tubes will have a greater collapse depth and they were probably the earliest boats capable of operating below 300m. The central tube houses the crew, armament and most of the electronics, while the narrower flanking tubes each contain a diesel, generator, propulsion motor and batteries. The rounded triangular cross-section is unique and results in a high uniform freeboard.

As can be seen, the class consists of two distinct pairs of boat, but these have been modified over the years to become near identical. Four were authorised in 1949, as the 032-35, of large dimensions to suit

service in the still-substantial Dutch Far-Eastern empire. Postwar financial problems delayed the laying down of the first pair until 1954, the second pair being held back with an eye — even at this date — to possible nuclear propulsion. By the time that the first two were complete, Indonesia was a republic, NATO a high reality and nuclear propulsion an over-ambitious dream, so a follow-on pair were constructed.

Though the radical layout has not been repeated the concept was worth exploring. They are due, officially, to be replaced from 1983 by the new 'Walrus' class boats but it has also been announced that their MAN diesels will shortly be replaced by Pielsticks, so retirement may be delayed.

Dolfijn is to be laid up for disposal.

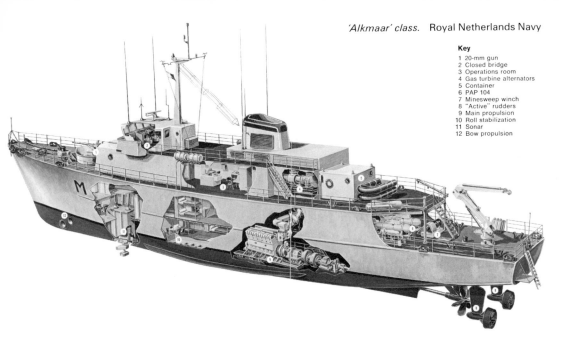

Key
1 20-mm gun
2 Closed bridge
3 Operations room
4 Gas turbine alternators
5 Container
6 PAP 104
7 Minesweep winch
8 "Active" rudders
9 Main propulsion
10 Roll stabilization
11 Sonar
12 Bow propulsion

Alkmaar   Minehunter   *Netherlands*

	Builders	Completed
M850 *Alkmaar*	GN	82
M851 *Delfzijl*	GN	82
M852 *Dordrecht*	GN	83
M853 *Haarlem*	GN	83
M854 *Harlingen*	GN	84
M855 *Hellevoetsluis*	GN	84
M856 *Maassluis*	GN	85
M857 *Makkum*	GN	85
M858 *Middelburg*	GN	86
M859 *Scheveningen*	GN	86
M860 *Schiedam*	GN	87
M861 *Urk*	GN	87
M862 *Vlaardingen*	GN	88
M863 *Willemstad*	GN	88
M864 *Zierikzee* (ex-*Veere*)	GN	89

Displacement: 510 tons standard; 545 tons full load
Dimensions: 49.1m×8.9m×2.5m
Armament: One 20mm gun
Machinery:
(Passage) Diesel, 2,300bhp on single centreline shaft
(Manoeuvring) Two electrically-driven active rudders
and two transverse bow thrusters
Speed: (Passage) 15kts

These 15 minehunters are the Dutch version of the so-
called 'Tripartite' programme, conducted jointly with
France and Belgium. With the latter navies planning to
built 15 and 10 respectively, a respectable force of
highly capable ships will be available for use largely in
the vulnerable waters from the Ems to Ushant. The
design was developed to meet the official requirement
'to be able to detect mines down to 80m or more at a
range greater than 500m, to identify mines to an
oblique distance greater than 150m in waters of up to
60m depth; to determine their location to within 15m;
to neutralise ground mines down to 80m with a 3kt
current and a 30kt wind, and to sweep moored mines
by mechanical means at up to 8kts. The whole to be
operative in sea state 5'. Following the British lead,
GRP was chosen as the building material, with special
facilities set up in each country. Electronics are
common to all and mainly of French origin, the EVEC
20 minehunting system processing a variety of inputs
from radars, sonars and ship's attitude, accelerations
and velocities to produce a comprehensive display.
Suspicious objects are positively identified and
destroyed by one of two PAP 104 remotely-controlled
submarine vehicles carried aboard. Six mine-clearance
divers are also carried. Interestingly the ship's function
can be changed by the shipping of variously-fitted 'containerised' facilities.

On passage and deploying a mechanical sweep, the
ships proceed powered by a Dutch Werkspoor diesel
but can hover and manoeuvre almost silently on two
Belgian ACEC directional active rudders and a side
thruster. Standardisation within NATO has here worked
well, yet Italy has still 'gone it alone' with the near-
identical 'Lerici' class (qv) and the British have produced something larger in the 'Brecons' (qv) yet so
expensive as to limit their numbers, however urgently
needed.

The 'Alkmaars' will replace the 18 remaining
'Dokkum' class coastal minesweepers (similar to the
UK's CMS). Sixteen 'van Straelen' inshore
minesweepers remain, most now over 20 years of age.

Zuiderkruis. Royal Netherlands Navy

Poolster   Fast combat support ship

Netherlands

	Builders	LD	L	C
A832 *Zuiderkruis*	VDS	73	74	75
A835 *Poolster*	RDM	62	63	64

Displacement: 16,850 tons full load
Dimensions: 171m × 20.3m × 8.3m
Armament: 20mm and 40mm guns when required
Machinery:
Steam turbines 22,000shp
Twin shafts
Speed: 21kts
Aircraft: Up to five helicopters, with hangar

Dutch flair for line, together with a fine hull, has produced a pair of support ships far and away more
handsome than the usual run. They carry up to 10,000
deadweight tons of oil (amidships) and dry stores/
ammunition (forward). An interesting feature is that
they can carry — and operate — a flight of five
helicopters, useful not only in vertical replenishment
underweigh but also for AS operations, for which the
ships carry both weapons and a hull-mounted sonar. In
heavy weather particularly, their presence would considerably reinforce the AS potential of an Atlantic
group, though a third unit will probably be needed to
complement the M class frigate group in time.

Oslo   Frigate

Norway

	Builders	LD	L	C
F300 *Oslo*	HV	63	64	66
F301 *Bergen*	HV	64	65	67
F302 *Trondheim*	HV	63	64	66
F303 *Stavanger*	HV	65	66	67
F304 *Narvik*	HV	64	65	66

Displacement: 1,450 tons standard; 1,750 tons full
load
Dimensions: 96.5m × 11.3m × 5.3m
Armament:
Four Penguin 1 SSMs (4 × 1)
One octal NATO Sea Sparrow BPDMS
Four 3in (76mm) guns (2 × 2)
One Terne AS weapon
Two triple AS torpedo tubes
Machinery:
One set geared steam turbines, 20,000shp
One shaft
Speed: 25kts

Though Norwegian-built, this class was 50% US-
funded and based heavily on the design of the
American 'Dealey' class DE. This postwar class took all
the desirable features of the various war-built DE

groups and combined them in a well-armed, seaworthy
vessel, driven economically by one set of steam turbines on a single shaft. Like the other postwar DE
group, the diesel-driven 'Claud Jones' (see under 'Berk'
Turkey), their life under the US flag was short, due to a
series of more highly capable frigates starting with the
Bronsteins, but the type proved to be adequate — with
suitable modification — for both Norway and Portugal
(qv).

For their modest size, the 'Oslos' are very well armed
indeed, mainly by virtue of not sacrificing space aboard
for a helicopter. Presumably, it is accepted that the AS
qualities of the ships will be used normally within range
of shore-based air support.

With mixed American and Norwegian sonars, the
Oslos' main AS punch lies in their home-produced
Terne system, which is an ahead-firing weapon throw-
ing a pattern of six rocket propelled 140kg charges out
to about 1,000m every 40 seconds. These are backed
by two triple banks of AS torpedo tubes mounted high
on the after superstructure. An eight-celled NATO Sea
Sparrow launcher is set in the superimposed position
aft, its director on a tower immediately forward of it.
Right aft, in the only remaining space on these well-
packed ships, are four Norwegian-built Penguin SSM
launchers. These missiles are of about 24km range with

a 120kg warhead and made a useful alternative for the smaller ship to the near-universal MM38 Exocet before the arrival of Harpoon.

Four US-pattern 3in (76mm) guns in twin Mk 33 DP

Stavanger, *note Sea Sparrow not fitted.* Mike Lennon

mountings complete the weapons fit. French search radar and HSA fire controls are fitted.

Sleipner Corvette   *Norway*

	Builders	LD	L	C
F310 *Sleipner*	NW	63	63	65
F311 *Aeger*	AMV	64	65	67

Displacement: 600 tons standard; 780 tons full load
Dimensions: 69m × 8m × 2.5m
Armament:
One 3in (76mm) gun
One 40mm gun
One Terne AS weapon
Two triple AS torpedo tubes
Machinery:
Four diesels. 9,000bhp
Two shafts
Speed: 21kts

Sleipner. Royal Norwegian Navy

Though there is only about 8m difference in length between the largest FACs and small 'orthodox' warships, typified by the 'Sleipners', there is all the difference in the world in their design philosphy. Here we have corvettes designed to stay at sea, to have a primarily AS bias yet be of use in general peacetime employment. In size and function, they equate to the West German 'Thetis' class and despite the lack of a helicopter (debatably necessary) would seem to have great potential as the basis of a patrol craft for Norway's large offshore zone.

They have a surprisingly shallow draught for a fleet not normally troubled by lack of water depth and the whole design is aimed at enclosure, loose water forward being cleared by a good sheer and the bridge face extending to the sides of the hull.

The Norwegian-built Terne AS system has been fitted very neatly abaft the superstructure (indeed, the ships were probably designed around it) getting its attack information from a home-produced sonar, with passive long range surveillance from a US pattern SQS 36.

Four MTU diesels are paired on to two shafts,

exhausting through a large, but well proportioned funnel. For one with an eye for these things, Norwegian masts have definite peculiarities; in this case, a substantial tripod supports the modern equivalent of a fidded topmast.

Five of the class were planned, but only two built.

Type 207   Patrol submarine   *Norway*

	Builders	LD	L	C
S300 *Ula*	RNE	62	64	65
S301 *Utsira*	RNE	63	65	65
S302 *Utstein*	RNE	62	65	65
S303 *Utvaer*	RNE	62	65	65
S304 *Uthaug*	RNE	62	65	66
S305 *Sklinna*	RNE	63	66	66
S306 *Skolpen*	RNE	63	66	66
S307 *Stadt*	RNE	63	66	66
S308 *Stord*	RNE	64	66	67
S309 *Svenner*	RNE	65	67	67
S315 *Kaura*	RNE	61	64	65
S316 *Kinn*	RNE	60	63	64
S317 *Kya*	RNE	61	64	64
S318 *Kobben*	RNE	61	64	64
S319 *Kunna*	RNE	61	64	64

Displacement: 370 tons surfaced; 435 tons submerged
Dimensions: 45.3m x 4.5m x 4.3m
Armament: Eight 53mm/21in torpedo tubes (all forward)
Machinery:
Two diesel generators. One drive motor 1,200hp
Single shaft
Speed: 10/17kts

Though labelled Type 207, these are really variants on the West German 205s and closely related to the

Danish 'Narhvalens'. Ordering almost on the reputation of the Germans as submarine builders, the Norwegians were fortunate in that their boats were commissioning even before the Germans' own 205s were being laid down. They were ahead of the latter's special steels problem therefore and proved reliable. Externally, they differ by having a cranked leading edge to the fin but retain the single-hulled construction with a powerful battery of eight forward tubes.

Though comparatively fast submerged (for a limited period) the hull form predates later post-'Albacore' ideas and the propeller is set above the lower rudder and abaft the upper, being forward of the hydroplanes for maximum effect.

Only 18 crew are required and conditions are somewhat 'hard lying', an acceptable state of affairs because of the likely short duration of patrols. With deep offshore waters, the Norwegians are more concerned with deep-diving capabilities than with minelaying. The boats have been, or are being, updated in electronics and the necessary gear for deploying long-ranged, wire-guided torpedoes.

By way of replacement for this class, the Norwegian Navy will be acquiring the new patrol submarine designed by IKL for the Bundesmarine, and likely to be a scaled-down Type 209. An order for six was placed with Thyssen Nordseewerke, Emden for delivery in 1989-90 with an option on a further two.

Skolpen, *Type 207.*   Royal Norwegian Navy

Geir, 'Hauk' class.   Royal Norwegian Navy

Hauk   FAC (Missile/Torpedo)   *Norway*

	Builders	Completed
P986 *Hauk*	BMV	77
P987 *Orn*	BMV	79
P988 *Terne*	BMV	79
P989 *Tjeld*	BMV	79
P990 *Skarv*	BMV	79
P991 *Teist*	BMV	79
P992 *Jo*	BMV	79
P993 *Lom*	BMV	80
P994 *Stegg*	BMV	80
P995 *Falk*	BMV	80
P996 *Ravn*	WMA	80
P997 *Gribb*	WMA	80
P998 *Geir*	WMA	80
P999 *Erle*	WMA	80

Displacement: 120 tons standard, 150 tons full load
Dimensions: 36.5m × 6.3m × 1.5m
Armament:
Six Penguin II SSMs
Four 533mm (21in) torpedo tubes   See below
One 40mm gun
Machinery:
Two diesels, 7,000bhp
Two shafts
Speed: 34kts

Developed directly from the 'Snogg' class boats, completed in 1970-71, the 'Hauks' are also closely related to the Swedish 'Hugins'. This is because the Swedes had a one-off evaluation boat, the *Jägeren*, built to the basic 'Snogg' design, eventually going ahead with a modified version, known as the 'Hugin'. As these were all Norwegian-built, they greatly influenced the 'Hauks'.

The steel hull has a GRP superstructure and is much smaller than many current SSM-armed FACs. Being shorter, only two shafts and diesels are required, though at the cost of a lowish speed. In all, size of boat and scale of weaponry reflect the short ranges and radius of action envisaged for the craft. Where the Swedes have opted for a useful 57mm Bofors gun forward, the Norwegians have shipped a 40mm weapon, rather small for this purpose but allowing more disposable topweight for alternative armament aft. Up to four 533mm torpedo tubes or six Penguin II SSMs can be fitted in various combinations dependent upon likely missiles.

Much cooperation between the Swedes and Norwegians is evident in the craft's inventory and fire control is by Kongsberg, whose MS1-80S system is enclosed in a distinctive, rotating helmet-shaped housing.

Snogg   FAC (Missile/Torpedo)   *Norway*

	Builders	Completed
P980 *Snogg*	BSM	70
P981 *Rapp*	BSM	70
P982 *Snar*	BSM	70
P983 *Rask*	BSM	71
P984 *Kvikk*	BSM	71
P985 *Kjapp*	BSM	71

Displacement: 100 tons standard; 125 tons full load
Dimensions: 36.5m × 6.3m × 1.2m
Armament:
Four Penguin SSMs
Four 533mm/21in torpedo tubes   See notes
One 40mm gun

Machinery:
Two diesels 7,000bhp
Two shafts
Speed: 32kts

Though of a similar size to the 'Hauks', the 'Snoggs' are apparently geared more to the usual fitting of four torpedo tubes, with a pair of Penguin I SSMs aft. A further pair of missile launchers can be fitted, though this looks as though it would be in lieu of the after tubes.

The steel hull design is shared with a further group of boats, the 20-strong 'Storm' class which have an enhanced missile and gun armament, but no tubes.

Each group complements the other for coordinated attack, a philosophy followed by other European fleets.

In appearance, the 'Snoggs' differ greatly 'up top' from the 'Storms', which have a much lower profile.

With these classes the Norwegians changed from their earlier choice of British Napier Deltic diesels to the West German MTU.

Storm   FAC (Missile/Gun)   *Norway*

	Builders	Completed
P960 *Storm*	BMV	68
P961 *Blink*	MBV	65
P962 *Glimt*	BMV	66
P963 *Skjold*	BSM	66
P964 *Trygg*	BMV	66
P965 *Kjekk*	BMV	66
P966 *Djerv*	BSM	66
P967 *Skudd*	BMV	66
P968 *Arg*	BMV	66
P969 *Steil*	BSM	67
P970 *Brann*	BMV	67
P971 *Tross*	BMV	67
P972 *Hvass*	BSM	67
P973 *Traust*	BMV	67
P974 *Brott*	BMV	67
P975 *Odd*	BSM	67
P976 *Pil*	BMV	67
P977 *Brask*	BMV	67
P978 *Rokk*	BSM	68
P979 *Gnist*	BMV	68

Odd, 'Storm' class. Royal Norwegian Navy

Displacement: 100 tons standard; 125 tons full load
Dimensions: 36.5m × 6.3m × 1.5m
Armament:
Six Penguin SSMs
One 76mm gun
One 40mm gun
Machinery:
Two diesels, 7,000bhp
Two shafts
Speed: 32kts

Built on a similar hull to that of the 'Snogg' class, the 'Storms' are not designed for torpedo-carrying but have a Bofors 76mm gun forward of the superstructure, a 40mm abaft it and six Penguin SSMs in single canister/launchers. The missiles are the Mark I version with a range of about 23km (as opposed to the Mark IIs in the later 'Hauks', which are capable of about 32km). Comparison of the canisters show significant differences.

The superstructure is a half-level lower than that in the 'Snoggs' and has a low quadrupod structure to support the inverted fishbowl radome.

Twenty-three boats were originally planned but this total became merged with the 'Snogg' follow-ons.

Tjeld FAC (Torpedo) *Norway*

	Builders	Completed
P343 ex-*Tjeld*	BSM	60
P348 ex-*Stegg*	BSM	61
P349 ex-*Hauk*	BSM	61
P357 ex-*Ravn*	BSM	62
P380 ex-*Skrei*	BSM	64
P381 ex-*Hai*	BSM	63
P387 ex-*Lyr*	BSM	66
P388 ex-*Gribb*	BSM	62

Displacement: 70 tons standard; 82 tons full load
Dimensions: 24.5m × 7.5m × 2.1m
Armament:
Four 533mm/(21in) torpedo tubes
One 40mm gun
Machinery:
Two diesels, 6,000bhp
Two shafts
Speed: 45kts

Descended directly from the British high-speed MTB of

WW2, the 'Tjeld' is small by current standards. Its open bridge is hardly the most suitable for Northern conditions, but its great speed and small silhouette make it formidable within the sheltered offshore Leads and, as these are usually ice-free, the mahogany hull is less likely to suffer abrasion damage than those of boats operating further south in the Baltic.

Batservis produced the design as a speculative venture, known as the 'Nasty', capable of carrying the above armament or shipping an additional 40mm weapon aft in lieu of the after pair of torpedo tubes. Having evaluated the prototype, the Norwegian navy ordered a series of 20, known from the leadship's name, as the 'Tjelds'. They were powered by the British Napier Deltic engine, then used in the Royal Navy's very similar 'Dark' class boats and offering, for its day, a very good power-to-weight ratio.

Lacking modern sensors and electronics for coordinating an action, the class is rapidly being rundown as newer boats are commissioned. Examples can still be found under the Greek and Turkish flags but the two built to US account have now been stricken.

Nordkapp Offshore patrol vehicle *Norway*

	Builders	Completed
W320 *Nordkapp*	BMV	81
W321 *Senja*	HVH	81
W322 *Andenes*	HMV	82

Displacement: 2,700 tons standard; 3,200 tons full load
Dimensions: 105.1m × 14.6m × 4.9m
Armament:
One 57mm gun
Four 20mm guns (2×2)
Two triple AS torpedo tubes
Machinery:
Four diesels, 14,400bhp
Twin shafts
Speed: 23kts

Though reduced from a planned seven to only three, the 'Nordkapp' class ships represent a significant improvement to Norwegian naval strength for although, like American cutters, they are under Coastguard control in peace, they are designed to act as escorts in times of war. As long as a frigate, they are significantly larger than any other vessels in the service; rather than

opt for a hull of about 81m overall, like the British and Irish, the Norwegians have built ships comparable with the largest of US cutters, well capable of operating in high latitudes to the north of the country. As ice can be a problem in such areas, the hull has features such as a cutaway forefoot, a moderate flare over the whole length and horns to protect rudders when going astern. The whole aspect of the topsides is one of enclosure, with a massive superstructure terminating at the after end on a helicopter deck of very generous proportions for the embarked Lynx. A keel-mounted sonar and, unusually, two sets of Mk 32 AS torpedo tubes are provided, it not being uncommon for strange submarine contacts to be made in Norwegian fjords. Forward is a single Bofors-made 57mm gun, perhaps a modest choice for this size of ship.

Two fully-enclosed lifeboats are carried, together with a navigational outfit that is comprehensive enough to cope with the dearth of 'aids' in northern waters. An upper conn is fitted in the rather odd structure that grows from the top of the funnel casing.

Besides the 'Nordkapps', the Norwegian coastguard service operates the 61.5m *Nornen* (W300), the 54m sisters *Farm* (W301) and *Heimdal* (W302), together with a variety of bareboat-chartered trawlers.

Vidar Coastal minelayer *Norway*

	Builders	Completed
N52 *Vidar*	MKB	77
N53 *Vale*	MKB	78

Displacement: 1,500 tons standard; 1,675 tons full load
Dimensions: 64.8m × 12m × 4m

Vale, 'Vidar' class. Royal Norwegian Navy

Armament: Two 40mm guns (2 × 1)
Machinery:
Two diesels, 4,200bhp
Two shafts
Speed: 15kts

Despite the general depth of Norwegian coastal waters, there are situations at which mines can be used effectively. Particularly, these are in the Leads (the shipping route running inshore of the islands) and at the mouths of many fjords, where there tend to be bars formed from the debris of the terminal moraines of the glaciers that formed them.

The two 'Vidar' minelayers are modern ships which, like many small Norwegian naval units, are the product of smaller shipyards, often using cooperative effort. Between 300 and 400 mines can be carried, dependent upon size, a moored deep or mid-depth mine being, with its sinker and mooring, very much bulkier than a ground-laid influence mine. Built very much on mercantile lines, the ships have a pair of hydraulic cranes serving a hatch at either end, the mines being stowed on three levels within the deep hull. Cargo lifts interconnect the levels for stowage and bringing the mines to the maindeck level for laying through doors in the square transom. Note how the uptakes are sided to allow unimpeded flow along the handling decks below.

Also noteworthy is the bulky superstructure, allowing all personnel to work above upperdeck level (machinery spaces can operate unmanned) during laying operations which, of course, carry an element of risk.

A comprehensive array of electronics is visible on the tripod, as accurate navigation is vital to a minelayer's trade.

MSC type   Coastal minesweeper   *Norway*

	Completed
M311 *Sauda* (ex-USS MSC102)	53
M312 *Sira* (ex-USS MSC132)	55
M313 *Tana* (ex-*Roselaere*, ex-MSC103)	54
M314 *Alta* (ex-*Arlon*, ex-MSC104)	54
M315 *Ogna*	55
M316 *Vosso*	55
M317 *Glomma* (ex-*Bastogne*, ex-MSC151)	54
M331 *Tista*	55
M322 *Kvina*	55
M334 *Utla*	55

Ten MSCs of standard type; for data and notes see under Greece.

Unusually, only M311 and M312 were built in US yards directly to Norwegian account. M313, M314 and M317 were acquired from Belgium in 1966 in exchange for two MSOs. The remaining five were built to the same design in Norwegian yards incorporating American machinery. Only M313 has undergone conversion to a minehunter. The advancing years of these and other NATO-operated mine sweepers indicates a need for a programme of, preferably standardised, replacements.

Commandante João Belo   Frigate   *Portugal*

	Builders	LD	L	C
F480 *Comandante João Belo*	ACN	65	66	67
F481 *Comandante Hermenegildo Capelo*	ACN	66	66	68
F482 *Comandante Roberto Ivens*	ACN	66	67	68
F483 *Comandante Sacadura Cabral*	ACN	67	68	69

For data and notes, see French 'Commandant Rivière' class.

To these they are virtually identical, through built in a commercial yard. They mount 40mm guns in place of the French units' 30mm and none is fitted with Exocet. All are to be fitted with a helicopter facility during modernisation; this will result in the loss of at least one of the after guns.

Baptista de Andrade   Frigate   *Portugal*

	Builders	LD	L	C
F486 *Baptista de Andrade*	ENB	72	73	74
F487 *João Roby*	ENB	72	73	75
F488 *Afonso Cerqueira*	ENB	73	73	75
F489 *Oliveira E. Carmo*	ENB	72	74	75

Displacement: 1,250 tons standard; 1,380 tons full load
Dimensions: 84.5m × 10.3m × 3.5m
Armament:
One 100mm DP gun
Two 40mm guns (2 × 1)
Two triple AS torpedo tubes
Machinery:
Two diesels, 11,000bhp
Two shafts
Speed: 23kts

A group of four follow-ons to the 'Coutinho' class, these were built by Bazan to a design apparently intermediate between the earlier vessels and the 'Descubiertas' for the Spanish Navy (qv). Essentially 'Continhos' with diminutive flight decks, they proved for some reason unpopular and were offered for sale as a class to Colombia. This fell through, the Colombians opting for the larger FS 1500 design from Howaldtswerke Deutsche Werft, and at the time of writing (1982) the ships remain available while the Portuguese Navy negotiates with the Netherlands to build a simplified 'Kortenaer' under licence in a home yard.

Though the larger Dutch design would be more weatherly, it is not apparently a lack of seaworthiness that is the problem as the older 'Continhos' have an identical hull. They are not even over ambitious in their weapons fit as can be seen from comparison with the slightly larger but very similar 'Descubierta'. Other ships of comparable size, but far more comprehensively fitted, are the French A69 and the Danish 'Niels Juel', each of which has a wider range of weaponry by virtue of not being saddled with a pocket handkerchief flight-pad, a feature of dubious worth.

In the 'Andrade' type, a single Franco-German 100mm gun has replaced the earlier classes US-pattern twin 3in and the large antenna of a British Plessey AWS-2 the Italian MLA-1 search unit. Two MM38 Exocet SSMs can be shipped.

João Coutinho   Frigate   *Portugal*

	Builders	LD	L	C
F471 *Antonio Enes*	ENB	68	69	71
F475 *João Coutinho*	BVH	68	69	70
F476 *Jacinto Candido*	BVH	68	69	70
F477 *General Pereira d'Eca*	BVH	68	69	70
F484 *Augusto de Castilho*	ENB	68	69	70
F485 *Honorio Barreto*	ENB	68	70	71

Displacement: 1,200 tons standard; 1,380 tons full load
Dimensions: 84.5m × 10.3m × 3.5m
Armament:
Two 3in (76mm) DP guns (1 × 2)
Two 40mm guns (2 × 1)
One Hedgehog AS spigot mortar
Machinery:
Two diesels, 10,600bhp
Two shafts
Speed: 24kts

Though the Portuguese shipbuilding industry demonstrated with the 'Dealeys' in the 1960s that it could build small warships, the expertise did not exist for their detailed design. Thus the French 'Belos' were followed by the 'Coutinhos', which, though based on Portuguese ideas, were German-designed. Blohm & Voss also built the first three of these and, in studying the basis for a suitable export line, conceived in them a measure of interchangeability of armament and electronics that developed eventually into the MEKO series that is now being successfully marketed.

The otherwise flush-decked hull has a low forecastle to increase freeboard; to obviate excessive sheer this has a 'Leander' type hance, likewise exaggerated flare is avoided by a prominent knuckle, a very German feature. For their size they have, by current standards, a poor and obsolete armament. A modernisation programme has been announced but its details are not clear. Realistically, this would be the exchange of the 3in 50's for a single 76mm Compatto and the provision of a multi-barrelled 375mm AS rocket launcher to superfire it. It is to be hoped that the temptation to add a flightpad will be resisted, the available deadweight being better devoted to sonars, possible a VDS, and a spare capacity for SSMs. In both these and the following 'Andrades', the relatively simple specification has kept the crew to about 100, leaving space for a Marine detachment of about 30.

Almirante Pereira de Silva   Frigate   *Portugal*

	Builders	LD	L	C
F472 *Almirante Pereira da Silva*	LL	62	63	66
F473 *Almirante Gago Coutinho*	LL	63	65	67
F474 *Almirante Magalhães Correa*	EVC	65	66	68

Based largely on the American 'Dealey' class destroyer escort; for details see under Norwegian 'Oslo' class. The Portuguese units differ greatly in armament, having two Bofors four-barrelled 375mm AS rocker launchers super-firing the forward twin 3in mounting. They lack the Norwegians' Sea Sparrow point defence system but right aft, in place of the 'Penguins', they have an American pattern VDS. Their mast is of more orthodox lattice form. Though they are of similar age to the 'Comandante' class, the Portuguese navy proposes to replace them with home-built, simplified versions of the Netherlands 'Kortenaer' though, again, a cheaper German-built alternative such as the FS1500 would also prove attractive.

Daphné   Patrol submarine   *Portugal*

	Builders	LD	L	C
S163 *Albacora*	DN	65	66	67
S164 *Barracuda*	DN	65	67	68
S165 *Delfin*	DN	67	68	69

Three of a group of four standard French 'Daphné' class vessels built to Portuguese account. For details see under France. The fourth boat, *Cachalote* (S165), was sold to Pakistan in 1975. Though they were not built by a State dockyard, it will be seen by comparison with the completion dates of the French-flag 'Daphnés' that they created a gap in the programme due to the reallocation of essential equipment.

It is this readiness on the part of the Government to sell off-the-shelf warships with attractive delivery times that makes for successful export.

NATO type   Coastal minesweeper   *Portugal*

	Completed
M401 *Sao Roque*	56
M402 *Ribeira Grande*	57
M403 *Lagoa*	56
M404 *Rosario*	56

For details see under United Kingdom. This group of four are virtually identical to the British 'Tons', though built in Portuguese yards. Two were financed under US offshore funds.

The Portuguese navy operates also one replenishment tanker, the *São Gabriel* (A5206), a 14,200-ton deep load ship based heavily on the early British 'Tide' class ships.

Principe de Asturias   Light aircraft carrier   *Spain*

	Builders	LD	L	C
R11 *Principe de Asturias*	ENB	79	82	86

Aircraft: About 20 V/STOL and helicopters, dependent upon mix

Displacement: 14,700 tons full load
Dimensions: 195.1m×24.3m×9.1m   (Flightdeck 175.5×30.3m)
Armament:
Two octuple Sea Sparrow SAM launchers
Four twelve-barrelled Meroka CIWS
Machinery:
Two gas turbines 40,000shp
One shaft
Speed: 25kts

One obvious vulnerability of the US navy lies in the great concentration of power vested in a comparatively small number of fleet carriers which, in turn require a large number of escorts. Though aware of this, American policy is to continue with the trend, in spite of extensive studies aimed at producing cheaper and less capable flightdecks which would improve flexibility and reduce the chance of a successful pre-emptive stirke by an enemy. Use of a fleet carrier in a small operation may well hazard her unnecessarily where a cheaper

Principe de Asturias. Spanish Official

vessel would be adequate. One proposal was to build a large number of small carriers, called Sea Control Ships (SCS), which would have closely paralleled the escort carrier of WW2. In view of their potential usefulness in ASW and the growing lack of old flightdecks that could be dedicated to this task, it seems a mistake not to have authorised them. Like the British 'Invincible' and the Italian 'Garibaldi', the SCS could be built to its modest dimensions owing to the development of V/STOL aircraft and helicopters. In contrast, however, it is far less ambitious and designed to be built cheaply and in quantity.

Once the project was turned down by the USN, the civilian designers were permitted to offer the design to foreign operators of small and ageing carriers. Only Spain is building one to date, however, with plans for a second.

Unusually, the flightdeck terminates some 20m short of the transom, a centreline elevator connecting it to the hangar deck. A second elevator is set just to starboard of the centreline forward of the island. The flight path itself was planned by the Americans to be moderately angled from port quarter to starboard bow, ie opposite to the normal layout.

Perhaps the most controversial design point is the single shaft. This is driven by two standard US LM2500 gas turbines where, economically, four diesels would have been a better, if noisier, choice.

A British-type 'ski-jump' is fitted forward to improve the takeoff weight for the Harriers, known by the Spaniards as Matadors.

An SPN-35 Aircraft Approach Control Radar is fitted beneath the radome abaft the funnel and the rectangular SPS-52C antenna provides three-dimensional data for targeting the defensive SAMs. The CIWS are the home-produced Meroka, a 12-barrelled 20mm gun whose barrels are fixed in two rows and not based on the revolving Gatling principle.

Dédalo   Light aircraft carrier   Spain

	Builders	LD	L	C
R01 Dédalo (ex-USS Cabot AVT3, ex-CVL28, ex-USS Wilmington, CL79)	NYS	42	43	43

Displacement: 13,000 tons standard; 16,400 tons full load

Dimensions: 189.9m × 21.8m × 8m (166 × 33m over flightdeck)

Armament: Twenty-six 40mm guns (2 × 4) + (9 × 2)

Machinery:
Four sets geared steam turbines 100,000shp

Four shafts
Speed: 30kts
Aircraft: Usually six V/STOL and about 20 helicopters

Shortly to celebrate her 40th birthday, Dédalo will not be deleted until the new carrier's much-delayed commissioning. She is the last of a group of the nine 'Cleve-

land' class light cruisers, converted by the Americans immediately after their launching to small carriers with a useful 32kt speed that enabled them to accompany a task group. Their original 'trade mark' was a row of four stubby funnels, cranked outboard on the starboard side; these have been reduced to only two in the course of subsequent modernisation.

Of the original group, *Cabot* and *Bataan* were converted to specialised ASW carriers, in the course of which their capacity was rearranged around about twenty aircraft of considerably larger size and weight than the original 40. Flightdeck and hangar deck were strengthened, elevators uprated and a catapult fitted. Specialised facilities and electronics were improved and re-arranged, and stability — a problem with a high freeboard, fine-lined ship — improved.

Transferred in 1967, she has operated mainly as a helicopter carrier with, usually, a mixed bag of Sea Kings and AB212s but a new dimension was added by the purchase of about a dozen Harrier V/STOLs. These have been deployed for some time and the new carrier will inherit a fully worked-up airgroup on her eventual completion.

Roger de Lauria   Destroyer   *Spain*

	Builders	LD	L	C
D42 *Roger de Lauria*	ENB	51	58	69
D43 *Marques de la Ensenada*	ENB	51	59	70

Displacement: 3,000 tons standard; 3,800 tons full load
Dimensions: 119.3m × 13m × 5.7m
Armament:
Six 5in guns (3 × 2)
Two 533mm (21in) torpedo tubes
Two triple A/S torpedo tubes
Machinery:
Two sets geared steam turbines 60,000shp
Two shafts
Speed: 31kts
Aircraft: One small helicopter, no hangar

Originally known as the 'Oquendo' class, these ships have had a somewhat chequered career. The design of the name ship dated from the mid-1940s, when British influence was still strong, but, considering that the ship was ordered in 1947, laid down in 1951, launched in 1956 and completed in 1960 it is scarcely surprising that the whole concept was dated well before completion even though the opportunity had been taken to change the original gun calibre from a German 4.1in to a British 4.7in and to install directors and electronics to about 'Battle' class standard. A planned torpedo tube fit of one triple and two twin banks was never shipped, the superstructure being in the form of a continuous house flanked by six single 40mm gun in sponsons.

By this time destroyers as a type were being built by only a few fleets, many existing units being rebuilt for other tasks. Thus the following two were not taken beyond the launching stage before being towed elsewhere for completion to a revised design, based largely on a FRAM 'Gearing'. As this involved more topweight, especially in the further increase of gun calibre to 5in, the hull was lengthened, widened and given a long forecastle design. The final planned six, to have been named *Blas de Lezo*, *Blasco de Garay*, *Bonifaz*, *Gelmirez*, *Langara* and *Recalde*, were all cancelled. *Oquendo* herself was scrapped in 1978.

Modernisation has included the provision of a pad for a small ASW helicopter, and in spite of rumoured machinery problems, they are reported to be receiving both short range SAMs and a Meroka CIWS.

Two further Spanish-built destroyers, the 1,200 ton *Audaz* of 1965 and the 1,850-ton *Liniers* for 1951 are still in service. Both are used for training and they have little potential as modern warships.

Gearing (FRAM I)   Destroyer   *Spain*

	Builders	LD	L	C
D61 *Churruca* (ex-USS *Eugene A. Greene*, DD711)	FSB	44	45	45
D62 *Gravina* (ex-USS *Furse*, DD882)	CSC	44	45	45
D63 *Mendez Nuñez* (ex-USS *O'Hare*, DD889)	CSC	45	45	45
D64 *Langara* (ex-USS *Leary*, DD879)	CSC	44	45	45
D65 *Blas de Lezo* (ex-USS *Noa*, DD841)	BIW	45	45	45

Standard FRAM I 'Gearings', details of which may be found under Greece. Transferred 1972-3.

Fletcher   Destroyer   *Spain*

D21 *Lepanto* (ex-USS *Capps*, DD550)
D23 *Almirante Valdes* (ex-USS *Converse*, DD509)
D24 *Alcala Galiano* (ex-USS *Jarvis*, DD799)
D25 *Jorge Juan* (USS McGowan, DD678)

Builders	LD	L	C
GSB	41	42	43
BIW	42	42	43
TPS	43	44	44
FSB	43	43	43

Four of five standard 'Fletchers' acquired from the US 1957-60. For data see under Greece. D21 retains five 5in gun layout but remainder have a triple 21in torpedo tube bank in lieu of 'Q' gun. The fifth unit, *Almirante*

Ferrandiz (D22) was deleted in 1978. Although plans have been announced for updating the ships' AS armament, these would amount to gilding somewhat faded lilies in view of their age and general obsolescence.

Perry   Frigate   *Spain*

	Builders	LD	L	C
F81 *Navarra*	ENB	81	83	85
F82 *Murcia*	ENB	82	84	86
F83 *Leon*	ENB	84	85	87

Three standard 'Perrys' being built under licence; for data see under USA. Where dates for Spanish naval

construction usually 'slip to the right', these have suffered the more in being subordinated to the construction of the new carrier. The choice of the 'Perry' logically follows that of the 'Knox' but continues the dubious trend of single-screw AA area-defence ships which, inevitably, must be used for escorting the carrier. They will, reportedly, be fitted with both Harpoon and the Spanish-built Meroka CIWS.

Knox   Frigate   *Spain*

	Builders	LD	L	C
F71 *Baleares*	ENB	68	70	73
F72 *Andalucia*	ENB	69	71	74
F73 *Cataluña*	ENB	70	71	75
F74 *Asturias*	ENB	71	72	75
F75 *Estremadura*	ENB	71	72	76

For details, see under USA. The licence to build these was obtained from the Americans after the UK, on political grounds, had refused an application to build 'Leanders'. Though the 'Knox' is larger, she is far less

weatherly, slower and of inferior manoeuvrability. She does, however, ship a heavier weapon and sensor payload, most supplied by the USA. The major difference between the Spanish and American units lies in the latter substituting a Standard MR system aft in place of a Sea Sparrow, the volume thus required meaning that the helicopter and facilities have been dispensed with. The area defence weapon makes them more suitable as carrier escorts.

Churruca, *'Gearing' class.* Spanish Official

Descubierta. Empresa Nacional 'Bazan'

Descubierta   Frigate

Spain

	Builders	LD	L	C
F31 *Descubierta*	ENB	74	75	78
F32 *Diana*	ENB	75	76	79
F33 *Infanta Elena*	ENB	76	76	79
F34 *Infanta Cristina*	ENB	76	77	80
F35 *Cazadora*	ENB	77	78	81
F36 *Vencedora*	ENB	78	79	82
F37 *Centinela*	ENB	78	79	82
F38 *Serviola*	ENB	79	80	83

Displacement: 1,235 tons standard; 1,480 tons full load
Dimensions: 88.8m × 10.5m × 3.3m
Armament:
Two quadruple Harpoon SSMs
One octal Sea Sparrow SAM
One 76mm gun
One 40mm gun, *or*
one 12 barrelled Meroka CIWS
Two triple AS torpedo tubes
Machinery:
Four diesels 16,000shp
Twin shafts
Speed: 25kts

Offering a comprehensive armament package on a very modest tonnage, this design could expect to have enjoyed more export success than it has so far achieved. Though officially styled a 'corvette', this is misleading as, with Harpoons and gun, it offers a good anti-ship capacity, whilst, in the Sea Sparrow and CIWS, it has the ability to survive close in aircraft attack, though a low-flying missile could present problems. This outfit has been bought at the expense of AS potential for, although a VDS is carried in addition to a hull-mounted sonar, only a twin Bofors-type mortar and short-range AS torpedoes are fitted. On so small a ship, the omission of a helicopter was wise, although a stretched GT-powered version with a similar armament fit, helicopter and hangar is under development.

Essentially a follow-on 'Coutinho', the 'Descubierta' has four diesels and an advertised 50% improvement in power, which makes the official speed questionable. The quixotic veed uptakes are an affectation in view of the diesel propulsion. Atop the foremast is the familiar egg-shaped WM 25 fire control radome from HSA, from which manufacturer came also the large DA 05 surveillance radar, used also by both the Dutch and Belgian navies.

The last two of the class are to be sold to Egypt. To be replaced by two extra FF67/'Perry' class.

Atrevida   Corvette

Spain

	Builders	LD	L	C
PA61 *Atrevida*	ENB	50	52	54
PA62 *Princesa*	ENB	53	56	57
PA64 *Nautilus*	ENB	53	56	59
PA65 *Villa de Bilbao* (ex-*Favorita*)	ENB	53	58	60

Displacement: 1,030 tons standard; 1,130 tons full load
Dimensions: 75.5m × 10.3m × 3m
Armament:
One 76mm gun
Three 40mm guns (3 × 1)
Two Hedgehog AS mortars
Machinery:
Two diesels 3,000bhp
Two shafts
Speed: 18kts

Atrevida.   Mike Lennon

Though six of the class were built, two have been discarded, the *Descubierta* (F63) and *Diana* (F66), both of whose names have been adopted by new-construction frigates. Far from old, particularly by Spanish standards, they can only be presumed to have been disappointing in service. This probably lay in the fact that they were designed as coastal AS ships, for which purpose they seem greatly underpowered. Having disposed of two units, the Spanish Navy changed the 'F' pennants of the remainder to 'PA' to underline a new and predominantly patrol role, even though the earlier armament was retained, the Hedgehogs complemented by up to eight DC throwers and racks. Fishery protection and offshore surviellance are now their likely functions.

They have a handsome hull which looks seakindly but lack a funnel as the diesels exhaust through the sides. Originally designed to carry a German-pattern 105mm gun, super-fired by a twin 37mm, together with three quadruple 20mm mounts, they now have a US-pattern single 3in/50m in B position and three single 40mm weapons aft. A useful feature is an ability to carry about 20 mines. An American GP radar is fitted, together with a small sonar.

Agosta   Patrol submarine   *Spain*

	Builders	L	C
S71 *Galerna*	ENB	81	82
S72 *Scirocco*	ENB	83	84
S73 *Mistral*	ENB	82	83
S74 *Tramontana*	ENB	84	85

For details see under France. These boats were ordered in two pairs from the Spanish yard and, although containing much home-produced equipment, are nearly identical with the French-built units. One reported difference is that they are fitted with French-pattern 550mm torpedo tubes, where the French boats have adopted the more standard 533mm (21in) tube. This might well make sense in order to simplify logistics vis-a-vis the Spanish-built 'Daphne' (qv) though doubt much exist in that they are also reported to be able to fire the encapsulated SM39 version of the Exocet from them.

Galerna, *'Agosta' class*.   Empresa Nacional 'Bazan'

Daphné   Patrol submarine   *Spain*

	Builders	L	C
S61 *Delfin*	ENB	72	73
S62 *Tonina*	ENB	72	73
S63 *Marsopa*	ENB	74	75
S64 *Narval*	ENB	74	75

For details see under France. They were ordered from the home yard in two pairs and were identical with the French boats, but now differ externally in that the French units have had a bow sonar dome of different profile fitted.

Guppy   Patrol submarine   *Spain*

	Builders	L	C
S31 *Almirante García de los Reyes* (ex-USS *Kraken*, SS370)	MSB	44	44
S32 *Isaac Peral* (ex-USS *Ronquil*, SS396)	PNY	44	44
S34 *Cosmsé García* (ex-USS *Bang*, SS385)	PNY	43	43
S35 *Narciso Monturiol* (ex-USS *Jallao*, SS368)	MSB	44	44

S31 is a modernised 'Balao' class boat and the remainder 'Guppy IIAs'. For details see under Greece. Transferred from US Navy between 1971 and 1974, except S31, acquired as far back as 1959. S35 has taken name of previous S33, deleted in 1977.

Now depth limited and likely to disappear on completion of 'Agosta' group.

Lazaga   FAC (Gun)   *Spain*

	Builders	Completed
PC01 *Lazaga*	LV	75
PC02 *Alcedo*	ENB	77
PC03 *Cadarso*	ENB	76
PC04 *Villamil*	ENB	77
PC05 *Bonifaz*	ENB	77
PC06 *Recalde*	ENB	77

Displacement: 275 tons standard; 400 tons full load
Dimensions: 58.1m × 7.5m × 2.5m
Armament:
One 76mm gun
One 40mm gun
Machinery:
Two diesels, 9,000bhp
Twin shafts
Speed: 29kts

Spain commonly purchases its warship designs, with the lead ship built in the country of origin and the remainder constructed under licence in homeyards. Having experienced satisfactory results from a Lürssen-designed S-boat type hull in the 1950s, the Spanish Navy acquired the 'Lazaga' type from the same source. The lines were used first for the Israeli 'Reshef' class, which had four diesels of about 10,500bhp total, powering two shafts. The 'Lazagas' are rather lower powered, with only two diesels, the leadship being built in parallel with the first of another derivative, the Bundesmarine's Type 143 (qv) which is a quadruple-shaft design. Where the Israeli and West German craft were heavily-armed with guns and missiles, however, the Spaniards were designed as patrol craft, carrying only guns. Though comparatively low-powered, the craft would almost certainly have space for a third engine to be added on the centreline. Each is equipped with a small sonar set and can reportedly ship AS torpedo tubes and depth charges. The long dodgers aft, nevertheless, would suggest two long tubes for wire-guided torpedoes launched over the transom, German-style, an impression heightened by the WM 22 fire control. Space in plenty exists aft for SSMs, should they be required and, indeed, a slightly-stretched triple-diesel variant with four Exocets has already been built for export.

Barcelo   FAC (Gun)   *Spain*

	Builders	Completed
PC11 *Barcelo*	LV	76
PC12 *Laya*	ENB	76
PC13 *Javier Quiroga*	ENB	77
PC14 *Ordoñez*	ENB	77
PC15 *Acevedo*	ENB	77
PC16 *Candido Perez*	ENB	77

Displacement: 135 tons full load
Dimensions: 36.3m × 5.8m × 1.9m
Armament: One 40mm gun and smaller weapons
Machinery:
Two diesels, 5,800bhp
Twin shafts
Speed: 34kts

Barcelo. Spanish Official

Like the 'Lazagas', the 'Barcelos' are of a Lürssen design, in this case similar to the 36m craft serving already under the flags of Chile and Ecuador. Though again operating in the lightly-armed patrol-boat role, they could easily be converted to carry torpedoes and/or SSMs. In this case, the optical director for the present small-calibre weapons would probably be supplemented by a more comprehensive system such as the HSA on the Lazagas. Although an official speed of 36kts is claimed for the class, their power would seem to be inadequate for this.

Galicia   Landing ship (Dock)   *Spain*

	Builders	LD	L	C
L31 *Galicia* (ex-USS *San Marcos*, LSD25)	PNH	44	45	45

Displacement: 4,800 tons standard; 9,400 tons full load
Dimensions: 139m × 23.2m × 5m
Armament: Twelve 40mm guns (2 × 4) + (2 × 2)
Machinery:
Two sets geared steam turbines, 7,000shp
Twin shafts
Speed: 15kts

Still having interests in enclaves on the African continent as well as in islands offshore, Spain has built up a comparatively large amphibious warfare force since WW2, necessary because of a lack of developed harbours. Following experience with a pair of ex-American Amphibious Transports, the Spanish Navy acquired the *Galicia* in 1971. Though amphibious transports can carry up to two battalions of troops, they rely on LCAs for landing them; as these are put over the side by the ship's own gear, operations can be constrained by heavy seas. An LSD, however, does not need to lift its landing craft, which can thus be larger, in the case of the *Galicia* up to three 36m LCUs or 18 LCM 6s. An LCU (Landing Craft, Utility) can carry about 200 tons of cargo or three medium tanks while the LCM 6 can stow 34 tons of mixed cargo. A larger version, the LCM8, can load a medium tank.

The illustration gives a good idea of an LSD's layout, with the docking well being open to a point amidships, spanned aft by light decks for transport stowage and helicopter operation. The forward part of the well is spanned by the elevated deck carrying the bridge structure and enclosing space for the short-haul transport of about 500 troops. Two heavy cranes for handling deck cargo are stowed with their jibs athwartships, immediately abaft the sided funnels. These 'Cabildo'-class LSD's differed from earlier vessels in having steam-turbine propulsion in place of the more interesting Skinner Uniflow steam engines. Even so, their speed was modest by today's standards.

In addition, the Spaniards operate two large amphibious transports (LPA), three 'County' class LSTs and seven LCTs.

MSO   Minesweeper   *Spain*

	Completed
M41 *Guadalete* (ex-USS *Dynamic*, MSO432)	53
M42 *Guadalmedina* (ex-USS *Pivot*, MSO463)	54
M43 *Guadalquivir* (ex-USS *Persistant*, MSO491)	56
M44 *Guadiana* (ex-USS *Vigor*, MSO473)	54

For data and illustration, see under Belgium. Unlike the Belgian units, this group all served in the US Navy, being transferred 1971-2. Though their sonars have been updated, they are still equipped only as minesweepers. *Guadalete* is used for patrol duties. It is reported that Spain would be interested in building NATO 'Tripartite' minehunters under licence.

MSC type   Coastal minesweeper

Spain

	Completed
M21 *Jucar* (ex-USS MSC220)	56
M22 *Ebro* (ex-USS MSC269)	58
M23 *Duero* (ex-USS *Spoonbill*, MSC202)	59
M24 *Tajo* (ex-USS MSC287)	59
M25 *Genil* (ex-USS MSC279)	59
M26 *Odiel* (ex-USS MSC288)	59
M51 *Nalón* (ex-USS MSC139)	54
M52 *Ulla* (ex-USS MSC265)	58
M53 *Mino* (ex-USS MSC266)	56
M54 *Turia* (ex-USS MSC130)	55
M55 *Sil* (ex-USS *Redwing* MSC200)	59

For details and illustration, see under Greece. The second group, M51-55, are used as patrol craft.

Östergötland   Destroyer

Sweden

	Builders	LD	L	C
J23 *Hälsingland*	KMV	55	57	59

Displacement: 2,150 tons standard, 2,600 tons full load
Dimensions: 112m × 11.3m × 3.8m
Armament:
Launcher for RB 08A SSM
One quadruple Seacat BPDMS
Four 120mm guns (2×2)
Four 40mm guns (4×1)
One sextuple 533mm (21in) torpedo tube bank
One triple-barrelled squid AS mortar
Machinery:
Two sets geared steam turbines, 47,000shp
Two shafts
Speed: 35kts

Present Swedish naval policy assumes that any surface warships larger than FACs would stand a slim hope of survival in any future Baltic war, a war that would be dominated by aircraft and missiles in waters already constricted by natural features. With this in mind, the cruisers and coast defence ships have gone, together with some fine destroyers that still have some life left in them. Thus, *Hälsingland* is the sole survivor of a quartette of particularly good-looking ships, her sisters

Gastrikland, *Östergötland* and *Södermanland* being stricken in 1979. It is surprising that they were not quickly purchased by a foreign power and it can only be assumed that this was due to Sweden's tight controls on selling armaments abroad.

Flush-decked ships with a long-easy sheerline, they presented a fort-like exterior, their crews covered against the effects of both nuclear and chemical warfare, and the rigours of the northern climate. Even the four 40mm guns, forward and aft, are enclosed in single mountings.

Assuming that enemy aircraft would be neutralised by friendly air cover a warship's main pre-occupation would be with her own kind and the 'Östergötlands' armament reflected this. Two paired 120mm guns (the Swedes retained the old British favourite, the 4.7in calibre) were backed up by a sextuple torpedo tube bank and a Saab RB 08A SSM, whose launcher was amidships and associated director adjacent, on a house abaft the forward funnel. A Sea Cat point defence SAM was immediately forward of the after gun mounting and a triple-barrelled Squid AS mortar was sited right aft. Like most Swedish ships, they had a minelaying capacity, in this case up to 60.

As her name has been allocated to one of the new A17 class submarines, her deletion can be expected shortly.

Halland   Destroyer

Sweden

	Builders	LD	L	C
J18 *Halland*	GVG	51	52	55
J19 *Småland*	EMV	51	52	56

Displacement: 2,800 tons standard; 3,400 tons full load
Dimensions: 121m × 12.5m × 4.5m
Armament:
Four 120mm guns (2×2)
Two 57mm guns (1×2)

Six 40mm guns (6×1)
Launcher for RB 08A SSM
Eight 533m (21in) torpedo tubes (1×5) + (1×3)
Two four-barrelled AS rocket launchers
Machinery:
Two sets geared steam turbines, 5,800shp
Two shafts
Speed: 35kts

Though slightly older than the 'Östergötlands', the

larger pair of 'Hallands' are being retained for the moment. They were Sweden's first postwar destroyers and, though they took from ordering in 1948 to commissioning in 1955/6, represented very much the 'state of the art' on their completion. A little longer than Britain's contemporary 'Darings', they featured the raised forecastle then common outside the USA. Their main armament was similar in layout but differed in having fully automatic 120mm guns in A and Y positions with the former super-fired by a more versatile 57mm pair. Although the main-calibre weapons were capable of a theoretical 40 rounds per barrel per minute, they were apparently not without problems, for the following class had a semi-automatic model of only half this rate of fire. Six fully enclosed single 40mm weapons are spaced along the ships. Torpedo tubes are retained and are carried high, similar to the earlier US practice. Uniquely, the forward banks is a triple and the

Halland.   Royal Swedish Navy

after, a quintuple, the latter acting also as a rotating support for the Saab-built RB08A SSM, an obsolescent 30-mile weapon. Right forward are two Bofors 375mm multi-barrelled AS rocket launchers and the stern is configured for mine-laying.

The squared-off, powerful appearance is beautifully set-off by a pair of perfectly proportioned funnels, the overall classic profile being marred only by the latter-day addition of a large Dutch-built surveillance antenna aft.

Camouflage is frequently used on Swedish warships, issuing as they often do from cavernous rock-bound shelters on the coast. Their 'J' flag superiors emphasise their non-NATO status. The ensign worn between the funnels when at sea is another Swedish touch.

Näcken   Submarine   *Sweden*

	Builders	L	C
Nak Näcken	KMV	78	79
Naj Najad	KV	78	79
Nep Neptun	KMV	79	80

Displacement: 980 tons surfaced; 1,125 tons submerged
Dimensions: 41m × 6m × 4.1m
Armament: Six 533m/(21in) torpedo tubes (all forward)

Machinery:
Two diesel generators
One electric propulsion motor, about 2,300bhp
Single shaft
Speed: 20/20kts

As Sweden envisages fighting only a defensive war in the constricted Baltic, her submarines tend to be small and handy, lacking great range or diving power. The

Neptun, *'Näcken' class*.   Royal Swedish Navy

three 'Näckens', or A14 class as they are officially known, exhibit these characteristics except that their safe operating depth of 300m suggests possible operations further west. An improved, and diminutive, version of the preceding 'Sjöormen' the design includes a six-tube battery forward; these are capable of firing either the wakeless and wire-guided M61 anti-ship torpedo or the smaller M42 AS torpedo, also wire-guided and small enough to be shipped two to a tube and swum-out as required. Mines may also be carried in lieu of torpedoes.

The illustration shows the X-configured after control surfaces. In this arrangement, each control surface is part-hydroplane and part-rudder. Controlled closely by computer, these are claimed by the Swedes to offer superior characteristics, though the effects of a failed computer or jammed surface would likely prove serious. Much effort has been made to reduce radiated noise and the large, slow-revving propeller is driven directly by a double-armature motor, water-cooled for heavy demands, as are the batteries. The careful mechanical de-coupling of machinery from the hull has been undertaken not only from the point of view of noise but also to minimise the effects of explosions, much magnified by shallow waters. Great use of automation has kept the crew down to a commendably small 19.

Four new boats, designated the A17s, have been ordered from Karlskronavarvet and Kockums. Developed from the A14 design, they are longer at 48.5m overall, though with a crew of only 20. For this programme, the former yard will build the bow and stern sections, and the latter will both build the amidships section and assemble the whole. They will take 'destroyer' names, *Hälsingland* (Hgd), *Östergötland* (Ogd), *Södermanland* (Söd) and Vastergötland (Vgd).

Sjoormen   Submarine   *Sweden*

	Builders	L	C
Sor Sjoormen	KMV	67	67
Sle Sjolejonet	KMV	67	68
Shu Sjohunden	KMV	68	69
Sbj Sjobjornen	KV	68	69
Sha Sjohasten	KV	68	69

Displacement: 1,125 tons surfaced; 1,400 tons submerged
Dimensions: 50.5m × 6.1m × 5m
Armament:
Four 533mm (21in) torpedo tubes
Two 400mm AS torpedo tubes (all forward)
Machinery:
Two diesel generators, 2,200bhp
One electric propulsion motor
One shaft
Speed: 15/20kts

Though less then six years span the commissioning of the last 'Draken' and the first 'Sjoormen', the boats are far apart in concept, although their respective official classifications of A11 and A11B suggest a closer relationship. Separating the two classes in time were the influential 'Albacore' experiments and the data reflects the resultant changes in shape, with the later boats, though of greater displacement, being shorter and fatter. They adopted the American-style fin-mounted forward hydroplanes and the X-configured control surfaces aft, a feature about which the Americans themselves since seem not too sure. The biassing of the performance to underwater use has resulted in a low surfaced speed.

A very deep hull has allowed two decks to be incorporated and the designs are reportedly depth-limited to less than 200m, sufficient for inner Baltic use where there are a few deep patches to justify a stronger construction. The large fin, of distinctive profile, is set unusually far forward.

A war-level crew of 23 can be supported for a three week patrol; of these, about 40% are officers, reflecting the high technical content of today's submarine operation, where advanced automation is employed.

Sjolejonet, *'Sjoormen' class.*   Royal Swedish Navy

Draken   Submarine   *Sweden*

	Builders	L	C
Del Delfinen	KV	61	62
Nor Nordkaparen	KMV	61	62
Spr Springaren	KMV	61	62
Vgn Vargen	KMV	60	61

Displacement: 835 tons surfaced; 1,110 tons submerged
Dimensions: 69m × 5.1m × 5m
Armament: Four 533mm (21in) torpedo tubes (all forward)
Machinery:
Two diesel generators
One electric propulsion motor, 1,600bhp
One shaft
Speed: 17/20kts

Looking rather older than their years, this quartette are the survivors of a class of 12 boats, divided into two equal subgroups, the 'Hajens' commissioned in 1957-60 and the 'Drakens' in 1961-62. Both groups had the long, slender lines of the 'classic' submarine but differed in that the 'Hajens' had a twin-screw arrangement and the 'Drakens' an early attempt at a large, single screw with cruciform control surfaces. The latter boats were also about 3.5m longer, probably because of improved electronics and/or greater battery capacity though, as the power of the propulsion motors was similar, improvements would likely to have been in terms of capacity rather than speed.

Compared with current submarines, with their ultra-clean lines, the 'Drakens' look cluttered and noisy. The low external conning position is backed by a higher casing enclosing the periscope and mast standards, an arrangement reminiscent of early 'Guppy' conversions.

As Sweden's first postwar design, they are now of limited performance and carry only four tubes with eight reloads. Like all Swedish submarines, they carry identification letters rather than numbers. Construction, as for all Swedish classes, was divided between the state dockyard at Karlskrona and the Malmo-based commercial yard of Kockums.

The 'Hajens' were discarded in 1978, and both the nameship and *Gripen* of the second group in 1981. The remainder will soon follow.

Hugin   FAC (Missile)   *Sweden*

	Builders	Completed		Builders	Completed
P150 *Jägaren*	BMV	72	P159 *Kaparen*	BMV	80
P151 *Hugin*	BMV	78	P160 *Väktaren*	BMV	80
P152 *Munin*	BMV	78	P161 *Snapphanen*	BMV	81
P153 *Magne*	BMV	78	P162 *Spejaren*	BMV	81
P154 *Mode*	BSM	79	P163 *Styrbjorn*	BMV	81
P155 *Vale*	BSM	79	P164 *Starkodder*	BMV	81
P156 *Vidar*	BSM	79	P165 *Tordon*	BMV	81
P157 *Mjolner*	BSM	79	P166 *Tirfing*	BMV	82
P158 *Mysing*	BSM	80			

Hugin. Royal Swedish Navy

Displacement: 120 tons standard; 150 tons full load
Dimensions: 36.5m × 6.3m × 1.6m
Armament:
One 57mm gun
Six SSMs
Machinery:
Two diesels, 7,200bhp
Two shafts
Speed: 35kts

Having embarked on a policy of gradual withdrawal of larger units without replacement, the Swedish navy needed a capable, missile-armed FAC to complement the torpedo/gun-armed 'Spicas'. It had built at the Norewegian Batservis yard at Mandal a prototype, name *Jägaren*, that was completed in 1972 for comprehensive evaluation. During the period of this programme, the Norwegians themselves adopted the design, of which they were to build 14, known as the 'Hauk' class. The same Norwegian yards were then invited to construct a further 16 to Swedish account;

the first of these was the *Hugin*, which became nameship for the class.

With a 70-calibre Bofors 57mm gun foward (the largest that could be mounted on this comparatively short hull) the 'Hugins' are more powerfully armed than the Norwegians. There is provision aft to mount a 40mm weapon for an all-gun role if required. With a missile armament to fit in aft, the bridge structure has had to be sited further forward than in the 'Spicas', limiting the big guns' firing arc to some extent.

With respect to the SSM armament, the originally-planned six Penguins are not now to be fitted, being replaced by the Swedish-built Saab-Bofors RBS-15 which, though lighter than even a Penguin 2, is reputed to have about four times the range (about 100km). They will not, however, be operational until the mid-1980s. Meanwhile, Penguins or a second gun could be fitted. Alternatively, mine rails can be shipped.

An interesting fitting is a small sonar: in view of the increasing number of 'unidentified' submarines discovered in Swedish inshore waters, this may prove useful.

Spica   FAC (Torpedo/Gun)   *Sweden*

	Builders	Completed
Spica I		
T121 *Spica*	GVG	66
T122 *Sirius*	GVG	66
T123 *Capella*	GVG	66
T124 *Castor*	KV	67
T125 *Vega*	KV	67
T126 *Virgo*	KV	67
Spica II		
T131 *Norrköping*	KV	73
T132 *Nynashamn*	KV	73
T133 *Norrtalje*	KV	74
T134 *Varberg*	KV	74
T135 *Västerås*	KV	74
T136 *Västervik*	KV	75
T137 *Umea*	KV	75
T138 *Pitea*	KV	75
T139 *Lulea*	KV	75
T140 *Halmstad*	KV	76
T141 *Stromstad*	KV	76
T142 *Ystad*	KV	76

Displacement: 200 tons standard; 230 tons full load
Dimensions: 41m × 7m × 2.5m
Armament:
One 57mm gun
Six 533mm (21in) torpedo tubes
Machinery:
Three gas turbines, 12,900bhp
Three shafts
Speed: 40kts

Torpedoes are still a potent weapon in a missile-dominated age, the one obvious advantage being that they damage a target where it hurts most — below the waterline. Long-range anti-ship and AS torpedoes can

be wireguided, transmitting and receiving coded signals as they run and are extremely difficult for the target to jam. Used in an attack coordinated with missile-armed craft, the torpedo-carriers can take advantage of a target with (apparently) more pressing preoccupations. Both groups of 'Spicas' were designed around six tubes for the launching of the Swedish Type 61 torpedo, carrying a 250kg warhead out to 25km. To give the 57mm gun the maximum firing arc, the superstructure is set far aft. The groups can easily be differentiated by the earlier craft having a higher bridge structure topped by the distinctive radome of a Dutch HSA M22 fire control and the later boats having the exposed antennas of a Swedish PEAB 9LV200 outfit used also in the

Ystad, *'Spica II' class.*   Royal Swedish Navy

'Hugins'. When the Saab-Bofors RBS-15 (see under 'Hugin') enters service, some of the 'Spicas' may be fitted with them, up to eight being carried in lieu of the four after tubes. *Pitea* (T138) has done trials with three missiles together with the full set of torpedoes.

The long foredeck makes the hull appear longer than it actually is, but despite only being 41m overall, it has sweet lines, seakindly and responsive to the high installed power from three Rolls-Royce Proteus gas tur-bines. No cruising diesels are fitted on the wing shafts.

An order for the first two of a planned six 'Spica III' class 'strike craft' has been placed. They will be pre-ceded by two follow-ons, the *Stockholm* (R11) and *Malmo* (R12). Armed with the RBS-15 SSM, guns of 57mm and 40mm calibre, as well as long and short torpedoes, they will be named *Göteborg* (R21), *Gälve* (R22), *Kalmar* (R23), *Sundsvall* (R24), *Helsingborg* (R25) and *Härnösund* (R26).

'T42' class   FAC (Torpedo)   *Sweden*

	Builders	Completed
V01 *Skanör*	KMV	57
V02 *Smyge*	KMV	57
V03 *Arild*	KMV	57
V04 *Viken*	KMV	57
V05 *Öregrund*	SND	58-60
V06 *Slite*	SND	58-60
V07 *Sandhamn*	SND	58-60
V08 *Lysekil*	SND	58-60
V09 *Marstrand*	SND	58-60
V10 *Lister*	SND	58-60
V11 *Torhamn*	SND	58-60
V12 *Dalaro*	SND	58-60

Displacement: 40 tons standard
Dimensions: 23m×6m×1.5m
Armament:
Two 533mm/(21in) torpedo tubes
One 40mm gun
Machinery:
Three diesel engines, 4,500bhp

Three shafts
Speed: 45kts

The last survivors of a once-numerous 'mosquito fleet', based on the MTBs of WW2 and virtual repeats of the T32 class of 1951, this class has recently been refitted and reclassed as 'Vedettes' or patrol craft. In size, power and layout they are closely similar to the British 'Gay' class boats of the time and had also their weakness of petrol-engine propulsion, which perpetuated totally unnecessary fire hazard in action in an age of excellent marine diesels. This recent refur-bishing included therefore a change to diesel pro-pulsion. Built of wood, they have lasted well, their hard-chine, flat vee sections still capable of producing very high speeds by modern standards.

Such small and fleet craft could pose a real problem for an enemy among the Skerries but they now lack the modern electronics required for coordinated action against a well-equipped and alert target and have been re-vamped for the very useful task of policing these complex offshore waters.

Carlskrona   Minelayer   *Sweden*

	Builders	L	Completed
M04 *Carlskrona*	KV	80	81

Displacement: 3,150 tons standard
Dimensions: 105.8m×15.3m×4.1m

Carlskrona. Royal Swedish Navy

Armament:
Two 57mm guns (2 × 1)
One 40mm gun
Machinery:
Four diesels, 10,600bhp
Two shafts
Speed: 20kts

Sweden has always taken the mine seriously and a large section of the fleet is devoted to laying and countering them, most larger units having also an auxiliary function as layers. It is, indeed, the rule rather than the exception for Swedish warships to be built with a designated secondary role. Such was the recently-retired *Alvsnaben*, 40-odd years old and built on to the mercantile-type hull of a Johnson liner. With her large mine-laying capacity of potential use only in wartime, she was employed as a sea-going training ship for over 60 naval cadets. Her successor, *Carlskrona* (note the historically-correct spelling), provides a contrast in purpose-design. Less than 4m longer, she is much beamier and of far shallower draught. As a training ship, she should prove more

efficient, her regular crew having been reduced from the earlier ship's 250 men to only 50, while the cadet complement has increased from about 60 to nearly 140: while accepting that today's automated ships require smaller crews, there still exists the impression that the cadets will be working rather harder in the day-to-day running of the ship.

Though very much a stretched 'Alvsborg' design, the *Carlskrona* differs greatly in having over twice the installed power, with two diesels in each of two machinery spaces, paired on to separate shafts. This arrangement offers greater economy and superior manoeuvrability than the earlier single-screw minelayers, while the smaller-diameter propellers contribute to the low draught.

A helicopter deck is provided aft, though an aircraft is not usually carried and no hangar is provided. An interesting small feature is the addition — in spite of the already imposing freeboard — of a bulwark forward. As with Swedish FAC practice, there has been a change from HSA fire control to Swedish-built PEAB and an increase in calibre for main armament from 40mm to 57mm.

Alvsborg Minelayer   *Sweden*

	Builders	L	C
M02 *Alvsborg*	KV	69	71
M03 *Visborg*	KV	75	76

Displacement:
2,650 tons standard (*Alvsborg*)
2,550 tons standard (*Visborg*)
Dimensions: 92m × 14.8m × 4m
Armament: Three 40mm guns (3 × 1)
Machinery:
Two diesels 4,200bhp
Twin shafts
Speed: 16kts

The very short space of time from launch to completion emphasises the essentially mercantile character of these ships, designed as they are to speedily load, stow and deposit their cargo. High-freeboard hulls are typical of the type, together with broad transoms containing the doors through which the mines are dropped over-

board. Fleets geared to offensive operations tend to view minelaying as a small-scale undertaking best carried out by aircraft so their purpose-built minelaying warships are rare but Sweden works in terms of defensive fields which may need large numbers of mines. This policy is obviously well established with the two 'Alvsborgs' now complemented by the new *Carlskrona*. These, with an average capacity of about 100 large mines, are backed up by nine smaller 'coastal' minelayers, which could each manage about 30 and 16 'inshore' layers, able to handle about a dozen apiece. The Baltic is ideal mine country and possession of its sea exits would be hotly disputed in any shooting war. Sweden would aim to stay neutral but would strongly deter any combatants that sought to use her territorial waters as a quiet way to sea.

Their available space is put to good use in peacetime, this pair acting as submarine depot ships as required and the newer *Visborg* doubling as a command ship.

Visborg, *'Alvsborg' class.*   Royal Swedish Navy

Arkö Coastal minesweeper

Sweden

	Completed
M57 *Arkö*	58
M58 *Spärö*	58
M59 *Karlsö*	58
M60 *Iggö*	61
M61 *Styrsö*	62
M62 *Skaftö*	62
M63 *Aspö*	62
M64 *Hasslö*	62
M65 *Vinö*	62
M66 *Vällö*	63
M67 *Nämdö*	64
M68 *Blidö*	64

Displacement: 285 tons standard; 300 tons full load
Dimensions: 42m × 7.5m × 2.5m
Armament: One 40mm gun
Machinery:
Two diesels 1,600bhp
Two shafts

Contemporary with the NATO-type coastal minesweeper programme, the 'Arkö' class units have the appearance of being rather smaller, even though the difference in length is minimal; the effect is due primarily to their lacking a high forecastle, being designed for work in rather more sheltered waters. They are of wooden construction with odd-numbered ships coming from the Karlskrona Varvet and the evens from the small yard at Halsingborg. All are really due for replacement and two prototypes of a nine-strong GRP-hulled M71 minehunter class have been ordered from Karlskrona Varvet but, with the usual extended nature of Swedish warship construction and evaluation times, the actual embarkation upon the full class programme is not likely for a while yet. Names of those under construction are *Landsort* (M71) and *Arholma* (M72). To follow are *Koster* (M73), *Kullen* (M74), *Vinga* (M75) and *Ven* (M76).

There exist in addition about 18 smaller 'sweepers for inshore use and the prototype for a new class of remotely-controlled GRP minesweeping catamarans has been ordered.

Kiliç Ali Paşa.   Selcuk Emre

Gearing (FRAM I and FRAM II) Destroyer

Turkey

	Builders	LD	L	C	Trans
D347 *Antitepe* (ex-USS Carpenter, DD825)	CSO	45	45	49	81
D348 *Savashtepe* (ex-USS *Meredith*, DD890)	CSO	45	45	45	79
D349 *Kilic Ali Paşa* (ex-USS *Robert H. McCard*, DD822)	CSO	45	45	46	80
D350 *Piyale Paşa* (ex-USS *Fiske*, DD842)	BIW	45	45	45	80
D351 *M. Fevzi Çakmak* (ex-USS *Charles H. Roan*, DD853)	BSQ	44	45	46	73
D352 *Gayret* (ex-USS *Eversole*, DD789)	TPS	45	46	46	73
D353 *Adatepe* (ex-USS *Forrest Royal*, DD872)	BSI	45	46	46	71
D354 *Kocatepe* (ex-USS *Norris*, DD859)	BSF	44	45	47	72
D355 *Tinaztepe* (ex-USS *Keppler*, DD765)	BSF	44	45	47	72
D (ex-USS *McKean*, DD784)	TPS	44	45	45	82

For data see under Greece. All FRAM I except for D354 and D355, both FRAM IIs. An unspecified number have been fitted with a 76mm gun on the flightpad aft, and the two FRAM IIs have a twin 35mm mounting in 'B' position.

Though some units have only recently been acquired, the Turkish destroyer force is obsolete and their replacement has been lent new urgency by the Greeks who, in the same position, have acquired a pair of 'Kortenaers'. It is reported that the Turks are interested in the Blohm & Voss MEKO 200. One of B+V's increasingly successful modular range, this 2,000-plus ton ship would probably have HSA electronics and an American armament of Harpoon, Sea Sparrow, Vulcan/Phalanx and a 5in 54.

Sumner Destroyer   *Turkey*

	Builders	LD	L	C	Trans
D356 *Zafer* (ex-USS *Hugh Purvis*, DD709)	FSD	44	44	45	72
DM357 *Muavanet* (ex-USS *Gwin*, DD772)	BSP	43	44	44	71

D356 is a FRAM II 'Sumner' and DM357 a minelaying version of the 'Robert H. Smith' sub-group. For data see under Greece.

Fletcher Destroyer   *Turkey*

	Builders	LD	L	C	Trans
D340 *Istanbul* (ex-USS *Clarence K. Bronson*, DD668)	FSB	42	43	43	67
D341 *Izmir* (ex-USS *van Valkenburgh*, DD656)	GSC	43	43	44	67
D343 *Iskenderun* (ex-USS *Boyd*, DD544)	BSP	42	42	43	69
D344 *Içel* (ex-USS *Preston*, DD795)	BSP	43	43	44	69

For data, see under Greece. *Izmit* (D342) the fifth of this group was formally deleted in 1980, probably for cannibalisation.

Berk Frigate   *Turkey*

	Builders	LD	L	C
D358 *Berk*	GI	67	71	72
D359 *Peyk*	GI	68	72	75

Displacement: 1,450 tons standard; 1,950 tons full load
Dimensions: 95m × 11.8m × 5.5m

Berk. Mike Lennon

Armament:
Four 3in guns (2×2)
Two triple AS torpedo tubes
Two Hedgehog AS spigot mortars
Machinery:
Four diesels. 24,000bhp
Two shafts
Speed: 25kts

Though a very simple pair of vessels, the 'Berks' are significant in being the first warships of any size to be built in Turkey. The design is based heavily on the American 'Claud Jones' class, all four of which were transferred to Indonesia in 1973-74. Like the Royal Navy, the USN has never really 'taken' to diesel-propelled surface warships and the quartette of 'Jones' represented something of an experiment in the building of a utility

escort, capable of quantity production in emergency. Fleet requirements at that time were for larger, and more capable, escort with a helicopter and the 'Jones' experiment was not taken further. The design was interesting in modifying the WW2 'Edsall' class machiney layout from its four diesel/two shaft arrangement to four diesels on a single shaft. Two stacks indicated a pair of machinery spaces and the Turks have adopted a single large funnel casing to accommodate the exhausts, reverting to two shafts.

Though the American ships demonstrated that they could deploy both VDS and advanced AS weaponry, the 'Berks' have a simple outfit. Similarly, the 3in gun armament is of dated US origin. Space is provided for a helicopter to land but there is no hangar and only minimal facilities.

This could be a useful little type of escort if the layout and fit were to be modified considerably.

Atilay   Patrol submarine   *Turkey*

	Builders	Completed
S347 *Atilay*	HWK	75
S348 *Saldiray*	HWK	75
S349 *Batiray*	HWK	78
S350 *Yildiray*	GI	80
S351 —	GI	82

Saldiray, Type 209. Selcuk Emre

For data see under 'Glavkos' class, Greece.

These are standard West German IKL-designed Type 209s, with the difference that Turkey is now building under licence. Plans to construct to a class of 12 are ambitious but timely, as the greater bulk of the submarine force is ex-American tonnage of WW2 vintage. It is possible that further units could be ordered from West Germany.

Guppy type   Patrol submarine   *Turkey*

	Type*	Builders	Completed	Trans
S333 *Ikinci Inonü* (ex-USS *Corporal*, SS346)	III	EBG	45	73
S335 *Burak Reis* (ex-USS *Seafox*, SS402)	IIA	PNY	44	70
S336 *Murat Reis* (ex-USS *Razorback*, SS394)	IIA	PNY	44	70
S337 *Oruç Reis* (ex-USS *Pomfret*, SS391)	IIA	PNY	44	72
S338 *Uluç Ali Reis* (ex-USS *Thornback*, SS418)	IIA	PNY	44	73
S339 *Dumlupinar* (ex-USS *Caiman*, SS323)	IA	EBG	44	72
S340 *Çerbe* (ex-USS *Trutta*, SS421)	IIA	PNY	44	72
S341 *Canakkale* (ex-USS *Cobbler*, SS344)	III	EBG	45	73
S342 *Turgut Reis* (ex-USS *Bergall*, SS320)	MB	EBG	44	58
S345 *Prevese* (ex-USS *Entemedor*, SS340)	IIA	EBG	45	73
S346 *Birinci Inonü* (ex-USS *Threadfin*, SS410)	IIA	PNY	44	73

* Type 'Guppy IA', 'IIA', 'III' or modified 'Balao'.

For data and notes see under Greece. At least five further old submarines are still in existence and could possibly be made operational to minimal standards.

Tang   Patrol submarine
Turkey

	Builders	L	C
S343 *Piri Reis* (ex-USS *Tang*, SS563)	PNY	51	51

For data see under United States. Transferred 1980.

Lürssen 58m   FAC (Missile)
Turkey

	Builders	Completed
P340 *Dogan*	LV	77
P341 *Marti*	TI	78
P342 *Tayfun*	TI	80
P343 *Volkan*	TI	81

Displacement: 410 tons full load
Dimensions: 5.8m × 7.5m × 2.8m
Armament:
Eight Harpoon SSMs (2 × 4)
One 76mm gun
Two 35mm guns (1 × 2)
Machinery:
Four diesels 18,000bhp
Four shafts
Speed: 38kts

With a leadship built in the yard of the West German designers and three locally-constructed follow-ons, the Turkish fleet has here a quartette with great potential.

In size they are at the top end of the FAC scale, larger even than the Greek 'Combattante IIIs', but by the adoption of the compact Harpoon missile, have double their firepower. If it is accepted that they operate within the range of shore-based air-power then the full 60-mile range of the missiles may be utilised. An HSA fire control is fitted for the powerful gun armament, a 76mm OTO/Melara forward and a paired 35mm Oerlikon-Bührle mounting right aft. Hulls are of steel with light alloy superstructure and, though well-designed, are well within the building capabilities of a comparatively simply equipped yard. Weapon and sensor fits can be bought 'off the peg' and an increasing trend towards this type of indigenously-built warship can be expected. In this case, German machinery is installed in a German-designed hull, with an Italian-American-Swiss armament fit directed by Dutch fire control.

The fifth hull was laid down in 1981 and three further units are believed planned.

Jaguar   FAC (Missile/Torpedo)
Turkey

	Builders	Completed
Group A		
P321 *Denizkusu*	LV	67
P322 *Atmaca*	LV	67
P323 *Sahin*	LV	67
P324 *Kartal*	LV	67
P325 *Meltem*	LV	68
P326 *Pelikan*	LV	68
P327 *Albatros*	LV	68
P328 *Simsek*	LV	68
P329 *Kasirga*	LV	67
Group B		
P330 *Firtina* (ex-P6086 *Pelikan*)	LV	62
P331 *Tufan* (ex-P6085 *Storch*)	LV	62
P332 *Kiliç* (ex-P6065 *Löwe*)	LV	60
P333 *Mizrak* (ex-P6087 *Hähner*)	LV	62
P334 *Yildiz* (ex-P6063 *Tiger*)	LV	59
P335 *Kalkan* (ex-P6062 *Wolf*)	LV	59
P336 *Karayel* (Ex-P6090 *Pinguin*)	LV	62

For data see under Greece.

Both groups of Turkish boats are of standard Lürssen 'Jaguar' (TNC42) design, the difference being that Group A boats were German-built to Turkish account while those of Group B were transferred from the Bundesmarine (along with three others for use as spares) in 1976.

Group A are known as the 'Kartal' class and, while they can carry four torpedo tubes, most seem to be armed with two Penguin II missile launchers right aft. Two more missiles or two tubes could be fitted. Supported by the all-torpedo, ex-'Jaguars', they would make a formidable group.

In spite of their advancing years, the 'Jaguars' seem to suit the Turks well for four new units are reported to be under construction at Lürssen. If reports of an eight-Harpoon armament are correct, then these will be very nearly the smallest craft to be so fitted.

Albatros, 'Kartal' class FAC. Selcuk Emre

SAR-33 FAC (Gun/Missile) *Turkey*

Numbers reported to be J61-J74 inclusive.

Displacement: 190 tons full load
Dimensions: 33m×8.5m×3m
Armament:
One 40mm gun
Two machine guns
Machinery:
Three diesels 12,000bhp
Three shafts
Speed: 40kts

As built for the Turkish Gendarmerie, these boats carry the small armament listed above, but in emergency, could easily be re-armed in a variety of ways. Together with a 76mm gun forward and a twin 35mm aft, they could carry an alternative fit of two Exocet, four Penguin IIs or two torpedo tubes. These would be con-trolled by an HSA installation with alternative active or passive sonars.

The design has a peculiarly aggressive appearance and, in an age when displacement hulls abound, is unusual in having deep V-sections with longitudinal spray chines. In spite of having the appearance of craft liable to pound heavily, they are reported to be very seakindly. Another unusual feature is the machinery, three French SCAM diesels driving the shafts through vee-gearboxes to give a compact arrangement.

Design and building of the lead ship were the province of the West German firm of Abeking & Rasmussen (more often associated with minesweepers and commercial craft) with the planned 13 follow-ons to be built at the Tazkizak Naval Yard. J61 was delivered by the Germans in 1978 and the Turkish units have, so far, averaged only one per year.

Interestingly, a class of 12 of the SSM-armed version have been ordered from Turkey by Libya.

Asheville Patrol gunboat *Turkey*

	Completed
P338 *Yildirim* (ex-USS *Defiance*, PG95)	69
P339 *Bora* (ex-USS *Surprise*, PG97)	69

For data, see under USA. Both were transferred in 1973 and both are gun-armed.

Bora, 'Asheville' class.   Selcuk Emre

Falster Minelayer *Turkey*

	Builders	LD	L	C	
N110 *Nusret*	FVF	62	63	64	For data, see under Denmark.

NATO type   Coastal minesweeper   *Turkey*

Group A   all completed 1960
M520 *Karamürsel* (ex-*Worms*)
M521 *Kerempe* (ex-*Detmold*)
M522 *Kilimli* (ex-*Siegen*)
M523 *Kozlu* (ex-*Hameln*
M524 *Kuşadasi* (ex-*Vegesack*)
M525 *Kemer* (ex-*Passau*)

Group B   all completed 1951-53
M530 *Trabzon* (ex-*Gaspe*)
M531 *Terme* (ex-*Trinity*)
M532 *Tirebolu* (ex-*Comax*)
M533 *Tekirdag* (ex-*Ungava*)

Both groups conform to the general NATO coastal minesweeper design, stemming from the British 'Tons' (qv). Group A above were all built in France with American funding, for West German account. Generally similar to the German-built 'Lindaus', they differ in appearance by virtue of a squat, rounded funnel. All transferred 1975-6, except M525, in 1979.

    Group B craft were Canadian-built and, again much like the British design, except for a more enclosed bridge and large, square-profile funnel. Transferred in 1958 after only a short service in the RCN.

MSC type   Coastal minesweeper   *Turkey*

M507 *Seymen* (ex-MSC131)
M508 *Selçuk* (ex-MSC124)
M509 *Seyhan* (ex-MSC142)
M510 *Samsun* (ex-MSC268)
M511 *Sinop* (ex-MSC270)
M512 *Surmene* (ex-MSC271)
M513 *Seddulbahir* (ex-MSC272)
M514 *Silifke* (ex-MSC304)
M515 *Saros* (ex-MSC305)
M516 *Sigacik* (ex-MSC311)
M517 *Sapanca* (ex-MSC312)
M518 *Sariyer* (ex-MSC315)

For data see under Greece. All American-built but of various ages and transferred between 1959 and 1970.

    The Turkish fleet's role in NATO is vital because it has to control the Dardanelles/Bosphorus exit, which

the Soviet Black Sea fleet must transit to reach the open Mediterranean. After considerable success with mines in WW1, the Turks have placed an emphasis on both laying and sweeping. Besides the large, purpose-built *Nusret* layer, there are six coastal layers. None of the sweeper fleet has been converted to a hunting role; this may be purely due to economic pressures or, probably, because the deep water of the exits precludes the use of bottom-laid influence mines.

    Soviet hostilities would, inevitably, include an attempt to sieze the exits by amphibious attack and Turkey has also a powerful amphibious arm, partly as an answer to that of Greece. This is spearheaded by five LSTs and no less than 34 LCTs.

    To act as a general-purpose depot and support ship, the 'Rhein' class *Ruhr* was purchased from the West Germans in 1975 and renamed *Cezayirli Gazi Hasan Pasa* (A579).

Invincible   Light aircraft carrier   *UK*

	Builders	LD	L	C
R05 *Invincible*	VSB	73	77	80
R06 *Illustrious*	SHW	76	78	82
R09 *Ark Royal*	SHW	78	81	84

Displacement: 16,000 tons standard; 19,500 tons full load
Dimensions: 206.5m×27.5m×7.5m. Width over flight-deck, 32m
Armament:
One twin Sea Dart SAM launcher
Two Vulcan/Phalanx CIWS
Machinery:
Four Olympus gas turbines 112,000shp
Twin shafts
Speed: Officially 28kts
Aircraft: Fourteen. Mixed Sea King and Harrier

Following a Government decision to run down the Royal Navy's carrier forces without replacement, a dedicated naval lobby fought the 'Invincibles' into existence in the belief that naval aviation had to be part of any fleet worthy of the name. Events in the South Atlantic early in 1982 graphically endorsed the wisdom of their cause.

    The expense of constructing and operating carriers large enough to handle high performance, fixed-wing aircraft is beyond the naval budget but the V/STOL aircraft, in the shape of the well-tried Harrier, offered the beginning of a new cycle of development. Benefiting greatly in terms of payload and/or range by getting a rolling take-off, the Harrier demanded a through flight-deck, which resulted in the original euphemism of 'Through-deck Cruiser'. Because of the nature of V/STOL operation, an angled deck was not required; nor were arrestor gear or catapults. An innovation was the 'ski jump' forward, designed to add impetus to the

Illustrious, 'Invincible' class; note CIWS forward and on starboard quarter; extra 20mm guns forward of after funnel. Mike Lennon

Harrier's rolling take-off. For no apparent reason, the flight deck ends about 25m short of the bows. On the centreline of the resulting forecastle deck is the Sea Dart launcher, whose advertised secondary anti-ship capacity replaced the earlier-mooted additional forward-mounted Exocets. Hard experience that all too many aircraft and missiles can penetrate defences have led to the acquisition of a pair of American Vulcan/ Phalanx CIWS, one forecastle-mounted, the other sited on the starboard quarter. Though an excellent weapon, and available, the CIWS has a calibre of only 20mm and cannot shoot into the zenith at diving missiles. Probably a better choice would have been the Oerlikon-Buhrle Seaguard with four 35mm guns, each with an individual feed. In view of the fact that the ship requires

an escort anyway, the layout would benefit from landing the Sea Dart system, continuing the flightdeck right forward in orthodox fashion and embarking two lightweight Sea Wolf systems for point defence.

The primary function of the 'Invincibles' is ASW and each has a hull-mounted sonar to supplement those on the helicopters. No AS weapons are mounted on the ships.

Long range surveillance radar is carried but experience has shown that a large helicopter with Air-borne Early Warning (AEW) radar would be invaluable. Command facilities are included as is space for the transport of a full commando unit. Whether the ship would be hazarded by landing this directly is another matter.

Hermes   Aircraft carrier   UK

	Builders	LD	L	C
R12 Hermes	VSB	44	53	59

Displacement: 23,900 tons standard; 28,700 tons full load
Dimensions: 227m×27.5m×8.7m. Width over flight-deck 48.8m
Armament: Two quadruple Sea Cat SAM launchers
Machinery:
Two sets geared steam turbines, 75,000shp
Twin shafts
Speed: 28kts
Aircraft: Up to 20. Mixed Sea King and Harrier

Laid down near the end of WW2 and intended as the fourth of the 'Albion' class, *Hermes* was completed so long after them that she incorporated all the postwar

innovatory features and became a 'one-off'. Joining the fleet in 1960, she was already too small to operate the most advanced fixed wing aircraft but spent a decade as a conventional carrier before being converted for a commando role in the early 1970s. Arrestor gear and catapults, together with the enormous Type 984 3-D radar system, were stripped out, though the angled deck was retained to support the side elevator. An all-helicopter aerial complement was embarked, four LCVPs were slung in davits aft and a large crane was added abaft the island. A new foremast carried a Type 965 surveillance antenna.

Further modifications came in 1976-7 when an additional capacity was added for ASW. This, primarily, involved adding the necessary facilities to operate both Sea Kings and Harriers.

Though targeted for disposal by successive defence reviews, *Hermes* maintained a precarious existence by

Hermes. Mike Lennon

virtue of slippage in the 'Invincible' programme. In 1981, she acquired a full 12-degree 'ski-jump' for her Harriers, a device as effective as it is hideous. The timely refit of which this was part enabled *Hermes* to act as flagship for the Falklands operation, where her lack of fixed wing capacity was much missed, in spite of the Harriers performing well beyond expectations.

If *Hermes* is to soldier on into the mid-1980s, to keep up the desired number of flight decks, her dated and inadequate armament of two Sea Cat launchers require modernisation.

Her eventual replacement — as replacement there must be — should be of about the same size, equipped with a Harrier derivative that would be a higher-performance, multi-purpose aircraft with, possibly, a sacrifice made by the adoption of only short take-off and land (STOL).

Type 82 Destroyer   *UK*

	Builders	LD	L	C
D23 *Bristol*	SHW	67	69	73

Displacement: 6,100 tons standard; 7,000 tons full load
Dimensions: 154.5m × 16.8m × 5.3m
Armament:
One twin Sea Dart SAM launcher
One Ikara AS missile launcher
One 4.5in (114mm) gun
Machinery:
Two Olympus gas turbines 44,000shp
Two sets geared steam turbines 30,000shp

COSAG configuration
Twin shafts
Speed: 30kts

Like the 'Counties', the only Type 82 illustrates the result of designing a ship around a missile system still under development — it will always turn out larger and more expensive than expected. The Type 82s were to have been 'County' replacements, ships to escort the next generation of aircraft carriers but, with the political decision to kill the carrier, they were no longer required. Only *Bristol* was completed, primarily as a trials ship for the Sea Dart SAM. With this weapon, the cumbersome

Bristol. Mike Lennon

D23

horizontal stowage and loading of the earlier Sea Slug made way for the more compact vertical arrangement, with a twin arm launcher. As with the later Type 42s, two separate fire controls are carried, under conspicuous radomes fore and aft. These give all-round coverage and allow two targets to be taken on simultaneously. Sea Dart is a semi-active radar homer, it requires the launching ship to 'illuminate' a target, the reflected signals being used by the missile. Only when the latter has 'locked-on' for a final approach can the ship's director shift to another target.

Unusually in a British ship of the size, a stand-off AS weapon is carried in the Ikara, mounted within the low breastwork abaft the gun mounting. As the ship was meant to operate with a carrier, no helicopter is normally carried, although space exists aft for one to land. The lack of a helicopter is somewhat offset by an unusually comprehensive sonar fit. A large surveillance radar over the bridge was designed to supplement that of a carrier.

Three funnels are unique in today's navy, the first design to incorporate them since the 'Manxmans' 30 years previously. The forward funnel exhausts the steam system on which the ship normally cruises. Each Olympus has its own after funnel an early solution that progressed to the even more ungainly 'veed' uptakes still being sported elsewhere. As in the 'Counties', the machinery is designed to run together in a COSAG arrangement.

County   Destroyer   *UK*

	Builders	LD	L	C
D18 *Antrim*	FSG	66	67	70
D19 *Glamorgan*	VSN	62	64	66
D20 *Fife*	FSG	62	64	66

Displacement: 5,450 tons standard; 6,200 tons full load
Dimensions: 158.7m × 16.5m × 6.3m
Armament:
Four MM38 Exocet SSM launchers
One Mk 2 Sea Slug SAM launcher
Two quadruple SeaCat SAM launchers
Two 4.5in (114mm) guns (1 × 2)
Machinery:
Two sets geared steam turbines, 30,000shp
Four Metrovik G6 gas turbines, 30,000shp
COSAG configuration
Twin shafts

Speed: 30kts
Aircraft: One medium helicopter and hangar

Designed concurrently with the Sea Slug missile system, the 'Counties' had to grow from a planned 4,000 tons to accommodate it. Although the missile itself was designed to be commendably short in length by wrapping its boosters around the main body, a fundamental error in arrangement resulted from the decision to handle the weapon horizontally. With stowage running virtually the whole length of the superstructure deck, freeboard became extremely high and the hull longer than planned. Nevertheless, the class is, aesthetically, easy on the eye, with a nicely balanced profile. One bonus of the extra dimensions was the ability to ship a Wessex helicopter in place of the then usual Wasp, through the need to site the hangar forward of the Sea Slug director was far from ideal.

Antrim, *'County' class.*   Crown Copyright

The class fell into two groups. Of these, the earlier four, *Devonshire* (D02), *Hampshire* (D06), *Kent* (D12) and *London* (D16), were fitted with the Mark 1 Sea Slug with capability only against aircraft. Of these, *Hampshire* has been broken up (1979), *London* has been sold to Pakistan (1982) and the other pair are non-mobile training ships. The present trio, together with the *Norfolk* (D21), had the Mark 2 Sea Slug, which had some potential against surface targets as well as aircraft. All surrendered their 'B' gun mounting forward for four MM38 Exocets; although these had no reload facilities, they gave the ships a more balanced armament. *Norfolk* was sold to Chile in 1982 with *Antrim* following in 1983.

By today's standards, the machinery is complex and expensive in crew numbers, having a steam turbine and two obsolete gas turbines on each shaft.

Judging by the rate at which the class has been deleted, it would seem that a major conversion would be uneconomic. Even so, in an age when numbers of missiles will be important in the penetration of a large ship's defences, it seems a pity that these still comparatively new ships cannot have their bulky Exocets taken out and — in default of the long-promised MM40 version — have Harpoons substituted.

Even with less-than-ideal stowage, sufficient of these could be housed in the magazine space to saturate any defence without the attendent need to harbour every round. With the Sea Slug director removed a hangar for two Sea King equivalents could easily be erected, with the means then to hand to realise the weapon's full over-the-horizon capability.

Type 22 Destroyer UK

	Builders	LD	L	C
F88 *Broadsword*	YSG	75	76	79
F89 *Battleaxe*	YSG	76	77	80
F90 *Brilliant*	YSG	77	78	81
F91 *Brazen*	YSG	78	80	82
F92 *Boxer*	YSG	79	81	83
F93 *Beaver*	YSG	80	—	—
F94 *London*	YSG	82	—	—
F95 *Brave*	YSG	82	—	—

Displacement:
(F88-F91) — 3,500 tons standard, 4,000 tons full load
(F92 on) —
Dimensions:
(F88-F91) 133m×14.8m×6.2m
(F92 on) — 143.5m×14.8m×6.2m
Armament:
Two sextuple Sea Wolf SAM launchers
Four MM38 Exocet SSM launchers
Two 40mm guns (2×1)
Two triple AS torpedo tubes

Machinery:
(F88-F91) — Two Olympus gas turbines 56,000shp
Two Tyne cruising gas turbines 8,500shp
(F92 on) — Four Spey gas turbines. About 70,000shp
COGOG configuration
Twin shafts
Speed: 30/18kts
Aircraft: Two Lynx helicopters with hangar

Supposedly designed to succeed the successful but ageing 'Leanders', the Type 22s are in a different league, having grown to such an extent that they have provided, in their cost, ammunition for a Treasury bent on warship economies and, in their complexity, guaranteed nil export sale potential. Though undoubtedly able AS ships, they have the appearance of having been put together by a committee; even so, where it may be argued that the first group are unacceptably large for their potential, the remainder will be over 12m longer in order to, it is hoped, improve their chances of future modernisation. Having two Lynx

Broadsword, Type 22; *shape of funnel varies from ship to ship.* Mike Lennon

helicopters aboard, availability of at least one is virtually guaranteed, and the ship's capabilities are enhanced by the airborne sensors, torpedoes and ASMs.

It can only be repeated that the lack of a medium-calibre gun, with its economy and versatility in shore bombardment and cold war enforcement, is by no means compensated by the four large and unreloadable Exocets. Surely it is possible to put a gun forward and mount two quadruple Harpoon launcher amidships. The two independent Sea Wolf systems are short-ranged but of proven effectiveness. They still appear to lack the all-important guaranteed kill rate on very low level aerial targets at very short ranges and need to be supplemented by a close-in weapons system, (CIWS). A vertical launcher (after the style of the Canadian 'Tribal' class ships' Sea Sparrow arrangement) could be

set into the superstructure at four points on the stretched versions, providing enough ready-use rounds to render automatic-loading unnecessary, unless improved fire-control permits a larger number of targets to be engaged simultaneously.

With the small carrier here to stay, there will be a continuing need for ships of this level of capability, to act as escorts and, savings achieved by reducing their numbers will be false economy.

Defence White Paper of December 1982 announced orders to be placed for four new T22's to replace 42s and 21s lost in the South Atlantic. Three of these will differ significantly in shipping also a 4.5in gun and will have 'twice as many', ie eight SSMs. This means either that the Exocet MM40 is assumed imminent or Harpoon SSMs have been adopted. Further stretching would seem inevitable.

Type 42   Destroyer   *UK*

	Builders	LD	L	C
D86 *Birmingham*	CLB	72	73	76
D87 *Newcastle*	SHW	73	75	78
D88 *Glasgow*	SHW	74	76	79
D89 *Exeter*	SHW	76	78	80
D90 *Southampton*	VTW	76	79	81
D91 *Nottingham*	VTW	78	80	82
D92 *Liverpool*	CLB	78	80	82
D95 *Manchester*	VSB	78	80	82
D96 *Gloucester*	VTW	79	82	—
D97 *Edinburgh*	CLB	80	82	—
D98 *York*	SHW	80	82	—
D108 *Cardiff*	VSB	72	74	79

Displacement:
(Up to Liverpool) 3,500 tons standarad; 4,100 tons full load
(Manchester on) 4,050 tons standard; 4,700 tons full load

Dimensions:
(Up to Liverpool) 125m × 14.3m × 6m (max)
(Manchester on) 141m × 14.9m × 6m (max)
Armament:
One twin Sea Dart SAM launcher
One 4.5in (114mm) gun
Two triple AS torpedo tube banks
Machinery:
Two Olympus gas turbines, 56,000shp
Two Tyne cruising gas turbines, 8,500shp
COGOG configuration
Twin shafts
Speed: 30kts
Aircraft: One Lynx helicopter with hangar

Where the Type 22s are designed for close defence of a task group, the 42s are equipped with Sea Dart area-defence SAMs and are meant to provide an outer perimeter defence, with a long-range surveillance radar to provide early warning. While both radar and SAMs

Newcastle, *Type 42; no pennant numbers, 1982 'South Atlantic' identification stripe, motor boats landed in favour of twin 30mm guns and extra 20mm guns added further aft.*   Mike Lennon

seem adequate at countering the high-flyer, the ships as designed have no defence except ECM against the surface-skimmer, a shortcoming all too easily exposed with the loss of the *Sheffield*. Resolutely conducted low-level bombing then accounted for *Coventry*, again the result of a situation demanding an adequate close-ranged weapons system. The basic 42s are known to have little built-in room for improvement (a much criticised feature from their very inception). British Aerospace has developed a lightweight version of the Sea Wolf, however, and space for at least one mounting should be found on the stretched units to provide the layered AA defence that is demonstrably so necessary, even at the expense of degrading the ship's primary function. *Glasgow* at least, post South Atlantic, has been fitted with a twin 30mm B-MARC/Oerlikon either side amidships (in lieu of seaboats!) together with two extra power-worked 20mm pieces further aft.

With the helicopter now becoming established as a multi-purpose platform, deploying AS sensors and weapons, air-to-surface missiles, acting as link for mid-course correction (when the Royal Navy finally gets an SSM with over-the-horizon capability) and airborne early warning as well as cast in the role of maid-of-all-work, a second unit is becoming rapidly essential. With the later stretched vessels having a beam increased to a figure greater than that of the 22's, it is to be hoped that a similarly large hangar will be worked-in.

The appearance is very clean-cut, though the distinctive radomes that cover the Sea Dart fire control radars are not always fitted and cannot be used as an identification feature. Ships from the *Exeter* onward have abandoned the enormous double Type 965 antenna for the improved Type 1022.

It was announced in 1983 that, during major refits, each Type 42 would acquire two sextuple Seawolf launchers in place of after Sea Dart radar.

Type 23 Frigate   *UK*

At the time of writing, little is known of the projected Type 23. Proposed as a cheap substitute for frigates that would, otherwise, require an expensive mid-life modernisation, the 23s were to commence deliveries by the mid-80s at a cost of about £70M. Already larger and more complex, the price has risen to £100M with the first coming forward after 1990. This supposedly 'export' orientated frigate is now being re-worked to include lessons learned in the South Atlantic. A competition is in progress to decide her SSMs, a choice of Sea Eagle (SSM derivative), Harpoon, Exocet or Otomat. The other known fact is the unusual choice of diesel-electric machinery. While they will have a helicopter landing pad, it is planned to garage the aircraft of up to six 23's on the accompanying specialist fast replenishment ship now being designed.

Type 21 Frigate   *UK*

	Builders	LD	L	C
F169 *Amazon*	VTW	69	71	74
E F171 *Active*	VTW	71	72	77
F172 *Ambuscade*	YSG	71	73	75
E F173 *Arrow*	YSG	72	74	76
E F174 *Alacrity*	YSG	73	74	77
E F185 *Avenger*	YSG	74	75	78

Displacement: 2,750 tons standard; 3,250 tons full load
Dimensions: 117m × 12.8m × 6m
Armament:
Four MM38 Exocets SSMs
One quadruple Seacat SAM
One 4.5in (114mm) gun
Two triple AS torpedo tubes
Machinery:
Two Olympus gas turbines, 56,000shp
Two Tyne cruising gas turbines, 8,500shp
COGOG configuration
Twin shafts
Speed: 32kts
Aircraft: One Lynx helicopter with hangar

Bearing all the rakish hallmarks of a Vosper-Thornycroft design, the Type 21s contrast strongly with the usual Royal Naval 'in-house' products. A joint product of VT and Yarrow, the class resulted from a requirement that arose while MoD design staffs were committed fully elsewhere and was the first commercially-produced RN warship of recent years. Although reportedly criticised officially, they have proved popular ships in the Service.

As GP frigates, they have a multi-purpose weapons fit and though they eventually received their four Exocet, none has been fitted, as planned, with Sea Wolf. This was unfortunate as two of their number, *Antelope* (F170) and *Ardent* (F184), were lost to conventional low-level bombing early in 1982 whilst supporting the Falklands landings. Their single Sea Cat, even though radar-laid by two GWS-24s which should have left no blind spots, was inadequate for their defence, either through lack of fast response or saturation due to the slow rate of reloading by hand. This obvious vulnerability to aerial attack must be remedied to give confidence in the ships' ability to fight a major war.

The hull is comparatively beamy which, combined with the rather over-criticised aluminium upperworks, should give a good margin for extra topweight resulting from an improved fit, although stability is apparently not a strong point of the design. A flat run aft, with a very wide transom, combined with the standard two-

Olympus, two-Tyne machinery, makes for a hull rather faster than most current frigates but, while the flight-deck is quite generously dimensioned as a result it is carried at a low level which is a drawback in adverse weather.

No long range surveillance radar was fitted, as was the case with the previous GP frigates, the 'Leanders', and it is noteworthy that the gun directors are of Italian

Amazon, *Type 21.* Crown Copyright

origin. Current Government plans are that these ships should not undergo a mid-life refit; should this be the case, there should be little problem in finding purchasers, as relative simplicity is an 'exportable' asset.

Leander Frigate   *UK*

	Builders	LD	L	C	Conv
(1) 'Ikara Leanders'					
F10 *Aurora*	JBC	61	62	64	76
F15 *Euryalus*	SSG	61	63	64	76
F18 *Galatea*	SHW	61	63	64	74
F38 *Arethusa*	JSW	62	63	65	77
F39 *Naiad*	YSG	62	63	65	75
F104 *Dido*	YSG	59	61	63	78
F109 *Leander*	HWB	59	61	63	72
F114 *Ajax*	CLB	59	62	63	73
(2) 'Exocet Leanders'					
F28 *Cleopatra*	HDD	63	64	66	75
F40 *Sirius*	HDP	63	64	66	77
F42 *Phoebe*	ASG	63	64	66	77
F45 *Minerva*	VAN	63	64	66	79
F47 *Danae*	HDD	64	65	67	80
F52 *Juno**	JTW	64	65	67	—
F56 *Argonaut*	HLH	64	66	67	80
F127 *Penelope*	VAN	61	62	63	81
(3) 'Broad-beam Leanders'					
F12 *Achilles*	YSG	67	68	70	—
F16 *Diomede*	YSG	68	69	71	—
F57 *Andromeda*	HDP	66	67	68	80
F58 *Hermione*	ASG	65	67	69	83
F60 *Jupiter*	YSG	66	67	69	83
F70 *Apollo*	YSG	69	70	72	—
F71 *Scylla*	HDP	67	68	70	83
F72 *Ariadne*	YSG	69	71	73	—
F75 *Charybdis*	HWB	67	68	69	82

* Remains unconverted

Phoebe, *Exocet 'Leander'; note SSMs now set lower, forward Seacat launcher removed and extra 20mm atop bridge and right aft.* Mike Lennon

F42

Displacements:
(1) 'Ikaras' — 2,450 tons standard; 2,850 tons full load
(2) 'Exocets' — 2,600 tons standard; 3,050 full load
(3) 'Broad Beams' — 2,500 tons standard; 2,950 tons full load
Dimensions: 113.5m × 12.5m × 5.5m ('Broad Beams' of 13.1m beam)
Armament:
'Ikaras' —
One Ikara AS missile launcher
Two/three quadruple Sea Cat SAM launchers
Two 40mm guns (2 × 1)
'Exocets' —
Four MM38 Exocet SSM launchers
Three quadruple Sea Cat SAM launchers
Two 40mm guns (2 × 1)
Two triple AS torpedo tubes
'Broad Beams' (as converted) —
Four MM38 Exocet SSM launchers
One sextuple Sea Wolf SAM launcher
Two triple AS torpedo tubes
'Broads Beams' (pre-conversion) —
Two 4.5in (114mm) guns (1 × 2)
One Limbo triple-barrelled AS mortar
Machinery:
Two sets geared steam turbines, 30,000shp
Twin shafts
Speed: 29kts
Aircraft: One Wasp helicopter with hangar
Lynx in 'Broad Beam' conversions

The 'Leanders' represented an updated and 'tidied-up' version of the earlier, and somewhat austere, Type 12s. Although preceded into service by the COSAG-powered Type 81s, they kept to the well-tried steam plant of the 12s; in the event, however, the class went to 26 units whose completions spanned a decade and three separate machinery arrangements. They retained the same basic hull with its excellent sea-keeping qualities and the high freeboard continued right aft to leave a well for the stowage of a new-style VDS. Further improvements were the addition of a helicopter

and a long-range surveillance radar.

By the time that mid-life refits became due their armament and electronics were somewhat dated, some of the earliest units having never even been fitted with Sea Cat. The 16 earliest hulls, all narrow-beam, were divided into two groups of eight for major alteration.

The first conversion programme concerned the 'Ikara' group. Here the twin 4.5in gunhouse forward was landed in favour of the Australian Ikara, an AS missile which, guided by instruction from the ship, could land a torpedo over a submerged target some 20km distant. Surveillance radar was also landed and AA defence enhanced by a second Sea Cat launcher. It seems a pity that the Ikara could not be accommodated aft, as the Australians have, in a pocket of the flight-deck and the heavy Mark 6 guns exchanged for a single modern Mark 8, to retain a measure of versatility.

In the 'Exocet' group, the gunhouse again had to make way, this time for four MM38 canister launchers and a third Sea Cat. AS potential was reduced to helicopter-launched weapons and torpedo tubes, the Limbo being landed. With the VDS also removed, the clutter aft was significantly reduced and a better arrangement would have been to mount the four SSMs on the extreme quarters, after the style of the Chilean-flag 'Leanders' and, again, adopting a single Mark 8 gun forward.

Being the newest, the 'broad-beamed' group came last for conversion, the claimed expense of which has been a plank for plans to reduce the number of frigates in RN service. *Andromeda* completed the pilot conversion in 1980. *Charybdis* followed in 1982 and three others are in the process of this work. Under the terms of the Defence White Paper, the remainder will not be updated. Alterations include the installation of a six-barrelled Sea Wolf forward, with only one director, that in place of the fire control of the guns, removed in favour of four Exocet canisters. Stern profile has been changed, possibly for a new-type VDS, the domed-top funnel casing has been squared off and a pole main-mast added. A Lynx has replaced the earlier Wasp helicopter.

Post-Falklands a twin B-MARC 30mm mounting has also been added on the starboard quarter.

At the time of writing *Bacchante* has been sold to New Zealand and renamed *Wellington*; the Ikara-armed *Dido* is due to follow her. *Juno* is to be demoted to an alongside training ship at Rosyth.

Naiad, *Achilles* and *Diomede* are to pay off by 1983.

Type 12   Frigate   *UK*

	Builders	LD	L	C
F 43 *Torquay*	HWB	53	54	56
F101 *Yarmouth*	JBC	57	59	60
F103 *Lowestoft*	ASG	58	60	61
F106 *Brighton*	YSG	57	59	61
F107 *Rothesay*	YSG	56	57	60
F108 *Londonderry*	JSW	56	58	60
F113 *Falmouth*	SHW	57	59	61
F115 *Berwick*	HWB	58	59	61
F126 *Plymouth*	HDD	58	59	61
F129 *Rhyl*	HDP	58	59	60

Displacement: 2,350 tons standard; 2,750 tons full load
Dimensions: 112.5m × 12.5m × 5.5m
Armament:
Two 4.5in (114mm) guns (1×2)
One quadruple Seacat SAM launcher
One Limbo triple-barrelled AS mortar
Machinery:
Two sets geared steam turbines 30,000shp
Twin shafts
Speed: 29kts
Aircraft: One Wasp helicopter with hangar (except F43)

Experience in WW2 showed that the destroyer could no longer hope to contain the range of weapons necessary to discharge a GP role, and the specialist AS frigate emerged. With higher submarine speeds also then becoming normal, fleet destroyers were converted to fast frigates (Types 15 and 16, none now extant) and some of the features of the 15s, the long forecastle deck, low superstructure and a much-reduced surface armament, set the tone for a purpose-built replacement class. Larger than a warbuilt destroyer, the Type 12 began with the six-ship 'Whitby' group, introducing the distinctive high-freeboard forecastle cranked up a half-level from the upper deck. This feature improved seaworthiness and allowed the large gunhouse to be set low enough to permit a view forward from the diminutive bridge. A roomy hull gained more space by having only half the installed power of a contemporary destroyer. In the original version, the superstructure was in two small, low masses, a vertical lattice mast amidships just forward of an equally vertical funnel, whose meagre proportions suited the general austere appearance of the whole ship. Two triple-barrelled Limbo mortars were set aft in a protected well leading on to the short, low quarterdeck. Up to eight fixed and two twin, trainable AS torpedo tubes were planned but few were ever fitted.

A two-year pause separated the 'Whitbys' from the second group, known as the 'Rothesays'. A different layout showed externally in a bulkier superstructure aft, with AA defence improved by the addition of a Sea Cat launcher. The mast was plated-in, the funnel thickened in section and given a rake that has never looked right. This second group was rebuilt considerably in 1966-72 to give them a Wasp helicopter. As a result the forward Limbo was removed and its location plated-over for the flight pad. Twelve 'Rothesays' were planned but only nine completed, the final three hulls becoming the first three of the succeeding 'Leanders'.

One, *Torquay*, remains of the 'Whitby' group. *Rhyl* and the much-modified trials ship *Londonderry* are currently due to pay off in 1982-3.

Yarmouth, *Type 12.* Mike Lennon

Gurkha, *Type 81*. Mike Lennon

Type 81 Frigate UK

	Builders	LD	L	C
F117 *Ashanti*	YSG	58	59	61
F119 *Eskimo*	JSW	58	60	63
F122 *Gurkha*	JTW	58	60	63
F124 *Zulu*	ASG	60	62	64
F125 *Mohawk*	VAB	59	62	62
F131 *Nubian*	HDP	59	60	62
F133 *Tartar*	HDD	59	60	62

Displacement: 2,300 tons standard; 2,700 tons full load
Dimensions: 109.7m × 13m × 5.5m
Armament:
Two 4.5in (114mm) guns (2×)
Two quadruple Sea Cat SAM launchers
One triple-barrelled AS mortar
Machinery:
One geared steam turbine set, 12,500shp
One gas turbine, 7,500shp
COSAG configuration
Single shaft
Speed: 25kts
Aircraft: One Wasp helicopter with hangar

The odd appearance of the Type 81's, or 'Tribals', gives the impression that they were built from a kit of parts. They have the air of conversions, which they were not, being designed to operate in extended independent roles, particularly in the Persian Gulf. Contemporary with the 'Counties', the 81s inherited the same COSAG machinery layout, here a single steam turbine boosted as required by a small gas turbine. As single-screw propulsion was chosen as being sufficient, machinery power has been limited to only 20,000shp with a corresponding low speed. In spite of this the machinery occupies a large volume with an unusual two-funnel layout, the forward exhausting the steam plant.

They were the first British frigates designed to carry a helicopter and the arrangement is unique. Instead of adopting a twin, 4.5in gunhouse forward, leaving the beamy after end clear, the designers put an old, handworked single mounting fore and aft. Thus the deckhouse immediately forward of the after gun is the hangar, crushing the Limbo into a constricted space between it and the after funnel. A folding deck covers both, to act as a flight pad. No mainmast can therefore be fitted and the foremast has been stiffened to the bulky proportions needed to support the longrange surveillance antenna.

VDS and AS torpedo tubes can be fitted but the current capability of the 'Tribals' is limited. Never really 'fitting in', they were denied mid-life refits and were listed for disposal until re-instatement following the Falklands losses. Too old now for a rebuild they could however, still be visualised with two derated Speys and longrange bunkers in place of the present plant, a Mark 8 gun forward and a Lynx/VDS layout aft. As it is they will exist in a sort of limbo, largely inactive yet listed for NATO use if required.

Resolution Nuclear-powered ballistic missile submarine UK

	Builders	LD	L	C
S22 *Resolution*	VSB	64	66	67
S23 *Repulse*	VSB	65	67	68
S26 *Renown*	CLB	64	67	68
S27 *Revenge*	CLB	65	68	69

Displacement: 7,500 tons surfaced; 8,400 tons submerged
Dimensions: 129.5m × 10.1m × 9m

Armament:
Sixteen launch tubes for Polaris SLBMs
Six 21in (533mm) torpedo tubes (all forward)
Machinery:
One PWC reactor
Two sets geared steam turbines driving single shaft. 15,000shp
Speed: 20/25kts

When the manned bomber became, in the early 1960s, vulnerable to defence systems, the Nation's nuclear deterrent was shifted to sea, in the same fashion as that of the United States. The range of the A2 Polaris SLBM, purchased for the purpose, required five SSBN's to give the necessary coverage. Financial restrictions and the newly-available 2,500-mile A3 version, resulted in a cut-back to four boats, less even than the French deem necessary for their own force, and vulnerable to reduction to unacceptable levels by damage or over-long refits.

Geared to accommodate 16 missiles similar to those used in the contemporary American force, the 'Resolutions' bear, not unsurprisingly, a close resemblance to the 'Lafayettes'. Though much has been made of the speed at which the British programme was planned and executed, the three to four years' building time for each boat still represents about twice that for their American equivalents. To get maximum use out of each boat, all have two complete crews, working alternately. Unlike attack boats, SSBNs do not rely so much on speed, so the power on the single propeller is not particularly high. SSBNs seek to remain undetected by a close attention to silent running; they avoid drawing atten-

Repulse, 'Resolution' class.   Mike Lennon

tion to themselves but carry a six-tube defensive torpedo armament for 'last ditch' use.

The American 'Lafayettes' were updated to deploy the Poseidon C3 and are now slated to receive the 4,000-mile Trident C4. No such future exists for the 'Resolutions', which are still tied to a missile which, in spite of its updated Chevaline warheads, is, by today's standards, short-ranged. By deciding to opt for the 6,000-mile Trident D5 the planners have committed themselves to a weapon too large for the 'Resolution' type hull.

Four monstrous 'Ohio' type SSBNs will now be required, boats with hulls longer than Winchester Cathedral. The massive investment in them is planned to give a viable weapons system 'into the 21st century' yet, with a 1,500-mile Tomahawk cruise missile already capable of being launched from the torpedo tube of an ordinary attack boat and an 8,000-mile weapon being investigated by the Defense Advanced Research Projects Agency in the USA, could this type of ship become no more than a dinosaur within the decade?

Swiftsure   Fleet submarine   *UK*

	Builders	LD	L	C
S104 *Sceptre*	VSB	74	76	78
S105 *Spartan*	VSB	76	78	79
S106 *Splendid*	VSB	77	79	81
S107 *Trafalgar*	VSB	78	81	82
S108 *Sovereign*	VSB	70	73	74
S109 *Superb*	VSB	72	74	76
S126 *Swiftsure*	VSB	69	71	73
Turbulent	VSB	79	82	83
Talent	VSB	81	—	—
Tactician	VSB	82	—	—
Tireless	VSB	—	—	—
Torbay	VSB	—	—	—

Displacement: 4,200 tons surfaced, 4,500 tons submerged
Dimensions: 82.9m × 9.8m × 8.2m
Armament: Five 21in (533mm) torpedo tubes (all forward)
Machinery:
One PWC reactor. Geared steam turbines, 15,000shp
One auxiliary propulsion diesel, 4,000bhp
Single shaft
Speed: 30kts submerged

A logical development of the preceding 'Valiants', the 'Swiftsure' design is much fuller, betrayed externally by a freeboard of constant height over the greater part of its length. In profile, too, the fin and visible part of the upper rudder both appear lower and longer. They are also shorter by about 4m but if, as published reports suggest, this is at the expense of weapon reload (as well as one tube less) then this is an expensive bonus.

The nuclear fleet submarine (known as an 'attack submarine' in the US Navy) is a prodigious weapon. Unhampered by weather conditions, she can outpace virtually any surface ship or hunt her own kind. To gauge her fighting potential merely in terms of 'torpedo tubes' is not to do her justice for, although 'steam' torpedoes are still in service, primarily for use against surface targets, so also are weapons like the Tigerfish. This large torpedo can pursue a submerged target out to better than 30km; it can 'loiter' while it carries out a pre-arranged search pattern or be wire-guided; once it has detected its target, it will home acoustically. The encapsulated Harpoon missile, announced as purchased from the USA, gives rapid anti-ship reaction out to almost 100km. Hovering silently in the depths, her passive sonars are much more effective than a surface ship's for pure surveillance. Operating alone, submerged for weeks on end, or forming part of a task-

Superb, 'Swiftsure' class. Item forward of fin is an aluminium brow, not a permanent fitting.
Mike Lennon

group's screen, her versatility is being recognised in the increasing numbers being commissioned.

One shortcoming is that she is a 'hot war' weapon — where a surface warship can deter by an obvious presence and meet a threat with an appropriate grade of response, a fleet submarine's presence can only be hinted at (sometimes enough in itself) and her response can only be to kill.

Valiant   Fleet submarine

UK

		Builders	LD	L	C
S46	*Churchill*	VSB	67	68	70
S48	*Conqueror*	CLB	67	69	71
S50	*Courageous*	VSB	68	70	71
S102	*Valiant*	VSB	62	63	66
S103	*Warspite*	VSB	63	65	67

Displacement: 4,400 tons surfaced; 4,900 tons submerged
Dimensions: 87m × 10.1m × 8.2m
Armament: Six 21in (533mm) torpedo tubes (all forward)
Machinery:
One PWC reactor

Geared steam turbines, 15,000shp
Single shaft
Speed: 28kts submerged

Britain's first class of nuclear-powered fleet submarine, the first of which, *Valiant*, was laid down well before the prototype 'Dreadnought' was commissioned. The latter boat, now discarded, was dependent to a great extent upon Anglo-American cooperation, with the propulsion machinery purchased out of the 'Skipjack' programme and a very fine after end influenced heavily by the then-recent experiments on the pioneer *Albacore*.

Conqueror.   Crown Copyright

Although the 'Valiants' echoed to some extent the fine afterbody, it was not as extreme as that of the older boat and the machinery was home-produced, based on accumulated experience from the navy's own reactor at HMS *Vulcan*, Dounreay.

Being so early in the overall development of the nuclear submarine, the 'Valiants' were probably geared more to combatting surface ships rather than other submarines. Against these, they are still formidable operators, particularly after all have completed their long mid-life refits. Both the 'Valiants' and the later 'Swiftsures' have diesel-electric 'get-you-home' systems; these, presumably, would require running at snort depth and, themselves, are a comment on the complexity of the nuclear-boiler-steam turbine machinery arrangement.

Type 2400   Patrol submarine   *UK*

Considering the established requirement for conventional patrol submarines to operate in conjunction with the nuclear-propelled fleet boats, together with the advancing years of the Royal Navy's present force, it becomes the more surprising that the long-awaited order for the first of the projected Type 2400s has not yet materialised, particularly as it will take at least three years to build a first-of-class.

The design, produced by Vickers under the direction of the Ministry of Defence, has already been offered for export, but those foreign fleets already operating 'Oberons' would obviously like the RN to order first — while we wait, the Germans take the orders for replacements.

Artist's impressions show a submarine bearing a close external similarity with the Netherlands' 'Walrus' class, except for the more conventional cruciform control surfaces and forward-mounted hydroplanes.

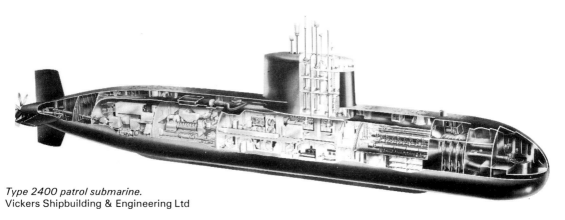

Type 2400 patrol submarine.
Vickers Shipbuilding & Engineering Ltd

Oberon/Porpoise   Patrol submarine   *UK*

	Builders	LD	L	C
S09 *Oberon*	HDC	57	59	61
S10 *Odin*	CLB	59	60	62
S11 *Orpheus*	VSB	59	59	60
S12 *Olympus*	VSB	60	61	62
S13 *Osiris*	VSB	62	62	64
S14 *Onslaught*	HDC	59	60	62
S15 *Otter*	SSG	60	61	62
S16 *Oracle*	CLB	60	61	63
S17 *Ocelot*	HDC	60	62	64
S18 *Otus*	SSG	61	62	63
S19 *Opossum*	CLB	61	63	64
S20 *Opportune*	SSG	62	64	64
S21 *Onyx*	CLB	64	66	67
S01 *Porpoise*	CSB	54	56	58
S07 *Sealion*	CLB	58	56	58
S08 *Walrus*	SSG	58	59	61

Displacement: 2,030 tons surfaced; 2,400 tons submerged
Dimensions: 90m × 8.0m × 5.5m
Armament: Eight 21in (533mm) torpedo tubes (six forward, two aft)
Machinery:
Two diesels
Two electric propulsion motors 6,000shp
Twin shafts
Speed: 15/17kts
Disposals: Rorqual (S02) 1976; *Narwhal* (S03) 1977; *Grampus* (S04) 1976; *Finwhale* (S05) 1978; *Cachalot* (S06) 1977

With *Sealion* and *Walrus* being newer than the oldest 'Oberons' and now being given a thorough refit, a homogeneous class of 15 boats should result, as the remaining differences should be minimal. This ageing

force represents the Royal Navy's only conventional submarine strength and, although the US Navy is persisting in its rather short-sighted 'all-nuclear' policy, the British have changed their mind and, it is hoped, will shortly order the first replacements. For shallow water operations and missions on the enemy's doorstep, the patrol submarine is ideally suited, being silent-running and unobtrusive though, being air-breathing, she must 'snort' from time to time. With enemy boats not wishing to betray themselves with active sonars, they rely on passive equipment and an Oberon when shut down is a quiet boat indeed. In turn, the lack of self-generated noise gives her own passive sets a better chance of detecting a target.

By the standard of today's portly, short boats with large diameter single screws, the twin-screw 'Oberons' may seem large and outdated. Interestingly, however,

Onslaught, 'Oberon' class.   Mike Lennon

the Soviets, who still believe firmly in the cost-effective 'conventional', are still building the 'Tangos', some 10 years after the beginning of their programme; also designed for ocean work when required, they are much of a size and reported to be triple-screwed.

Like fleet submarines, the conventional could deliver a variety of ordnance from her tubes, including mines.

Additionally, she can carry the SLAAM (Submarine-launched AA missile) on a retractable mounting to discourage the attentions of helicopters during 'snorting'.

Although the 'Oberon' exported well, 14 being sold to Australia, Brazil, Canada and Chile, their eventual replacements will be in fierce competition with foreign designs, particularly from IKL.

Engadine   Helicopter support ship

_UK_

	Builders	LD	L	C
K08 _Engadine_	HRL	65	66	67

Displacement: 9,000 tons full load
Dimensions: 129.3m × 17.9m × 6.7m
Armament: None in peacetime
Machinery:
One diesel, 5,500bhp
Single shaft
Speed: 15kts
Aircraft: Four medium and two small helicopters, _or_ two large helicopters

Engadine's odd appearance results from her being designed for an unusual function — that of training

sea-going helicopter pilots. Her generously-dimensioned flightdeck, high freeboard and actively-stabilised hull engender confidence. She is RFA-manned with a small naval contingent but her full, mercantile lines contain accommodation sufficient to more than double the complement, to nearly 200, if required. The greater part of the superstructure abaft the funnel is devoted to hangar space for her visiting helicopter contingent. She carries no permanently-assigned aircraft but can stow either four Wessex and two Wasp, or a pair of Sea Kings. For her size, the latter option would seem meagre, which suggests that her dimensions were not particularly well chosen. With all three types now being phased out even more 'broken stowage' may result. Atop the hangar is a flight control and a 'garage' for remotely-controlled target drones.

A very simple ship in almost every respect, she even has a mercantile mast forward and a pair of derricks for handling dry stores in union purchase, where a crane would reasonably be expected. Her name perpetuates that of one of the two earliest railway steamers taken into naval service in WW1 for use as seaplane carriers.

Intrepid, *'Fearless' class.*   Crown Copyright

Fearless   Amphibious transport docks   *UK*

	Builders	LD	L	C
L10 *Fearless*	HWB	62	63	65
L11 *Intrepid*	JBC	62	64	67

Displacement: 11,100 tons standard; 12,100 tons full load
Dimensions: 158.5m × 24.4m × 6.2m
Armament:
Four quadruple Sea Cat SAM launchers
Two 40mm guns (2 × 1)
Machinery:
Two sets geared steam turbines 22,000shp
Twin shafts
Speed: 20kts
Aircraft: Up to five medium helicopters, no hangar

Best viewed as a self-propelled floating dock, the LPD is derived from those introduced by the US Navy for amphibious operations in the Pacific. A few of the latter served under the White Ensign after WW2 but the type lapsed after their return, until its re-introduction with the *Fearless.*

The basic LST can land troops and armour on to the beach directly but has limited range and facilities, while expensive conversions of such as *Hermes* can handle personnel and light transport but no heavy gear and armour. Advantages of both are combined in the LPD, the 'Fearless' aproximating to the American 'Raleighs'. Their docking well is comparatively short, just large enough to accommodate four LCM 9s. Each of these can be pre-loaded with two main battle tanks and can load further armour on return trips via an internal 'beach', sloping from a heavily-reinforced tank deck. Lighter transport, artillery etc, can be stowed below on further vehicle decks on the upper deck in place of helicopters. All are inter-connected by moveable ramps to facilitate loading. Some 5,000 tons of water ballast are taken aboard to flood the ship down. Four LCAs are stowed under davits, and can each carry about 35 personnel or a small vehicle. A battalion-sized force of troops can be carried for short periods, the large super-structure accommodating also extensive command, control and communication facilities for the direction of amphibious operations. Boiler and turbine rooms are staggered, the need to 'side' the uptakes to flank the vehicle decks resulting in the characteristic echeloned funnel arrangement.

Their armament is purely defensive, as they would normally operate as part of a properly constituted amphibious force.

Sir Lancelot   Landing ships, logistic   *UK*

	Builders	LD	L	C
L3004 *Sir Bedivere*	HLH	65	66	67
L3027 *Sir Geraint*	ASG	65	67	67
L3029 *Sir Lancelot*	FSG	62	63	64
L3036 *Sir Percivale*	HLH	66	67	68

Displacement: 3,300 tons standard; 5,650 tons full load
Dimensions: 125.2m × 19.5m × 4.3m
Armament: Light armament can be carried

125

Sir Lancelot class, 'Sir Bedivere'. Mike Lennon

Machinery:
Two diesels, 9,400bhp
Twin shafts
Speed: 17kts

These useful auxiliaries have few foreign equivalents, the nearest being the rather smaller Soviet 'Alligators'. Like the Soviet ships, they too adopt clam-shell doors in the bows to protect the ramp and to improve seakeeping, though at the cost of extra complexity. In conjunction with a larger stern door, this facility offers full drive-through Ro-Ro capability, with extra versatility available by using pontoon units as a bridge to the shore or motorised as flat lighters. The interior vehicle deck is connected with the upper deck by ramps; heavy gear or deck-stowed LCAs can also be handled by means of the 20-ton and two 5-ton SWL cranes. The

superstructure is continued right aft to provide temporary accommodation for about 500 troops with a helicopter deck above. Up to 20 medium helicopters or 16 main battle tanks can be carried. Originally operated by the British India company on behalf of the government, the ships have been full RFAs only since 1970. *Sir Galahad* (L3005) was a casualty of the Falklands operations, the *Sir Tristram* (L3505) being badly fire-damaged and with her future still undecided.

LCTs are represented only by comparatively new *Ardennes* and *Arakan*, operated by the Army's Royal Corps of Transport. Fully loaded, these craft displace 1,600 tons and, at over 73m in length, can stow up to give large tanks. Compared with the earlier generation of LCTs, their superstructure seems vulnerably bulky.

Defence White Paper of December 1982 announced that a replacement for *Sir Galahad* would be built and *Sir Tristram* would be towed home for repair.

Abdiel Minelayer

UK

	Builders	LD	L	C
N21 *Abdiel*	JTW	66	67	67

Displacement: 1,375 tons standard; 1,450 tons full load

Dimensions: 80.4m × 11.7m × 2.9m
Armament: Normally unarmed
Machinery:
Two diesels, 2,700bhp
Twin shafts
Speed: 16kts

Abdiel. Mike Lennon

The first minelayer of any size to be built for the Royal Navy since WW2, *Abdiel's* main role is in laying mines for the purpose of exercising mine countermeasures forces. Her subsidiary function, well illustrated in the re-opening of the Suez Canal, is to act as support ship to MCMVs. The flush decked-hull, with its high freeboard, is typical of the minelayer as a type, with the mines themselves being stowed in tunnels down either side and launched through apertures in the transom. Depending on the type, up to 44 can be carried, brought aboard by a crane aft and struck below through a small hatch. Diesel-driven, the ship is of simple construction and completed in a short space of time. Her name was carried by a minelaying destroyer of WW1 and a fast minelayer of WW2.

Hunt Mine countermeasures vessel   UK

	Builders	LD	L	C
M29 *Brecon*	VTW	75	78	80
M30 *Ledbury*	VTW	77	79	81
M31 *Cattistock*	VTW	79	81	82
M32 *Cottesmore*	YSG	79	82	82
M33 *Brocklesby*	VTW	80	82	82
M34 *Middleton*	YSG	—	—	—
M35 *Dulverton*	VTW	81	82	—
M36 *Hurworth*	VTW	—	—	—
M37 *Chiddingfold*	VTW	82	—	—

Displacement: 615 tons standard; 725 tons full load
Dimensions: 60m × 10m × 2.5m
Armament: One 40mm gun
Machinery:
Two diesels, 2,000bhp
Twin shafts
Speed: 16kts

Size for size, the 'Hunts' are the fleet's most expensive ships and reflect the complexity that is built into them in order to counter today's mines. Mining remains an exceedingly cost-effective means of pursuing a maritime war and both the advancing years and diminishing numbers of the 'Ton' class NATO-type coastal 'sweepers was a matter of concern. The new class is timely, though their cost will preclude replacement on a hull-for-hull basis, though about 30 should be considered a desirable minimum force.

Though wood has proved a durable medium for the construction of small ships, glass reinforced plastic (GRP) was chosen as an alternative, mainly because the expertise of high-quality wood-working is being lost. Vosper Thornycroft constructed a purpose-built GRP facility, gaining experience with *Wilton* and guaranteeing a good run of orders. Once established, the facility was repeated at Yarrow, providing a useful back-up.

Though rather larger than the coastals, the 'Hunts' bear more than a passing resemblance to them, with a long forecastle and high freeboard, but with a larger superstructure to keep more of the crew topside. They are equipped to hunt for all types of magnetic/acoustic mines and can also sweep for moored varieties. In this respect it is interesting to note their lower installed power compared with earlier 'sweepers. Divers are carried for positive identification of suspicious objects on the bottom which, if mines, are destroyed by charges placed remotely by the French-built PAP 104 miniature submersibles.

Utmost care has been taken in the reduction of 'magnetic signature' by the use of both non-ferrous materials and thorough de-gaussing. Silence, too, is essential and resilient mounting of machinery is backed by two Pleuger-type active rudders for creeping at low speed when required.

Excellent ships though these are, their cost is enforcing investigation into an inexpensive, less-capable minehunting alternative.

Orders for two more of this class announced in Defence White Paper of December 1982. Complementary to the 'Hunt' class, these will be more capable to hunt mines but will be a single role vessel, cheaper but unable to sweep moored mines.

Brocklesby, 'Brecon/Hunt' class.   Mike Lennon

Kirkliston, *CMS.* Mike Lennon

Ton Coastal minesweeper/hunter   *UK*

Completed

a) *Minehunters*

M1110 *Bildeston*	53
M1113 *Brereton*	54
M1114 *Brinton*	54
M1115 *Bronington*	54
M1116 *Wilton*	73
M1133 *Bossington*	56
M1140 *Gavinton*	54
M1147 *Hubberston*	55
M1151 *Iveston*	55
M1153 *Kedleston*	55
M1154 *Kellington*	55
M1157 *Kirkliston*	54
M1165 *Maxton*	57
M1166 *Nurton*	57
M1181 *Sheraton*	56

b) *Minesweepers*

M1103 *Alfriston*	54
M1109 *Bickington*	54
M1124 *Crichton*	54
M1125 *Cuxton*	53
M1141 *Glasserton*	54
M1146 *Hodgeston*	54
M1158 *Laleston*	54
M1173 *Pollington*	58
M1180 *Shavington*	56
M1187 *Upton*	56
M1188 *Walkerton*	58
M1195 *Wotton*	57
M1200 *Soberton*	57
M1204 *Stubbington*	57
M1208 *Lewiston*	60
M1216 *Crofton*	58

Displacement: 360 tons standard; 440 tons full load
Dimensions: 46.3m × 8.5m × 2.6m
Armament:
One 40mm gun
Two 20mm guns (2 × 1)
Machinery:
Two diesels, 2,400bhp
Twin shafts
Speed: 15kts

The Korean War abruptly reminded the West that it faced an alliance skilled in mine warfare. Though well provided for in ocean minesweepers the Royal Navy had only a few basic Motor Minesweepers (MMS, or 'Mickey Mice') remaining from WW2 for near seas use. A crash building programme was initiated, based on two designs, the 360-ton Coastal and the 120-ton Inshore types. Both sound and used widely by NATO navies for their own fleets, so that they have become known as Weston Union or NATO standard. A glance at the list of builders (116 Coastals and 89 Inshores) reveals the strength and versatility of the British ship-building industry at that time.

With J. I. Thorneycroft acting as lead yard, these little ships were constructed in dozens of yards, from giant concerns such as Harland & Wolff, through those specialising in smaller ships such as Richards Ironworks (sic) to yacht builders of the size of Camper and Nicholson. Their double mahogany skin on aluminium frame construction has proved remarkably durable, with 30 coastals still under the White Ensign and a further 37 scattered among fleets from Argentina to Malaysia. Very good seaboats, though lively, they have changed little in appearance over the years. Early versions had an open bridge and lattice mast though all have now adopted the tripod mast and enclosed bridge of later units. All sport the so-called 'Thornycroft' top to the funnel, a device for keeping stack gases clear of the bridge, and which enjoyed some popularity in the 1950s.

With influence mining becoming a greater threat, many were re-equipped as minehunters, betrayed externally mainly by the specialised antennas on the bridge roof. Some of the remaining sweepers have Mirrlees diesels but all hunters have faster-running Napier Deltics and have been fitted with active rudders for 'silent-creeping'.

Wilton is a one-off, a repeat built in GRP as an experiment prior to the embarkation on the new 'Hunt' class programme. As the EEC has now effectively destroyed Britain's once-large trawler fleet, the navy can no longer look to this as a pool of auxiliary minesweepers for use in emergency and four 800-ton trawler-based minesweepers have been ordered from Richards, Lowestoft. Meanwhile, a pair of commercial stern trawlers have been bareboat-chartered for trials, particularly on the 'team sweep', used to counter deep-laid AS minefields.

Castle Offshore patrol vessel   UK

	Builders	LD	L	C
P258 *Leeds Castle*	HRA	79	80	81
P265 *Dumbarton Castle*	HRA	80	81	82

Displacement: 1,430 tons standard
Dimensions: 81m × 11.5m × 3.5m
Armament: Usually one 40mm gun
Machinery:
Two diesels, 5,600bhp
Twin shafts
Speed: 20kts

Though from the same builders as 'OPV Mark 2', the 'Castle' bears no resemblance to the Mark I 'Island' and has all the hallmarks of DG ships. Over 21m longer in the hull, the class are not substitutes for the 'Islands' and their greater capabilities are reflected in the price tag which, approaching three times that of the earlier ships, will greatly influence the numbers built. Nevertheless, they do answer criticism of the 'Island' design in that they are faster and can land a large helicopter, though it is not thought necessary to carry one normally, thus saving the space required by a hangar. The four-knot increase in speed was obtained on an increase in power of little over 25%, the longer hull also giving more comfortable movement, an important consideration when one considers that their planned range of 10,000 miles at 12kts means that they could be at sea for over a month. Being very roomy, a 'Castle' can accommodate her sizeable crew of 50 in comfort and still have space for a 25-strong Royal Marine contingent. An interesting omission is the seaboat, each ship stowing two high speed rigid inflatables abaft the superstructure and four liferafts surprisingly high up on the bridge deck. The rigid inflatables are intended primarily for boarding purposes, or 'crash boats' as fishery protection will be a major occupation. In this connection the ships have a CANE 2 (Computer-assisted navigation equipment) on the bridge, capable among much else, of tracking nearly 40 surface targets and producing a hard print-out with accurate navigational data of a standard acceptable to any Court of Law wherein an errant trawler skipper may find himself.

Perhaps the most interesting feature of the 'Castle' is invisible, a built-in capacity for upgrading. Hulls are designed to be stretched by some 5m and space is available for a one-third increase in installed power, giving a speed of 25kts. A folding hangar could then be installed for a Lynx-sized helicopter. The 40mm gun's underpinnings are sized for a 76mm weapon if required, and there would be no problem in fitting a range of missiles and/or AS torpedo tubes. Given an emergency, the 'Castle' class could blossom into a series as long as that of the earlier 'Castles' of WW2.

Island Offshore patrol vessel   UK

	Builders	LD	L	C
P277 *Anglesey*	HRA	78	78	79
P278 *Alderney*	HRA	78	79	79
P295 *Jersey*	HRA	75	76	76
P297 *Guernsey*	HRA	75	76	77
P298 *Shetland*	HRA	76	76	77
P299 *Orkney*	HRA	76	77	77
P300 *Lindisfarne*	HRA	77	77	78

Displacement: 925 tons standard; 1,250 tons full load
Dimensions: 59.5m × 11m × 4.3m
Armament: One 40mm gun
Machinery:
Two diesels, 4,400bhp
Single shaft
Speed: 16kts

Anglesey, *'Island' class.* Mike Lennon

The old-established problems of fishery protection and surveillance of foreign trawlers in UK waters has been magnified in recent years by an ever-increasing number of astronomically-expensive offshore rigs engaged in the economic exploitation of the British exclusive economic zone, or EEZ. To discharge this dual role, five 'Islands' were ordered in 1975, followed two years later by a further pair. Typically British in concept, they are neither fast nor heavily armed, being designed primarily to keep the seas for an extended period in a part of the world known for the ferocity of its weather. All were built by Hall, Russell, an Aberdeen yard with a well-established reputation for trawler construction, a pedigree readily visible in the rather pretty hull. Two diesels drive a single shaft, though only one engine would normally be used for economy.

For sometime from its inception, the class was criticised heavily for its lack of speed, armament and lack of helicopter. Certainly there have been times when extra capability may have been useful but, in general, these little ships have built for themselves a good reputation. They can carry a detachment of 16 Royal Marines to meet an emergency and, in truth, it is only such an instance that will prove early comment to be valid or ill-founded. A clue may lie in the OPV Mark 2, later the 'Castle' class, being considerably larger and inevitably, more expensive. Nevertheless, these ships are first-class platforms for learning basic seamanship, a subject in danger of becoming submerged in a sea of technology.

Peacock   Patrol craft

UK

	Builders	LD	L	C
P239 Peacock	HRA	82	—	—
Plover	HRA	—	—	—
Starling	HRA	—	—	—
Swallow	HRA	—	—	—
Swift	HRA	—	—	—

Displacement: 700 tons full load
Dimensions: 62.2m × 10m × 3.5m
Armament:
One 76mm gun
Some smaller
Machinery:
Two diesels, 14,400bhp
Twin shafts
Speed: 24kts

These little ships are designed to replace the elderly ex-'Ton' class minesweepers used as patrol craft in Hong Kong waters. As such the HK government is paying three-quarters of the total cost of £40M. Unlike the older ships, the 'Peacocks' will have a gun of reasonable calibre and a comparatively high speed for the apprehension of the numerous illicit or suspect craft that abound in the waters. The OTO-Melara makes its first appearance under the White Ensign, with a Sperry Sea Archer fire control. Interestingly, the diesels are 16-cylinder medium-speed Pielsticks, compact but noisy and, presumably, capable of low 'loitering' speeds.

The craft are due for delivery between mid-1983 and end-1984.

Endurance   Ice patrol ship

UK

	Builders	LD	L	C
A171 Endurance (ex-Anita Dan)	KR	55	56	56

Displacement: 3,600 tons standard
Dimensions: 91.5m × 14m × 5.5m
Armament: Light automatic weapons

Machinery:
One diesel, 3,220bhp
Single shaft
Speed: 14kts
Aircraft: Two light helicopters, with hangar

Endurance.   Mike Lennon

he Danish shipping concern of J. Lauritzen once perated a substantial number of ice-strengthened hips for servicing Denmark's interests in Greenland nd the Faroes. Most were engines-aft ships but an xception was the German-built *Anita Dan*, which was urchased in 1967 by the UK for conversion as a eplacement for the ageing ex-net layer *Protector*, then mployed as a support ship for the British Antarctic Survey. Conversion was by Harland & Wolff, Belfast, in the course of which the after cargo holds were rebuilt as accommodation and plated over with a helicopter deck one level above and the accommodation block virtually doubled in size to include a hangar for two Wasps. Forward, No 2 hold was also converted, but,

where the after bipod mast was removed, the forward was retained to work the remaining No 1 hold. Over No 2 hatch a low house was constructed with two large launches stowed under heavy davits for work in the ship's other important role, oceanography and hydrography.

In addition to scientific staff, the ship can also carry a detachment of Royal Marines. These were used to good effect in the 1982 confrontation with Argentina, as were the helicopters, whose light AS 12 missiles disabled the submarine *Santa Fe*. Though the ship was on the point of being withdrawn, a re-appraisal of the navy's role in the South Atlantic kept her for further service.

Hovercraft and Hydrofoils   *UK*

Though the Royal Navy has carried out extensive trials n numerous classes of hovercraft, a definite role does not yet seem to have emerged. Interest has centred on comparatively small designs with flexible sidewalls, a line incidentally, also taken by the Soviets, while American work has been toward a frigate-sized SES with rigid sidewalls.

Experience has shown the 10-ton SRN6 to be a useful small assault vehicle, though inhibited by its noise. They have served as Hong Kong patrol craft and with US forces in the swampy delta of the Mekong in Vietnam.

The 55-ton BH7 can carry fully equipped troops or light vehicles and can act, as those under the Iranian flag, as an alternative to an FAC. In terms of cost, range and lack of vulnerability the conventional FAC must win handsomely, however.

Trials with the large commercial-type SRN4 in the role of mine countermeasures vessel were promising. Far less expensive than the new GRP/hulled MCMVs, an SRN4 can, for a reasonably inshore role, deploy most of the sweep and detection gear of the MCMV,

while having an exceptionally low acoustic and magnetic signature, and a high degree of immunity to underwater explosions in close proximity.

Further trials in this direction have been carried out by the navy's sole VT2, a 100-ton Vosper Thornycroft design with two ducted propellers and a 24-ton payload. With cuts in naval budgets, however, further interest in the hovercraft looks limited and the assessment to date must be that, while interesting, these lightly-built craft cannot really offer much that a more conventional warship does not.

Hydrofoils never really interested the ocean-orientated Royal Navy until its assumption of new responsibilities with the declaration of the 200-mile UK offshore zone. The American Boeing Jetfoil offered a means of fast response to an emergency and one was acquired for evaluation in 1979, being commissioned in 1980 as HMS *Speedy* after a degree of conversion. She was used in a fishery protection role and for exercises in comparing with West German FACs but, although officially satisfactory, she was offered for sale in 1982.

Speedy. Crown Copyright

Olmeda, 'O' class. Mike Lennon

'O' class   Fleet tanker (large)   UK

	Builders	C
A122 Olwen (ex-Olynthus)	HLH	65
A123 Olna	HLH	66
A124 Olmeda (ex-Oleander)	SHW	65

Displacement: 10,900 tons light; 36,000 tons full load
Dimensions: 197.5m × 25.5m × 11m
Machinery:
One set geared steam turbines, 26,500shp
Single shaft
Speed: 19kts
Aircraft: Up to four medium helicopters with hangar space

Developed from the immediately preceding 27,500-ton 'Tidesprings', the 'Os' are by far the largest vessels currently in the Royal Fleet Auxiliary. Retaining the same layout, they carry 'wet' cargo in the spaces between the after superstructure and the bridge, and dry stores forward. Three massive gantries support the specialised cranes that carry the hoses for alongside underweigh replenishment, and a stern manifold can supply fuels to a ship astern. Dry stores can be transferred either by a modified jackstay or by one of the four Sea Kings normally aboard.

Displacement tonnages, quoted above, are of course the usual warship yardstick and not really applicable to tankers. The differences between the two, approxi-

mately 25,000 tons, represents the ships' more realistic measurement of deadweight tons. This is low for a vessel of these dimensions and illustrates the specialised nature of the design. By comparison, the 'Appleleaf' type freighting tankers were built for mercantile service and have a much fuller hull, enabling them to carry 33,000 deadweight tons, though nearly 30m shorter overall.

Noting the unadopted proposed names for Olwen and Olmeda, it is surprising that they were even considered, 'Olynthus' being too easily confused with 'Olympus' and 'Oleander' with 'Leander'.

The embarked Sea King flight obviously has a further potential as an AS force during hostilities, although British RFAs are entirely civilian-manned and unarmed in peacetime. This capability is to be further extended in the new class of auxiliary now under development, the first of which is hoped to be ordered in 1984.

On the basic premise that a replenishment vessel will usually accompany a frigate force, the new Type 23s may have facilities only for landing helicopters, which will be garaged (up to six) in their attendant auxiliary, whose ample deck will also serve V/STOL aircraft, if necessary. Another departure will be the arming of these ships, a second feature that will require a part-naval, part-mercantile crew. The design will allow for a higher proportion of wet-to-dry cargo and it is anticipated that the class will do the work of current tanker and dry-store classes.

Rover   Fleet tanker (small)   UK

	Builders	C
A268 Green Rover	SHH	69
A269 Grey Rover	SHH	70
A270 Blue Rover	SHH	70
A271 Gold Rover	SHH	74
A273 Black Rover	SHH	74

Displacement: 4,700 tons standard; 11,500 tons full load
Dimensions: 140.5m × 19.3m × 7.3m

Machinery:
Two diesels, 15,400bhp
Single shaft
Speed: 19kts

With their fine-lined hulls, these small tankers are surprisingly elegant. Indeed, while on the subject of ship aesthetics — a very personal thing — the only displeasing feature is the funnel top and black band, both of which should have been near horizontal in line.

They are combination 'wet-and-dry' ships, their

Black Rover, *'Rover' class.* Mike Lennon

6,700 ton deadweight capacity devoted primarily to oils, transferred at sea via a single gantry. Interconnection of the many spaces is complex for, like mercantile 'parcels' tankers, they must deal in many products. Steamers still require heavy bunker fuel, gas turbine ships need lighter fractions; most need diesel oil for generators, all need lubricating oils, with aviation spirits for those operating helicopters.

A lighter goalpost abaft the funnel supports derricks for the transfer of dry stores. These are brought topside by a large elevator which also serves the flightdeck for

the purpose of 'vertical replenishment', using a Sea King helicopter.

The first three of class were equipped with a British Ruston diesel of a type which were particularly trouble-prone. As a result all now have French-built medium-speed Pielsticks, twinned into a common gearbox, with astern power given by a variable-pitch propeller. It was a pity that Rustons marketed that particular machinery, for their products are usually of excellent quality, those, for instance, installed in the new 'Castles' being highly thought of.

Fort   Fleet replenishment ship   *UK*

	Builders	C
A385 *Fort Grange*	SLG	78
A386 *Fort Austin*	SLG	79

Displacement: 23,600 tons full load
Dimensions: 184m×24.1m×9m
Machinery:
One diesel, 23,000bhp
Single shaft
Speed: 22kts
Aircraft: Four medium helicopters and hangar

Though considerably larger, this pair of ships was derived directly from the 'Ness' class, since sold to the US. Where the latter's appearance is messy to the point where it would look as though they are conversions (which they are not), the 'Forts' have used cranes to good effect and the modern mercantile practice of a broad, flat transom has been adopted, which is more

sympathetic to the large flight deck aft. With a substantial beam available, it has been possible to accommodate a hangar large enough for four Sea King equivalents. Only one is carried in peacetime, for vertical replenishment purposes, but this could be increased quickly to a useful AS flight in the event of hostilities, with space for a naval detachment already fitted out. Power is provided by a large, low-speed diesel on a single shaft; the hull is of fine line and is capable of a useful 22kts for underweigh transfer but at the cost of a low deadweight of barely 8,000 tons. No liquid stores are carried, the available space being devoted to naval stores, foodstuffs and ammunition.

Interestingly, the only other pair of fleet replenishment ships, the *Regent* and *Resourse*, which were contemporary with the 'Ness' type, are laid out similarly to the 'Tide' class tankers. They are steam turbine driven yet, in spite of being slightly larger than the diesel-propelled 'Forts', are credited with an RFA complement of only about 120 as opposed to some 140.

Fort Austin, *'Fort' class; note 20mm guns and chaff launchers abaft bridge.* Mike Lennon

Challenger   Seabed operations vessel

	Builders	C
K07 *Challenger*	SLG	83

Displacement: 6,800 tons standard
Dimensions: 134m × 18m × 5.5m
Machinery:
Five diesel-generator sets totalling 6,500bhp
Three transverse thrusters forward and two Voith-Schneider cycloidal propellers aft
Speed: 15kts

Ostensibly a replacement for the old *Reclaim*, *Challenger* will be in a different league altogether. Her function is to be able to investigate any seabed phenomenon, from pure research projects to specific tasks such as the recovery of hardware. To locate her area of interest she is equipped with a range of her own sensors or can work in conjunction with a vessel carrying more specialised equipment. Depending on the nature of the investigation, depth of water, etc, *Challenger* can then put over a manned submersible by a pivoting gantry over the transom or employ divers from the outset. Amidships is a 'moonpool', a well through which a pressurised 'bell', containing a diving team, can be lowered to considerable depths, guided on a pair of weighted lines. To avoid lengthy delays caused by decompression cycles when working deep, several teams of divers can work around the clock, supported in a 'saturated' state in a set of pressurised chambers in which they live for the duration of the job, transferring to and from the bell via an airlock.

During such operations, it is necessary for the ship to keep station possibly for days on end to an accuracy of a few metres, in varying weather and tidal conditions, possibly no visual fixes and in great depths of water. For this, she employs a dynamic positioning system, the seabed site being ringed with transponders which can be continuously interrogated. Any change in time response represents a movement by the ship, and this time is fed as an 'error signal' into the ship's prime movers as appropriate. These will probably all be running continuously, and at constantly varying thrusts. They consist of three transverse thrusters forward and two Voith Schneider cycloidal propellers aft, the latter capable of producing full thrust at almost any angle. By adopting diesel-electric machinery, power can be directed as required to any of these electrically-driven propulsors.

Nimitz   Nuclear-propelled aircraft carrier

	Builders	LD	L	C
CVN68 *Chester W. Nimitz*	NNS	68	72	75
CVN69 *Dwight D. Eisenhower*	NNS	70	75	77
CVN70 *Carl Vinson*	NNS	75	80	82
CVN71 *Theodore Roosevelt*	NNS	81	85	87

Displacement: 81,600 tons standard, 91,500 tons full load
Dimensions: 333m × 40.8m × 11.3m (Max width over flightdeck 77m)
Armament:
Three Sea Sparrow point defence SAM
Three/four Vulcan/Phalanx CIWS
Machinery:
Two PWC reactors
Four sets geared steam turbines 260,000shp
Four shafts
Speed: Over 30kts
Aircraft: 90-100

In major dimensions, displacement, propulsive power, complement, strike power, or virtually any statistic, these vessels set new records. Unfortunately their other record statistic lies in their cost and this must limit their numbers in spite of the fact that, in response to the perceived Soviet threat at sea, the Reagan administration reversed the policy of the preceding management in committing funds for long-lead items for three further units. Obviously the 'big-carrier' lobby still flourishes in spite of an announced intention to move down in size (a phonomenon active also in the submarine arm). It cannot be gainsaid that the versatility of a large carrier enables her to grade her response flexibly to any situation, from the need for a 'presence' to a full nuclear strike. The weakness is in the argument that they are the least vulnerable of ships because of their power. This is true only for limited war — in a Falklands-style involvement for example, the combination of airborne early-warning and long-ranged strike aircraft would prove devastating at breaking up any incoming attack far removed from the carrier herself or any landing zone. However, in an East-West conflict, low yield nuclear weapons can be expected in use at sea from the outset (or even before). These could be in the form of obsolescent ballistic weapons from 'Golf' or 'Hotel' class submarines, nuclear-tipped cruise weapons from a 'Charlie' or even a ballistic weapon from deep inside the Soviet Union, targeted by satellite. Any of these would stand a good chance of laying waste a complete carrier task force — the value of any of these task forces would be worth the risk of escalation, and these risks would not increase for several task forces being so obliterated. The answer must be to accept a down-grading of capability and opt for more, smaller flightdecks, though this view pre-supposes that the Soviets themselves do not opt to build large carriers. With more and more CVNs being built, Newport News, as the only US shipyard capable handling them, must inevitably be saturated — a problem rendered no less worrying by the vulnerability of the yard to destruction in the event of war.

The two lead ships were completed as CVAN, or attack carriers, but the steady attrition in war-built flightdecks still available for AS work meant that all

Eisenhower, 'Nimitz' class. Tophamper of 'California' class CGN visible over starboard quarter.
US Navy Official

have had to be re-classified CVN. This signifies a multi-purpose capability, the ships' strike capability being diluted for the other needs of ASW as well as AEW and reconnaissance.

Layout was heavily based on experience gained with the pioneering *Enterprise*, with a similarly double-overhung flightdeck with three deck-edge elevators to starboard and one to port, and four steam catapults, two forward and two on the angled deck.

In the decade between the laying down of *Enterprise* and *Nimitz*, advances in nuclear technology allowed

reduction in the number of reactors from eight to only two. These have an expected life of about 13 years which, for the currently-expected span of an American carrier, looks like coinciding with a quarter-life refit!

Externally, there is little that does not appear in earlier classes, the radar suite being very similar. The Sea Sparrow point defence systems are to be backed up by the 'last-ditch' Vulcan/Phalanx CIWS.

CVN72 and CVN73 reportedly named *Abraham Lincoln* and *George Washington* respectively.

Enterprise Nuclear-propelled aircraft carrier   *USA*

	Builders	LD	L	C
CVN65 *Enterprise*	NNS	58	60	61

Displacement: 75,700 tons standard; 89,500 tons full load
Dimensions: 335.8m×40.5m×10.8m (Max width over flightdeck 76.8m)
Armament:
Two Sea Sparrow point defence SAM
Three Vulcan/Phalanx CIWS
Machinery:
Eight PRC reactors
Four sets geared steam turbines, 260,000shp
Four shafts
Speed: Over 20kts
Aircraft: 85-90

As the world's first nuclear carrier and largest warship, the reign of the 'Big E' lasted over 13 years, until the entry into service of the *Nimitz*. Basically a slightly stretched 'Kitty Hawk' she resulted from an imaginative programme to put nuclear propulsion to sea in three separate types of surface warship, with the idea of

testing the feasibility of an all-nuclear squadron. The other ships involved were the cruiser *Long Beach* (CGN9) and the frigate *Bainbridge* (DLGN25).

Externally her profile was original in the small cross-section of the island, no longer built around conventional uptakes. A further departure was in the virtual elimination of rotating radar antennas. Like *Long Beach*, *Enterprise* was fitted with four 'bill-board' fixed phased-array antennas, one pair of each of the island's four faces to cater for horizontal and vertical scanning to give range and bearing in 3-0 as well as target tracking. Known as 'Scanfar' (officially SPS32 and 33) it had a theoretical range of over 4,000 miles but limitations are apparent in its removal from both ships in their major modernisations. Of these, that on *Enterprise* was completed in 1981, though a conversion from CVAN to CVN was carried out in 1975. The array of rotating hardware now installed is interchangeable with those on other US warships and occupies the limited space atop the island, previously taken by the ship's characteristic bee-hive-shaped stack of ECM gear.

Enterprise's mid-1950s design demanded eight PRC reactors, each raising steam from conventional boilers

via four heat exchangers. Three years' steaming exhausted the first charge of fuel, the second cores lasted over four years; between them they accounted for over half a million miles.

Where the 'Kitty Hawks' had been armed with Terrier or Sea Sparrow SAM systems, *Enterprise* had initially nothing but allocated space. She has since acquired Sea Sparrow launchers on either quarter and, lately, three Vulcan/Phalanx weapons.

Enterprise, *after rebuild.*   US Navy Official

It should be noted that though, as a unit a nuclear carrier can steam almost indefinitely, this does not make her fully independent, as, particularly at war footing, her needs in other basics, eg aviation fuel for up to 90 aircraft and ordnance, to say nothing of the prodigious quantity of foodstuffs for the total of about 5,500 men aboard need assuaging at least fortnightly.

Kitty Hawk   Aircraft carrier

USA

	Builders	LD	L	C
CV68 *Kitty Hawk*	NYS	56	60	61
CV64 *Constellation*	NYD	57	60	61
CV66 *America*	NNS	61	64	65
CV67 *John F. Kennedy*	NNS	64	67	68

Displacement: (average) 61,150 tons standard; 80,500 tons full load
Dimensions: (average) 323m × 39.5m × 11.1m (width over flightdeck 76.5m)
Armament:
Three Sea Sparrow point defence SAM
(Two twin Terrier SAM in Constellation)
Three Vulcan/Phalanx CIWS

Machinery:
Four sets geared steam turbines 280,000shp
Four shafts
Speed: 30kts
Aircraft: 85-90

Though developed from the immediately preceding 'Forrestals', this group can easily be recognised by having their islands set noticeably farther aft, a fashion which remained with the later-nuclear propelled carriers. The object was to improve the flightdeck layout, something which is appreciated in plan. Where both classes have four deckedge elevators, the earlier class had that on the portside at the forward end of the angled deck and the aftermost of the three starboard

Constellation, *'Kitty Hawk' class; note Terrier launcher on starboard quarter.*   Mike Lennon

installations so close to the angled deck limit that aircraft would have to be moved over it. During flying operations, they are in effect, reduced to two fully effective elevators.

All were classified CVA (Attack Carriers) on completion, but have since been rebuilt internally as CV (Multi-function Carriers) to include AS capability with strike. This introduces considerable complexity when one considers the typical mix of two attack squadrons of A-7 Corsairs, and one of A-6 Intruders, two fighter squadrons of F-14 Tomcats, a flight of E-2 Hawkeyes for airborne early warning, and one of EA-6B Prowlers for electronic warfare, a squadron each of S-3 Vikings and SH-3 Sea Kings for ASW, together with a flight of RA-5C Vigilantes equipped for reconnaissance work. This increased versatility has to be acquired at the expense of reduced striking power.

It will be noted how *Enterprise's* pendant, CVN56, came from the block allocated to the 'Kitty Hawks', and indeed, it was intended originally that *Kennedy* also should be nuclear powered. Though she eventually was not, the debate set back her construction sufficiently for her to incorporate differences. One of these was the adoption of Sea Sparrow point defence SAMs in place of the Terriers on the first three. These obsolete systems are being removed at major refits and only *Constellation* remains so fitted.

America of this group is fitted with an SQS-23 sonar in a bow dome, the only large carrier so fitted. This set can work in either a passive or active mode but must be of limited use in that a ship of this size could tailor her speed to optimum sonar operation only in an ideal world.

Forrestal   Aircraft carrier   *USA*

	Builders	LD	L	C
CV59 *Forrestal*	NNS	52	54	55
CV60 *Saratoga*	NYD	52	55	56
CV61 *Ranger*	NNS	54	56	57
CV62 *Independence*	NYD	55	58	59

Displacement: (average) 59,500 tons standard; 77,500 tons full load
Dimensions: (average) 318m × 38.5 × 11.3m (width over flightdeck 78m)
Armament: Two eight-celled Sea Sparrow point defence SAM
Machinery:
Four sets geared steam turbines, 280,000shp
Four shafts

Speed: 33kts
Aircraft: About 80

As the world's first carriers designed and built for the operation of jet aircraft, it is hardly surprising that they showed a considerable increase in size over the preceding 'Midways'. There was, however, an intermediate step in the ill-starred *United States* (CVA58), a large vessel intended for the operation of nuclear-armed bombers, which was commenced and cancelled in the same year 1949, a time of great re-appraisal in carrier roles and equipment. Based in large measure on this design, the first-of-class *Forrestal* was laid down in 1952. At this stage, she incorporated an axial flight deck but an angled deck was worked in during con-

Saratoga, *'Forrestal' class.*   Mike Lennon

struction. Other departures from earlier practice included a plated-in 'hurricane bow' and a protected flightdeck, both standard features in British ships.

For their size, the ships were clean-lined with a neat rectangular island, out of which the funnel casing barely protruded. This casing needed, in fact, to be raised at a later date. An earlier feature that was carried on into this class was a gun armament of eight single 5in weapons, sponsored out, two to a corner. In most, the forward guns were soon removed, together with their sponsons which, on such fine lined ships, tended to drive under on pitching. Later, the after weapons were also removed, and a pair of eight-cell Sea Sparrow point defence systems installed.

The steam plant was an improved 'Midway' fit,

uprated from 212,000shp to 260,000shp in *Forrestal*. Later units had further improvements incorporated to produce 280,000shp.

Like later ships, they were modified from CVA to CV but, interestingly, the first two were laid down as CVB, a categorisation for large aircraft carrier.

The 'Forrestals' are the first candidates for the so-called SLEP programme (Service Life Extension) where each in turn will undergo a 28-month facelift to enable them to operate current aircraft, improved electronics and enhanced armament. Due to complete the first of these in 1983 is *Saratoga*, supposed to be then good for service until the year 2000, by which time the hull will be 48 years of age.

Midway Aircraft carrier *USA*

	Builders	LD	L	C
CV41 *Midway*	NNS	43	45	45
CV43 *Coral Sea*	NNS	44	46	47

Displacement: (average) 51,700 tons standard; 62,200 tons full load
Dimensions: 398.5m×36.9m×10.8m (width over flightdeck 72.5m)
Armament:
Two eight-celled Sea Sparrow point defence SAM (in Midway)
Three Vulcan/Phalanx CIWS
Machinery:
Four sets geared steam turbines, 212,000shp
Four shafts
Speed: 33kts
Aircraft: About 75

Of six planned units of this class, originally classified CVB, only three were ever completed. CVB44 being cancelled as early as 1943 and the later CVB56 and 57 in 1945. Since then CV42 (*Franklin D. Roosevelt*) was discarded in 1977. The CVB status arose from their disparity in size compared with the long programme of 'Essex' class ships then being built. The toughness and survivability of British fleet carriers, due to their armoured flightdecks, influenced the basic design. American thinking before was toward light flightdecks and side scantlings over a protected hangar deck but hard experience showed that fires in the hangar could

still be fatal. To increase length and push the protection up about eight metres would have given stability problems but for the decision to increase the beam to the extent where passage of the Panama Canal — a cherished quality for a two-ocean navy — was no longer possible.

First-of-class, *Midway*, was completed just too late to see active service in WW2 and, following the death of the President, the second unit, *Coral Sea*, was renamed after him with the third then assuming the name of the battle. Despite their years, neither ship has ever been in reserve, though *Coral Sea* is now a sort of 'standby' ship without a designated air wing but useful for operations where unexpected needs arise.

Both have been extensively modernised and, due to their smaller proportions, have angled deck overhangs of seemingly larger dimensions than their larger running mates. Overall, their profiles are much lower and they are the only US carriers with a pronounced stack. Originally fitted with two centreline elevators and one on the port deckedge they now have two starboard deckedge elevators, one before and one abaft the island, and the port side unit has been moved further aft to clear the added angled deck.

Although *Coral Sea* is due to pay off during 1983, *Midway* will need to soldier on for at least two years more — possibly until the completion of *Theodore Roosevelt*. She will, therefore, receive two Sea Sparrow point defence SAMs and, possibly, some CIWS.

Essex and Improved Essex Aircraft carrier *USA*

	Builders	LD	L	C
a) *'Essex' class*				
CVS12 *Hornet*	NNS	42	43	43
CVS20 *Bennington*	NYD	42	44	44
b) *'Improved Essex' class*				
AVT16 *Lexington* (ex-*Cabot*)	BSQ	41	42	43
CVA31 *Bonne Homme Richard*	NYD	43	44	44
CV34 *Oriskany*	NYD	44	45	50

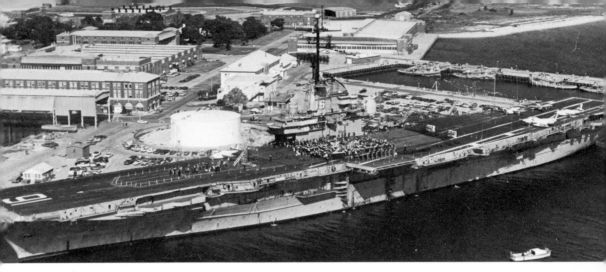

Displacement:
a) 33,000 tons standard; 40,600 tons full load
b) 23,500 tons standard; 41,900 tons full load
Dimensions: 274m×30.8m×9.4m (width over flight-deck 52.5m-59.5m)
Armament: Up to four 5in (127mm) guns (4×1)
Machinery:
Four sets geared steam turbines, 150,000shp
Four shafts

An early appreciation of the vital importance of air power in the Pacific war led the Americans to prepare a carrier of a design that would lend itself to rapid series production in a minimum number of yards. Of 32 'Essex' class ships ordered, 24 were eventually completed, the five listed above being the survivors.

As a design it followed both Japanese and earlier American practice rather than British in having a protected lower hull topped with a 60-70mm hangar deck, above which was the hangar level with comparatively lightly-built sides and a 35mm flightdeck over. As a construction philosophy it proved inferior to the British method from the point of view of survival after heavy damage but, on the other hand, enabled far more aircraft to be embarked. In short, the resulting ships were more effective in an offensive sense but more vulnerable to attack. No 'Essex' class ships were, in fact, lost

Lexington, *'Improved Essex' class.*   US Navy Official

to enemy attack but several were heavily damaged. As improvements spurred by experience were incorporated into each ship as built, there existed a host of minor variations into the class, that being most different being the *Oriskany*, completed later than the remainder and incorporating an experimental aluminium flightdeck.

All surviving 'Essex' class carriers have been modernised to varying degrees, the main difference between the two groups being that the 'improved' units have steam catapults to match their uprated facilities for handling modern aircraft. They carry a variety of categorisations: CVS — AS carrier, AVT — training carriers, CVA — attack carriers (ie no ASW wing embarked). Only *Lexington* is currently active but, with a dearth of ready flightdecks available to meet the planned US naval expansion, *Oriskany* and *Bonne Homme Richard* are set for a major modernisation, the remaining units probably being deleted or cannibalised.

Though considered small by US naval standards, the 'Essex' class carriers are of a size that would be approaching the ideal for a new group to act as an alternative (CVV) to the dauntingly expensive (and vulnerable) CVNs.

Iowa   Battleship   *USA*

	Builders	LD	L	C
BB61 *Iowa*	NYD	40	42	43
BB62 *New Jersey*	PND	40	42	43
BB63 *Missouri*	NYD	41	44	44
BB64 *Wisconsin*	PND	41	43	44

Displacement: 45,000 tons standard; 59,000 tons standard load
Dimensions: 270.4m×33m×11.6m
Armament:
(before modernisation) Nine 16in (406mm) guns (3×3)
Twenty 5in (127mm) guns (10×2)

Machinery:
Four geared steam turbines, 212,000shp
Four shafts
Speed: 33+kts

Possibly the most controversial warship project ever, the re-activation of the world's four last battleships is probably not the whimsical bout of sentiment that many have held it to be. Even before the limited Falklands operation it was readily apparent that paper-thin modern warships trading SSMs would have a limited chance of surviving a hit. In the event, it was not only high technology but also good old-fashioned courage and iron bombs that did the damage. Either way, the

loss of the ships on the receiving end pointed to the continuing need to be able to absorb punishment as well as inflict it. This is just what a battleship is designed for and there can be few missile manufacturers rash enough to claim that their product could pierce the 310mm main belt of an *Iowa*. In addition, once the up-dating is complete, the range and number of the installed missiles would make her a most difficult target for any of today's potentially hostile surface ships.

Owing to trim problems it is unlikely that the after turret will be removed in favour of a major aviation facility as was first planned, so the *New Jersey*, the first to be dealt with, was to re-commission in early 1983 with her full nine-gun main battery, effective out to about 34km with AP rounds weighing up to 1,225kg. Six of the 20 gun secondary battery will be landed to make way for 16 Harpoon launchers with potential out to about 100km with mid-course correction from one of the ship's four LAMPS helicopters. Space should be available for reloads. Beyond this, she will strike to 400km with no less than 32 Tomahawk cruise missiles housed in eight armoured launchers. No SAM systems are planned and only four Vulcan/Phalanx CIWS as last-ditch defence. Depending absolutely on an escort for AA and AS defence, she would seem to carry a large number of dated 5in guns with no apparent function.

Critics have pointed out that the concussive shock of a main battery shoot will derange modern electroncis. This may be so and encourage the development of a laser-guided subcalibre round with discarding sabots.

A futher bonus is that at least three of the quartette should still be able to outrun a modern cruiser, their speed being a somewhat dated virtue, as is their undoubted 'presence' as flagships. In spite of their years they have spent surprisingly few years in active commission and should still have plenty of life left in them. The longish re-activation programme, however, — BB61 to complete in 1985, BB63 in 1986 and BB64 in 1987 — will span administrations and may run foul of a change of policy.

This re-juvenation is planned as a 'Phase I' of a comprehensive rebuild which will the after end increased in height over the redundant after turret to act as a flight-deck, with two forward-facing ski-jump split by the after superstructure, set over a hangar housing V/STOL aircraft and helicopters. On the centreline will be set a VLS for about 140 mixed missiles. Whether this Phase II will ever be more than a plan must remain as conjectural as the four projected surface battlegroups built around the battleships.

Virginia and Modified Virginia Nuclear-powered cruiser *USA*

	Builders	LD	L	C
a) 'Virginia' class				
CGN38 *Virginia*	NNS	72	74	76
CGN39 *Texas*	NNS	73	75	77
CGN40 *Mississippi*	NNS	75	76	78
CGN41 *Arkansas*	NNS	77	78	80
b) 'Modified Virginia' class				
CGN42	—	—	—	—
CGN43	—	—	—	—
CGN44	—	—	—	—
CGN45	—	—	—	—

Displacement:
a) 11,000 tons full load
b) 12,000 tons full load

Dimensions:
a) 178.3m × 19.2m × 9m
b) 179.6m × 19.2m × 9m
Armament:
Two quadruple Harpoon SSM launchers
Two twin standard MR/ASROC launchers
Two 5in (127mm) guns (2 × 1)
Two triple AS torpedo tubes
Machinery:
Two PWC reactors
Two sets geared steam turbines, 100,000shp
Twin shafts
Speed: Over 30kts
Aircraft: Two LAMPS helicopters with hangar

Essentially improved 'Californias', the 'Virginias' represent a greater step forward than a cursory glance

would suggest. Probably the most fundamental is a substantial up-rating of machinery power, speed being of vital importance to a large carrier escort. Further, the space aft has been used to stow two LAMPS helicopters below the flightpad, a neat arrangement that avoids the space-consuming topside hangar, but at the cost of the complexity of an elevator. The helicopters not only can be used for over-the-horizon targeting for the Harpoon SSMs but also in conjunction with targeting ASROC, the rounds for which are launched from the twin-arm Mark 26 launchers. This saves the deckspace occupied on the earlier class by the separate ASROC launcher and re-load facility and advantage has been taken of this by shortening the hull by about 3.5m. As the class may well be candidates during their lifetime for retro-fitting a vertical launch system, this 'saved' space my be regretted. Only one pair of SAM control directors, SPG 51Ds is fitted. The vacated space forward is occupied by SPG 60 dish and the radome-covered SPQ-9 which, together make up the Mark 86 fire control, which caters both for the

Virginia. Mike Lennon

forward Standard/ASROC launcher and the guns.

With the demise of the so-called·'Strike Cruiser' project, the US Navy has opted for an Aegis-equipped version of the 'Virginia', commencing with CGN42.

In view of the criticisms of the CG47 (Ticonderoga) Aegis destroyer, this would seem sound. Aegis, when fully operational, will have the capability of countering any form of aerial target, aircraft or missile, as well as being able to operate in the usual tracking, illumination and surveillance modes. In addition it can control friendly aircraft. It is hoped that, by means of data linking, the Aegis-equipped ship of a task group will also be able to control the defence systems of the whole group, assessing each threat and allocating the best available weapon system to meet it. Delivery of the first seems unlikely before 1995.

Delays in the 'Virginia' programme have highlighted the vulnerability of putting the navy's nuclear carrier and cruiser series into only one yard.

California   Nuclear-powered cruiser   *USA*

	Builders	LD	L	C
CGN36 *California*	NNS	70	71	74
CGN37 *South Carolina*	NNS	70	72	75

Displacement: 9,550 tons standard; 10,700 tons full load
Dimensions: 181.7m × 18.6m × 9.7m
Armament:
Two quadruple Harpoon SSM launchers
Two single Standard MR SAM launchers
Two 5in (127mm) guns (2 × 1)
One 8-cell ASROC AS rocket launcher
Two triple AS torpedo tubes
Machinery:
Two PWC reactors
Two sets geared steam turbines
Speed: Over 30kts

The imaginative construction of a prototype nuclear-propelled squadron in the early 1960s might fairly be assessed as having scored two out of three for, where the *Enterprise* proved a sound design upon which to base future CVNs, the *Long Beach* did not start a new

line in cruiser development which, rather surprisingly, grew from the smaller 'frigate' *Bainbridge*. Her double-ended layout was the basis for the two 'Californias' which are only about nine metres longer in the hull. Though also originally designated as 'frigates', their importance in their function as dedicated escorts for the large carriers was reflected in their up-grading to cruiser and in their names, which commenced a new trend in adopting the 'State' names once reserved for battleships (this has been complicated by the new SSBNs also being similarly named). As task group escorts, their bias is toward AAW and in this they are well endowed in having two Standard MR systems, based on two single-armed Mk 13 launchers on a 40-round magazine. Two SPG-51D fire control systems are fitted, with separate tracker and illuminator dishes, with 3D early warning coming from the rectangular SPS 48 at the forecastle head.

As the two launchers are not equipped for dual operation, a separate ASROC launcher is fitted, immediately forward of the bridge, with an adjacent structure housing a reload facility. The weakness of the arrangement is that the 'Californias' do not carry

helicopters (having only a pad right aft) and ASROC data must come either from the SQS-26 active/passive search sonar mounted in the hull (not likely to be very effective because of the need for the ships to proceed almost continuously at high speed) or via the NTDS inter-ship data link.

A great improvement over the basic *Bainbridge* concept has been the re-adoption of a pair of 5in 54s, weapons whose versatility and economy are still very marked in a missile-ridden era. The ships' anti-ship

California. Mike Lennon

capability has been further augmented by the addition of Harpoon, but here again a helicopter would be useful to realise these weapons' full potential range. CIWS can be expected to be fitted.

The official rating of the machinery at only 60,000shp would seem to be on the low side to propel so large a ship at about 30kts.

Ticonderoga Cruiser

USA

	Builders	LD	L	C
CG47 *Ticonderoga*	ISP	80	81	83
CG48 *Yorktown*	ISP	81	83	84
CG49 —	ISP	—	—	—
CG50 —	ISP	—	—	—
CG51 —	ISP	—	—	—
CG52 —	ISP	—	—	—
CG53 —	ISP	—	—	—
CG54 —	ISP	—	—	—
CG55 —	ISP	—	—	—

Displacement: 9,050 tons full load
Dimensions: 171.1m × 17.6m × 9.5m

Armament:
Two twin launchers for Standard MR/ASROC
Two quadruple Harpoon SSM launchers
Two 5in (127mm) guns (2 × 1)
Two Vulcan/Phalanx CIWS
Two triple AS torpedo tubes
Machinery:
Four gas turbines, 80,000shp
Twin shafts
Speed: c30kts
Aircraft: Two LAMPS helicopters with hangar

Ticonderoga. US Navy Official

An irony of the successful 'Spruance' design is that it was offered by its builders as the basis for a range of optional variants, up to and including a mini-aircraft carrier. So far, the US Navy has opted for only one variant, the CG47, which was none of these and, although the baseline 'Spruance' hull is capacious and easily capable of accommodating a variety of fits, the CG47 would seem to have over-taxed it. The same hull and propulsion system used in the DD963 series is now reported to be burdened so that it is at least 1,250 tons up on deep-load displacement, deep-draughted, slowed to the extent where it may have difficulty keeping up with the task group that it is designed to protect and blessed with a less-than-adequate stability range. As the class is destined to be at least twenty-strong a reduction in fit and/or an increase in beam would seem in order, though an up-rating of installed power would also be required. Officially this is denied, it being claimed that a 600 ton margin for extra equipment is built-in.

Even so, the *Ticonderoga* has the first Aegis system in an operational warship, its fixed phased arrays working in each quadrant and shared between the faces of the heightened bridge and hangar structures. Known as SPY-1, the system has been reported as coping with 20 simultaneous targets whilst under development in the trials-ship *Norton Sound*. Though the system can command weapons on other platforms in the force, it depends also on two Standard MR launchers on the same hull and these, with their dual ability to launch ASROC rounds, have accounted for a large measure of the increase in displacement. Harpoon may be a likely casualty in the early ships.

In profile the CG47 is not dissimilar to the double-ended *Kidd* (DD993) variant but can be distinguished at present by the forward bulwark, added to increase freeboard. From the fifth of the class onward, a vertical launch system will permit a freer mix of missiles with no penalty in top-weight though Tomahawk, in its armoured launchers, would seem questionable. Though ship-launched missiles are Aegis-controlled, Mark 91 fire controls are mounted high up at either end of the superstructure, presumably as 'look-down' detection for incoming SSMs, to be countered by ECM and Vulcan/Phalanx.

Truxtun   Nuclear-powered cruiser   *USA*

	Builders	LD	L	C
CGN35 *Truxtun*	NYS	63	64	67

Displacement: 8,200 tons standard; 9,150 tons full load
Dimensions: 172m × 17.7m × 9.4m
Armament:
Two quadruple Harpoon SSM launchers
One twin Standard ER/ASROC launcher
One 5in (127mm) gun
Four fixed AS torpedo tubes
Machinery:
Two PWC reactors
Two sets steam turbines, 60,000shp
Twin shafts
Speed: 30kts
Aircraft: One LAMPS helicopter with hangar

Congress itself dictated that the tenth 'Belknap' should be nuclear-powered; the resultant *Truxtun* was slightly longer than the remainder of the class, though shorter than *Bainbridge*, and lacking the knuckle in the forward hull. An interesting feature was the reversal of gun and missile systems with the latter now in a more sheltered position aft. It is credited with the same mixed 60-round magazine, which must have been a tight squeeze into the narrower sections of the after hull. As a result, the area forward of the bridge looks strangely under-utilised with a roomy forward extension of the bridge structure at 01 level occupied only by a brace of chaff launchers. Though, however, one would expect the access to the reactors for re-coring, etc, to be through the small amidships gap, it may well be forward, following some mercantile practice. In either case the *Truxtun* remained a one-off, for the first major derivatives, the 'Californias', reverted to separate SAM and ASROC launchers, enabling more targets to be engaged simultaneously, even at the expense of a larger ship.

Where the 'macks' of the remainder of the programme might well have been expected to inspire rigid plated-in masts in the funnel-less *Truxtun*, the designers eschewed these in favour of a pair of graceless lattice structures which, while stiff, offer no protection and would look better in a test-rig ashore.

Like *Bainbridge*, she is a cramped and rather low-speed experiment which is unlikely to out-live the remainder of the class.

Truxtun. Mike Lennon

Belknap *after rebuild.* US Navy Official

Belknap Cruiser

	Builders	LD	L	C
CG26 *Belknap*	BIW	62	63	64
CG27 *Josephus Daniels*	BIW	62	63	65
CG28 *Wainwright*	BIW	62	64	66
CG29 *Jouett*	PSD	62	64	66
CG30 *Horne*	SFD	62	64	67
CG31 *Sterett*	PSD	62	64	67
CG32 *William H. Standley*	BIW	63	64	66
CG33 *Fox*	TSS	63	64	66
CG34 *Biddle*	BIW	63	65	66

Displacement: 6,570 tons standard; 7,950 tons full load
Dimensions: 166.7m × 16.7m × 8.7m
Armament:
One twin launcher for Standard ER/ASROC
Two quadruple Harpoon SSM launchers
One 5in (127mm) gun
Two Vulcan/Phalanx CIWS
Two triple AS torpedo tubes
Machinery:
Two sets geared steam turbines, 85,000shp
Twin shafts
Speed: 33kts
Aircraft: One LAMPS helicopter with hangar

First derivatives of the 'Leahy' type, the 'Belknaps' are geared to a GP, all-round capability yet, in spite of being only 'single-ended' and having adopted the Mark 10 launcher which can fire both Standard MR and ASROC rounds, they are over 4m longer. This could have been from necessity but, more probably, was due to an uneconomic use of space. As the first US escorts to carry a helicopter with full facilities, their flight pad was

placed well forward, instead of aft, where it has minimum impact on ship layout. This stemmed from the requirement to add the 5in gun that the 'Leahy's' conspicuously lacked. The problem of layout can be solved far more neatly; for instance in the Netherlands' 'Tromps', which carry a similar armament on a hull some 28.5m shorter. Where the double-ended 'Leahy' hull could house some eighty extended-range Standard missiles (SM-2s) with a range of 75-miles and a, probably, non-reloadable ASROC launcher, the Belknaps have a single 60-round magazine, one third of which can be ASROCs. At the moment, most have the SM-1 Standard ER with a 35-mile range but, commencing with the re-constructed nameship, they will be re-equipped. The question of reliability must be paramount in the Mark 10 system as, where the earlier ships had three separate launchers for their AAW and ASW, their follow-on have only the one.

Their adherence to the steam turbine probably resulted from the resolution to develop nuclear propulsion as the alternative, rather than the gas turbine, which was becoming established in both the British and Soviet fleets.

Originally, two large-calibre AS torpedo tubes were built into their after superstructures but these have been superseded by the usual short range Mk 32 triple mountings on deck. Interestingly, however, the renascent *Belknap* has been rebuilt with a flatter transom in which appears to be set two covered apertures.

The so-called DDG51 design continues as a planned replacement for 'Belknap', 'Leahy' and 'Coontz' classes. It is hoped to order the first of up to 50 hulls in 1985. They are planned to have a modified AEGIS system, vertically-launched missiles, a gun and a helicopter.

Bainbridge   Nuclear-powered cruiser   *USA*

	Builders	LD	L	C
CGN25 *Bainbridge*	BSQ	59	61	62

Displacement: 7,600 tons standard; 8,600 tons full load

Dimensions: 172.5m × 17.6m × 7.8m

Armament:
Two quadruple Harpoon SSM launchers
Two twin Standard MR SAM launchers
One eight-cell ASROC AS launcher
Two triple AS torpedo tubes

Machinery:
Two PWC reactors
Two sets geared steam turbines, 60,000shp
Twin shafts

Speed: 30kts

Bainbridge slightly predates the 'Leahy's' but she is, nevertheless, one of the same type and with an identi-cal armament disposition on a hull necessarily some 10m longer to accommodate an experimental nuclear power plant. With the remainder of the group having 'macks', her lack of funnel does not so readily betray her propulsion system. She has to be seen as a highly successful experiment as, although she was meant to be something of a prototype for a large frigate, she proved to be the beginning of the new cruiser genre, in place of the *Long Beach* which remained a 'one-off'. In spite of the bulk of her propulsion system, however, only 60,000hp were available at the shafts, barely two-thirds that developed by the steam-turbine units, which has resulted in her being considerably slower. Though she underwent an AAW up-rating 1974-76, she retains her SM-1 Standard ERs and it will be interesting to see if she will be given the longer-range SM-2s as a guarantee of her future or whether, as a prototype, her span will be comparatively short.

Leahy   Cruiser   *USA*

	Builders	LD	L	C
CG16 *Leahy*	BIW	59	61	62
CG17 *Harry E. Yarnell*	BIW	60	61	63
CG18 *Worden*	BIW	60	62	63
CG19 *Dale*	NYW	60	62	63
CG20 *Richmond K. Turner*	NYS	61	63	64
CG21 *Gridley*	PSB	60	61	63
CG22 *England*	TSS	60	62	63
CG23 *Halsey*	SFD	60	62	63
CG24 *Reeves*	PSD	60	62	64

Displacement: 5,670 tons standard; 7,800 tons full load

Dimensions: 162.5m × 16.8m × 7.5m

Armament:
Two quadruple Harpoon SSM launchers
Two twin-arm Standard ER SAM launchers
One eight-cell ASROC AS launcher
Two Vulcan/Phalanx CIWS
Two triple AS torpedo tubes

Machinery:
Two geared steam turbines, 85,000shp
Twin shafts

Speed: 33kts

Contemporary with the extensive 'Adams' class GM destroyers, the 'Leahy' design was aimed at producing a large, weatherly escort for a carrier group. Thus, where the 'Adams' is still recognisably a destroyer, the 'Leahy' introduced a new class of combatant which, though first classed as a frigate has, since 1975, been elevated to the status of cruiser. (This problem of categorisation is not unknown elsewhere, for instance the Royal Navy's 'Counties'.)

The first noticeable departure was from the long sheerline of generations of flush-decked destroyers to a higher freeboard with a single level drop aft to the quarterdeck. Besides improving seakeeping qualities, the design gives a useful discontinuity for the incor-poration of reload facilities for the after Standard MR launcher. The forward launcher of this 'double-ended' design requires a distinctive 'glacis'-style structure for the purpose.

Being dedicated carrier escorts, their bias is very much to AA defence, a bias enhanced further in AAW updates from 1967-72. Their early anti-ship defences all rested entirely upon two twin 3in mountings but these have all been superseded by two of the ubi-quitous Harpoon quadruple launchers.

145

Harry E. Yarnell, 'Leahy' class; note Harpoon abaft boats. Mike Lennon

AA strength has been bought also at the expense of AS potential. Though a pad is sited right aft, no helicopter is carried — the carrier will provide such support by a hull-mounted SQS-23 sonar of comparatively limited performance.

Another innovation in the class was the 'mack', a combined mast and stack. With tripod masts becoming ever more heavily braced and loaded, this was a sound departure for it proved a solid, vibration-free base for

antennas and a protection for vulnerable waveguides and cables.

The comprehensive array of antennas topside speak much for the ships' functions. A TACAN beacon tops the pole extension to the mainmast with a 3D search antenna, an SPS 48 on the foremast. Paired SPS55 fire control directors are sited at either end for tracking and illumination, radars developed originally to work with the beam-riding Terrier SAM.

DDG-51 ('Burke' class) Destroyer *USA*

	Builders	LD	L	C	Armament:
DDG51 *Arleigh Burke*	—	—	—	85	Two vertical launch systems, capable of firing Standard MR SAM, Harpoon SSM, and probably ASROC AS rounds
DDG 52-54 FY1987	—	—	—	—	Tomahawk SSMs
DDG55-99 Proposed	—	—	—	—	One 5in (127mm) gun

Displacement: 8,500 tons full load
Dimensions: 156m × 18.3m × 6m

Armament:
Two vertical launch systems, capable of firing Standard MR SAM, Harpoon SSM, and probably ASROC AS rounds
Tomahawk SSMs
One 5in (127mm) gun
One/two Vulcan/Phalanx CIWS
Two triple AS torpedo tubes

Arleigh Burke, DDG-51 class.
US Navy Official

Machinery:
Four gas turbines 80,000shp
Twin shafts
Speed: 30kts

Though the artist's impression shows what appears to be an Aegis installation in the bridge structure, the DDG51s are less capable than the 'Ticonderogas' and are designed to work in conjunction with them. About 50 ships are planned for the class, which is designed to replace the 30 ships of the 'Belknap', 'Leahy' and 'Coontz' classes, as well as further buttressing of the continuously diminishing number of hulls in the US Navy's destroyer force. Innovative steps for the USN, but standard for RN ships designed 'in-house', are the adoption of steel topsides and a built-in ability to operate in areas of heavy fallout.

Long Beach   Nuclear-powered cruiser   *USA*

	Builders	LD	L	C
CGN9 *Long Beach*	BSQ	57	59	61

Displacement: 14,200 tons standard; 15,550 tons full load
Dimensions: 219.9m × 22.3m × 9.2m
Armament:
Two quadruple Harpoon SSM launchers
Two twin Standard ER SAM launchers
One eight-cell ASROC AS launcher
Two 5in (127mm) guns (2 × 1)
Two Vulcan/Phalanx CIWS
Two triple AS torpedo tubes
Machinery:
Two PWC reactors
Two geared steam turbines, 80,000shp
Twin shafts
Speed: 30kts

Long Beach, *picture before rebuild.*
US Navy Official

Conceived as the 'cruiser' element of the three-ship nuclear squadron of the late 1950s. Long Beach proved ultimately to be no more than a final version of the WW2 cruiser concept, while the smallest of the three, the 'frigate' Bainbridge, proved to be the forerunner of cruisers to come. From the outset, the exact role of the ship was rather vague — being the world's first nuclear-powered surface warship, she needed to have strike power to suit her image. Guns were at that time, mistakenly, believed to be subjects for histories and an all-missile armament would herald the future shape of the fleet. Not only would she have the intermediate and shorter ranged Talos and Terrier SAM systems but also the cumbersome Regulus II, a cruise missile with a 1,000-mile potential. This weapon died in favour of the ballistic Polaris, the ship being re-designed to deploy these. With building costs rocketing, however, and the feasibility of the less-vulnerable Polaris-armed SSBNs about to be proved, it was decided to give the ship a second Terrier system. Thus the final disposition was a pair of twin-armed Terrier launchers forward and a Talos at the forward end of the wide quarterdeck that acted as a helicopter landing pad. Like the *Enterprise,* she featured the enormous 'bilboard' arrays of the Scanfar radar built into the four sides of a square bridge structure. Hardly a year after completion two single 5in guns were added in the waist, it being realised that the ship had no means of dealing with minor surface targets.

In the mid 1970s, it was proposed to convert *Long Beach* to the first Aegis platform in the course of a 1978-81 mid-life refit. Considering that she was of a good size for the task, it was somewhat surprising that these plans were cancelled. On completion of this refit in 1982, she will emerge with two Standard ER systems and the obsolete Talos and its associated SPG-49 directors removed. She will offer only one 5in gun more than the weapon fit put into the much smaller 'Virginias' — and still lack their two LAMPS helicopters. Her 120-round Standard magazine would be of benefit in a prolonged shoot-out but the ship still has the air of having no real function. (Perhaps a CVLN?) The last two CG conversions, *Albany* and *Chicago,* are laid up awaiting disposal.

Des Moines   Cruiser   *USA*

	Builders	LD	L	C
CA134 *Des Moines*	BSF	45	46	48
CA139 *Salem*	BSF	45	47	49

Displacement: 17,000 tons standard; 21,500 tons full load
Dimensions: 218.4m × 23.3m × 7.8m

'Des Moines' class. Mike Lennon

Armament:
Nine 8in (203mm) guns (3×3)
Twelve 5in (127mm) guns (6×2)
Sixteen 3in (76mm) guns (8×2)
Machinery:
Four sets geared steam turbines, 120,000shp
Four shafts
Speed: 33kts
Disposal: Newport News (CA148) — 1978

The three units completed, of a planned class of 12, represented the ultimate development of the classic cruiser. Developed directly from the preceding 'Oregon City' class, they feature the armament layout that was virtually standard at this time, the main battery split between two triple turrets forward and one aft, with both ends superfired by a twin 5in 38 with two more of these gunhouses at either beam. Further, these vessels were completed late enough to incorporate 3in AA armament from the outset, carrying 20 or 22 in twin mountings. With this variety of major calibres on board they seem to have reached a point in design analogous to that of the all-big-gun 'Dreadnought' in the same way that the missile-armed ship usurped the role of the big cruisers.

Newport News was much used as a flagship and served near continuously until her retirement, but the remaining pair have each seen little more than a decade in actual commission and, like the 'Iowas', offer potential. Their fully automatic guns, with cased ammunition, required the large hull which, itself, is well protected.

Never modernised, they would be a liability in their present form, good only for shore bombardment support with no viable self-defence capacity. Possible updating could see the secondary and tertiary armament stripped out, retaining only the centreline superimposed 5in gunhouses. Besides creating more platforms for Tomahawk, it would be possible to mount Harpoon on a scale generous enough for firing in the salvoes necessary to guarantee penetration of an enemy defence system. This would involve a vertical launch system which could replace the after 8in turret (stability problems permitting) and building facilities into the extreme after end for a brace of LAMPS helicopters for long-range targeting. With their massive steam plants and enormous number of guns, their complement, at over 1,300, is about three times that of the 'Virginias'. Although this would be reduced by a part-missile armament it makes the prospect of their re-employment less attractive.

Spruance/Kidd Destroyer *USA*

	Builders	LD	L	C
a) 'Spruance' class				
DD963 *Spruance*	ISP	72	73	75
DD964 *Paul. F. Foster*	ISP	73	74	76
DD965 *Kinkaid*	ISP	73	74	76
DD966 *Hewitt*	ISP	73	74	76
DD967 *Elliott*	ISP	73	74	76
DD968 *Arthur W. Radford*	ISP	74	75	77
DD969 *Peterson*	ISP	74	75	77
DD970 *Caron*	ISP	74	75	77
DD971 *David R. Ray*	ISP	74	75	77
DD972 *Oldendorf*	ISP	74	75	78
DD973 *John Young*	ISP	75	76	78
DD974 *Comte de Grasse*	ISP	75	76	78
DD975 *O'Brien*	ISP	75	76	77
DD976 *Merrill*	ISP	75	76	78
DD977 *Briscoe*	ISP	75	76	78
DD978 *Stump*	ISP	75	77	78
DD979 *Conolly*	ISP	75	77	78

	Builders	LD	L	C
DD980 *Moosbrugger*	ISP	75	77	78
DD981 *John Hancock*	ISP	76	77	79
DD982 *Nicholson*	ISP	76	77	79
DD983 *John Rodgers*	ISP	76	78	79
DD984 *Leftwich*	ISP	76	78	79
DD985 *Cushing*	ISP	76	78	79
DD986 *Harry W. Hill*	ISP	77	78	79
DD987 *O'Bannon*	ISP	77	78	79
DD988 *Thorn*	ISP	77	78	80
DD989 *Deyo*	ISP	77	79	80
DD990 *Ingersoll*	ISP	77	79	80
DD991 *Fife*	ISP	78	79	80
DD992 *Fletcher*	ISP	78	79	80
DD997 *Hayler*	ISP	80	81	83
b) *'Kidd' class*				
DDG993 *Kidd* (ex-*Kouroosh*)	ISP	78	79	81
DDG994 *Callaghan* (ex-*Daryush*)	ISP	78	79	81
DDG995 *Scott* (ex-*Nader*)	ISP	79	80	81
DDG996 *Chandler* (ex-*Anoushirvan*)	ISP	79	80	81

Displacement:
a) 5,850 tons light, 7,800 tons full load
b) 6,200 tons light, 8,300 tons full load
Dimensions: 171.7m × 55.1m × 8.8/9.1m
Armament:
a) Two quadruple Harpoon SSM launchers
One eight-cell Sea Sparrow SAM launcher
Two 5in (127mm) guns (2 × 1)
Two Vulcan/Phalanx CIWS
Two triple AS torpedo tubes
b) Two launchers for Standard ER/ASROC
Two 5in (217mm) guns (2 × 1)
Two Vulcan/Phalanx CIWS
Two triple AS torpedo tubes
Machinery:
Four gas turbines, 80,000shp
Twin shafts
Speed: 33kts
Aircraft: Two LAMPS helicopters with hangar

This extensive group of ships was produced to replace the mass of WW2 built destroyers which, even after FRAM conversions, had reached the end of their useful lives as first-line ships. Though they could not be replaced on a hull-for-hull basis, the number involved still made worthwhile the establishment of a purpose-built 'ship facility' for their series construction. While offering great benefits, it also posed problems in labour allocation and funding, the latter being particularly troublesome in a programme lasting over a decade of high inflation.

The result is an excellent ship, surprisingly the first major units of the US Navy to be gas-turbine propelled. Though criticised initially for their lack of punch when compared with, say, a Soviet 'Kresta II' of similar size, they have the generously-scaled capacity to be modified considerably over their career. They have the size, speed and weapons fit to act as the ASW component of a task group, complementing the nuclear-powered AAW cruisers. As such, they have an eight-cell ASROC launcher forward with two dozen reloads, AS torpedo tubes mounted within the superstructure for last-ditch defence and, most importantly, a pair of LAMPS helicopters. The latter can carry sensors as well as AS weaponry supplementing the SQS-53 sonar sited in an enormous bulb at the ship's forefoot. Beyond this weapons fit the standard Spruance carries only two 5in guns, a Sea Sparrow point-defence missile system and two CIWS. The latter are still being fitted in fact, along with two quadruple Harpoon SSM launchers, and it will be several years before the class is uniformly armed. Tomahawk is planned for the future, probably sharing a launcher with Harpoon.

The four General Electric LM2500 gas turbines are in two separate spaces and their exhausts are via square stacks echeloned to the sides of the ship, an arrangement that also keeps the hot gasses clear.

The four 'Kidd' class destroyers were ordered

originally for the Iranian navy, their cancellation being a windfall for the USN. All are double-ended missile ships with two Standard ER/ASROC launchers earning them the 'DDG' categorisation.

In association with these is the distinctive rectangular antenna of the SPS 48, 3D search radar on the mainmast. The Mark 26 launchers occupy the sites of the ASROC and Sea Sparrow in the Spruance type, the proportions of the ship allowing this degree of inter-changeability, marking a step on the road to the fully modularised weapon systems and sensors which make sound economic sense if sufficient hulls are ever to be provided in an era of ever-tighter defence spending.

Charles F. Adams   Destroyer   *USA*

	Builders	LD	L	C
DDG2 *Charles F. Adams*	BIW	58	59	60
DDG3 *John King*	BIW	58	60	61
DDG4 *Lawrence*	NYS	58	60	62
DDG5 *Claude V. Ricketts*	NYS	59	60	62
DDG6 *Barney*	NYS	59	60	62
DDG7 *Henry B. Wilson*	DSC	58	59	60
DDG8 *Lynde McCormick*	DSC	58	60	61
DDG9 *Towers*	TSS	58	59	61
DDG10 *Sampson*	BIW	59	60	61
DDG11 *Sellers*	BIW	59	60	61
DDG12 *Robinson*	DSC	59	60	61
DDG13 *Hoel*	DSC	59	60	62
DDG14 *Buchanan*	TSS	59	60	62
DDG15 *Berkeley*	NYS	59	60	62
DDG16 *Joseph Strauss*	NYS	60	61	63
DDG17 *Conyngham*	NYS	61	62	63
DDG18 *Semmes*	ASN	60	61	62
DDG19 *Tattnall*	ASN	60	61	63
DDG20 *Goldsborough*	PSB	61	61	63
DDG21 *Cochrane*	PSB	61	62	64
DDG22 *Benjamin Stoddert*	PSB	62	63	64
DDG23 *Richard E. Byrd*	TSS	61	62	64
DDG24 *Waddell*	TSS	62	63	64

Displacement: 3,370 tons standard; 4,500 tons full load
Dimensions: 133.2m × 14.3m × 6.1m
Armament:
Two quadruple Harpoon SSM launchers
One Tartar SAM launcher
One eight-cell ASROC launcher
Two 5in (217mm) guns (2 × 1)
Two triple AS torpedo tubes

Charles F. Adams. Mike Lennon

Machinery:
Two sets geared steam turbines, 70,000shp
Twin shafts
Speed: 31kts

The speed at which the SAM has developed is typified by the 'Adams' class destroyers. Originally designed as gun-armed, ASW destroyers, improved 'Forrest Sher-mans', the first batch of eight were given the pennants DD962-9. The decision to fit them with the Tartar system was made early enough for modifications to be made to hull dimensions. Reallocated DDG numbers (starting at DDG2 because the 'Gearing' class con-version *Gyatt* was acting as trials ship, carrying DDG1) those up to and including Buchanan were given a Mk II Mod O twin-armed launcher and the remainder the improved single-armed Mk 13 Mod O. The 10-mile Tartar has since been replaced by the smaller, but 25-mile ranged, Standard MR. About 40 rounds are carried.

The main AS system is the amidships-mounted ASROC and, although the RIM-66A version of the Standard MR can be fired from ASROC cells as an SSM, the class is also being fitted with Harpoon. No-point-defence system is fitted but a multi-round exper-imental Chaparral launcher has been evaluated by two of the class.

During the 1980s the class was to have been extensively modernised to aim at a life extended to 35 years. Funds for these plans were cancelled by the Carter administration and it now looks as though the later 10 hulls (DDG15-24) will get a less ambitious up-date and the remainder will begin to be retired as they approach 30 years of age.

Three 'Adams', suitably modified, were built also for each of the Australian and West German navies.

Coontz; note quadruple Harpoon near after funnel.
Mike Lennon

Coontz   Destroyer

USA

	Builders	LD	L	C
DDG37 *Farragut*	BSQ	57	58	60
DDG38 *Luce* (ex-*Dewey*)	BSQ	57	58	61
DDG39 *MacDonough*	BSQ	58	59	61
DDG40 *Coontz*	PSD	57	58	60
DDG41 *King*	PSD	57	58	60
DDG42 *Mahan*	SFD	57	59	60
DDG43 *Dahlgren*	PND	58	60	61
DDG44 *William V. Pratt*	PND	58	60	61
DDG45 *Dewey*	BIW	57	58	59
DDG46 *Preble*	BIW	57	59	60

Displacement: 4,700 tons standard; 5,850 tons full load
Dimensions: 156.3m × 15.9m × 7.5m
Armament:
Two quadruple Harpoon SSM launchers
One Standard ER SAM launcher
One 5in (127mm) gun
One eight-celled ASROC launcher
Two triple AS torpedo tubes
Machinery:
Two sets geared steam turbines, 85,000shp
Twin shafts
Speed: 33kts

Conceived as uprated versions of the all-gun large frigates of the 'Mitscher' class, the 'Coontz' were re-designated DLG before the first was even laid down. In the process, two of the original three 5in guns were replaced by ASROC and a Terrier launcher. *Farragut*, one of the earliest of the class to be completed has a forward extension of the bridge to accommodate an ASROC reload facility, after the style of the 'Mitschers', but the remainder were not so fitted. Although 20 of the class were planned, developments were rapid enough to enforce a revamping of the second half of the programme, which became the 'Leahy' class.

The 'Coontz' hull was the last to exhibit the long sheerline of generations of destroyers, subsequent classes having flatter sheers and a drop in level aft to a quarterdeck. Their profiles are most distinctive, with lofty capped funnels and massive lattice structures to bear an array of antennas far more comprehensive than any ships of the size had ever carried, the large SPS 48, 3-D search unit having to be distanced from the SPS-37 surface search. Examination will show that the introduction of the 'Mack' in succeeding classes made sense.

All have had an extensive AAW modernisation, the Terrier being up-graded to the SM-2 version of the Standard ER. Improved guidance radars were installed and the obsolete 3in guns removed.

Though their all-round capability is good, the 'Coontz' share with all too many ships of their size a vulnerability to air attack that has succeeded in getting to close quarters, particularly at low level. A compact 'look-down' radar might be a useful addition to an, already overloaded, LAMPS helicopter. Even in this event, the 'Coontz' belong to the LAMP-less generation that could not take advantage of it, only a pad for use in VERTREP being provided right aft.

Forrest Sherman   Destroyer

USA

	Builders	LD	L	C	Con
a) *GM conversions*					
DDG31 (ex-DD936) *Decatur*	BSQ	54	55	56	67
DDG32 (ex-DD932) *John Paul Jones*	BIW	54	55	56	67
DDG33 (ex-DD949) *Parsons*	ISP	57	58	59	67
DDG34 (ex-DD947) *Somers*	BIW	57	58	59	68
b) *AS conversions*					
DD933 *Barry*	BIW	54	55	56	68

	Builders	LD	L	C	Conv
DD937 *Davis*	BSQ	55	56	57	70
DD938 *Jonas Ingram*	BSQ	55	56	57	70
DD940 *Manley*	BIW	55	56	57	71
DD941 *Du Pont*	BIW	55	56	57	70
DD943 *Blandy*	BSQ	56	56	57	70
DD948 *Morton*	ISP	57	58	59	70
DD950 *Richard S. Edwards*	PSB	56	57	59	71
c) *Unconverted*					
DD931 *Forrest Sherman*	BIW	53	55	55	—
DD942 *Bigelow*	BIW	55	57	57	—
DD944 *Mullinnix*	BSQ	56	57	58	—
DD945 *Hull*	BIW	56	57	58	—
DD946 *Edson*	BIW	56	58	59	—
DD951 *Turner Joy*	PSB	57	58	59	—

John Paul Jones, *'Forrest Sherman' DDG.* Mike Lennon

Displacement:
a) 2,950 tons standard; 4,150 tons full load
b) 3,000 tons standard; 4,200 tons full load
c) 2,800 tons standard; 3,950 tons full load
Dimensions: 127.5m × 13.8m × 6.9m
Armament:
a) One Tartar SAM launcher
One 5in (127mm) gun
One eight-cell ASROC launcher
Two triple AS torpedo tubes
b) Three 5in (127mm) guns (3×1)
Two 3in (76mm) guns (1×2) in some
Two triple AS torpedo tubes
Machinery:
Two sets geared steam turbines, 70,000shp
Twin shafts
Speed: 33kts

These 18 ships were the first destroyers to be built to embody all the lessons learned by the US Navy in WW2. Compared with earlier destroyers, they were longer by over eight metres and had a marked increase in freeboard forward. This resulted directly in having to put any superimposed main calibre weapon aft. These were single, 54 calibre weapons in place of the earlier twinned 38-calibre guns; though fewer, however, they had improved range and rate of fire, and threw a heavier projectile. Superfiring 'A' gun was a twinned

3in mounting flanked by Hedgehog AS spigot mortars. Speed was also important as the submarine was rapidly increasing in submerged speed and endurance while the helicopter was not yet in general use at sea. Improved stability was achieved through an extensive use of aluminium alloy in the superstructure.

The late 1960s saw the conversion of four ships to a GM role. All guns except 'A' mounting were landed and a single-armed Terrier launcher added aft, over a 40-round magazine. Forward of this, a sizeable house remains as a memory of the ill-fated DASH AS helicopter system, which would have complemented the eight-round ASROC launcher abaft the after funnel. A large lattice mainmast was built around the after funnel, to support the SPS 48 3-D search antenna. In spite of the increase in topweight that these modifications must have added, there is talk of adding Harpoon.

This modification must have been cramped compared with the Tartar installation on the purpose-built 'Adams' for further plans of similar conversions were dropped in favour of a group of eight less-ambitious AS conversions.

In these, both the 'A' and 'Y' guns were retained, the ASROC being sited further aft, abaft the structure that may include a magazine. Two Mk 32 triple AS torpedo tubes were sited forward of the bridge and a VDS right aft, no attempt being made to include DASH.

Even these more modest improvements appear to have been difficult for the conversions on the final six

were cancelled. One of these, *Hull*, has since conducted extensive trials on the new lightweight 8in gun. Although successful, the project was cancelled in 1979, the plans for issue to a variety of major classes being dropped. With continuing improvements in guided projectiles, this would have been an accurate, versatile, and inexpensive weapon and its abandonment would seem ill-judged.

All the unconverted units are likely to be assigned to naval reserve training to replace the WW2 vintage destroyers now for disposal. As newer ships commission the AS conversions are likely to follow suit.

Perry Frigate   *USA*

	Builders	LD	L	C
FFG 7 *Oliver Hazard Perry*	BIW	75	76	77
FFG 8 *McInerney*	BIW	77	78	79
FFG 9 *Wadsworth*	TSP	77	78	80
FFG10 *Duncan*	TSS	77	78	80
FFG11 *Clark*	BIW	78	79	80
FFG12 *George Philip*	TSP	77	78	80
FFG13 *Samuel Eliot Morison*	BIW	78	79	80
FFG14 *Sides*	TSP	78	79	81
FFG15 *Estocin*	BIW	79	79	81
FFG16 *Clifton Sprague*	BIW	79	80	81
FFG19 *John A. Moore*	TSP	78	79	81
FFG20 *Antrim*	TSS	78	79	81
FFG21 *Flatley*	BIW	79	80	81
FFG22 *Fahrion*	TSS	78	79	81
FFG23 *Lewis B. Puller*	TSP	79	80	81
FFG24 *Jack Williams*	BIW	80	80	81
FFG25 *Copeland*	TSP	79	80	82
FFG26 *Galery*	BIW	80	81	81
FFG27 *Mahlon S. Tisdale*	TSP	80	81	82
FFG28 *Boone*	TSS	79	80	82
FFG29 *Stephen W. Groves*	BIW	80	81	82
FFG30 *Reid*	TSP	80	81	82
FFG31 *Stark*	TSS	79	80	82
FFG32 *John L. Hall*	BIW	81	81	82
FFG33 *Jarrett*	TSP	81	81	83
FFG34 *Aubrey Fitch*	BIW	81	81	82
FFG36 *Underwood*	BIW	81	82	83
FFG37 *Crommelin*	TSS	80	81	83
FFG38 *Curts*	TSP	81	82	83
FFG39 *Doyle*	BIW	81	82	83
FFG40 *Halyburton*	TSS	80	81	82
FFG41 *McClusky*	TSP	81	82	83
FFG42 *Klakring*	BIW	82	82	83
FFG43 *Thach*	TSP	82	82	84
FFG45 *Dewart*	BIW	82	83	83
FFG46 *Rentz*	TSP	82	83	84
FFG47 *Nicholas*	BIW	82	83	84
FFG48 *Vandergrift*	TSS	81	82	84
FFG49 *Robert G. Bradley*	BIW	83	83	84
FFG50 *Taylor*	BIW	83	84	84
FFG51 *Gary*	TSP	82	83	85
FFG52 *Carr*	TSS	83	83	85
FFG53 *Hawes*	BIW	83	84	85
FFG54 *Ford*	TSP	83	84	85
FFG55	BIW	84	84	85

FFG56-58 Approved
FFG59-70 Proposed

Displacement: 3,600 tons full load
Dimensions: 135.6m × 13.7m × 7.5m
Armament:
One Standard MR/Harpoon launcher
One 76mm DP gun

McInerney, *'Perry' class, fitted with extended counter for LAMPS III evaluation.*   US Navy Official

One Harpoon/Phalanx CIWS
Two triple AS torpedo tubes
Machinery:
Two gas turbines, 41,000shp
One shaft
Speed: 28.5kts
Aircraft:Two LAMPS helicopters with hangar

Following-on to the extensive 'Knox' class AS frigate programme, the 'Perrys' are recognisably derivatives but with a very different fit for a GP role. Originally classified as Patrol Frigates (PF) they were later designated FFG, a logical Guided Missile Frigate label to follow the six 'Brookes'. The hull is similar to that of the 'Knox', incorporating the forward bulwark from the outset to improve dryness. Where the 'Knox' has been heavily caned for its lack of speed, the 'Perry' has had a 16% increase in power by adopting a pair of LM2500 gas turbines but, on the same waterline length, the beam has been clipped by about 0.7m to improve the lines further. This would seem questionable for, where the speed has been improved by little more than a knot, the weight of machinery below has been decreased and the addition of a second helicopter has increased topweight, all doing little to improve stability. One casualty has been the only medium calibre gun, where the US Navy's traditional 5in (127mm) has been

superseded by the OTO-Melara 76mm. Built under licence, this calibre gun is inadequate for a GP frigate, its performance being further reduced by its situation in the only spot available, nearly amidships on the roof of the long, box-like superstructure. Its forward arcs are limited by the array of electronics whose lattice towers are perched like a strange collection of apparent afterthoughts ahead of it. Immediately abaft the gun is the stack, which has, perforce, been reduced to a low pot, exuding gases hot enough to do the CIWS sited about 14m further aft — no good at all.

The uptakes divide the forward end of the double hangar, the extra helicopter being bought at the expense of ASROC. Forward is a single-armed Mark 13

Mod 14 launcher for firing both Standard MR and Harpoon rounds, a mixed load of about 40 of which are carried.

Another 'Knox' problem, poor manoeuvrability at low speeds, has been countered by the provision of a pair of retractable low power azimuthal thrusters, which also provide emergency propulsion.

Lacking the enormous bulb of the SQS-26 sonar, which gives the 'Knox' a tendency to slam, the 'Perrys' have the smaller, keel-mounted SQS-56, with the later addition of the TACTAS towed array planned. Besides the Italian-designed gun, the class features also the Mark 92 weapons control system, an Americanised version of the Dutch HSA WM-28.

Brooke/Garcia Frigate   *USA*

	Builders	LD	L	C
(a) 'Brooke' class				
FFG1 Brooke	LSC	62	63	66
FFG2 Ramsey	LSC	63	63	67
FFG3 Schofield	LSC	63	63	68
FFG4 Talbot	BIW	64	66	67
FFG5 Richard L. Page	BIW	65	66	67
FFG6 Julius A. Furer	BIW	65	66	67
(b) 'Garcia' class				
FF1040 Garcia	BSS	62	63	64
FF1041 Bradley	BSS	63	64	65
FF1043 Edward McDonnell	ASN	63	64	65
FF1044 Brumby	ASN	63	64	65
FF1045 Davidson	ASN	63	64	65
FF1047 Voge	DSC	63	65	66
FF1048 Sample	LSC	63	64	68
FF1049 Koelsch	DSC	64	65	67
FF1050 Albert David	LSC	64	64	68
FF1051 O'Callaghan	DSC	64	65	68
FF1098 Glover	BIW	63	65	65

Displacement: 2,650 tons standard; 3,250 tons full load
Dimensions: 126.3m × 13.5m × 7.5m

Armament:
One Standard MR SAM launcher (in 'Brookes')
One eight-cell ASROC launcher
One 5in (127mm) gun (two in 'Garcias')
Two triple AS torpedo tubes
Machinery:
One geared steam turbine, 35,000shp
One shaft
Speed: 27kts
Aircraft: One LAMPS helicopter and hangar

Stemming directly from the prototype pair of 'Bronsteins', the 'Brookes' and 'Garcias' are mutually nearly identical except that the former group has a lightweight Standard MR launcher immediately forward of the hangar where the latter group have a second 5in gun. When first built they were classed as DEG and DE but, in the general re-classification of 1975, assumed FFG and FF. Though 19 'Brookes' were planned, their numbers were curtailed by cost, the 'Garcias' being increased in numbers as partial compensation. Though their SAM magazine capacity is small, the 'Brookes' must be considered as useful escorts in as much as their ASW fit includes a LAMPS helicopter (in place of the original abortive DASH installation, an ASROC

Garcia. Mike Lennon

launcher (re-loadable automatically in FFG4-6), two triple Mk 32 AS torpedo tubes (the fixed Mk 25s firing through the transom have been removed), and a large SQS-26 bow sonar.

The 'Bronsteins' lacked speed, their single screw being driven by only 20,000shp and this deficiency was partially rectified by an increase in power of 75% in the 'Brooke'/'Garcia' classes. This, together with full helicopter facilities, caused a 13m increase in length, in spite of the installation of compact boilers of advanced design which, themselves, have not been entirely trouble-free.

From the recognition standpoint, this group have a pronounced hangar aft, lacking in the 'Bronsteins', but have a far shorter 'mack', than the following 'Knox' class ships.

Glover acts as a trials ship and changes appearance quite drastically according to fit.

Knox Frigate

	Builders	LD	L	C
F1052 *Knox*	TSS	65	66	69
F1053 *Roark*	TSS	66	67	69
F1054 *Gray*	TSS	66	67	70
F1055 *Hepburn*	TSP	66	67	69
F1056 *Connole*	ASN	67	68	69
F1057 *Rathburne*	LSC	68	69	70
F1058 *Meyercord*	TSP	66	67	69
F1059 *W. S. Sims*	ASN	67	69	70
F1060 *Lang*	TSP	67	68	70
F1061 *Patterson*	ASN	67	69	70
F1062 *Whipple*	TSS	67	68	70
F1063 *Reasoner*	LSC	69	70	71
F1064 *Lockwood*	TSS	67	68	70
F1065 *Stein*	LSC	70	70	72
F1066 *Marvin Shields*	TSS	68	69	71
F1067 *Francis Hammond*	TSP	67	68	70
F1068 *Vreeland*	ASN	68	69	70
F1069 *Bagley*	LSC	70	71	72
F1070 *Downes*	TSS	68	69	71
F1071 *Badger*	TSS	68	68	70
F1072 *Blakeley*	ASN	68	69	70
F1073 *Robert E. Peary*	LSC	70	71	72
F1074 *Harold E. Holt*	TSP	68	69	71
F1075 *Trippe*	ASN	68	69	70
F1076 *Fanning*	TSP	68	70	70
F1077 *Ouellet*	ASN	69	70	70
F1078 *Joseph Hewes*	ASN	69	70	71
F1079 *Bowen*	ASN	69	70	71
F1080 *Paul*	ASN	69	70	71
F1081 *Aylwin*	ASN	69	70	71
F1082 *Elmer Montgomery*	ASN	70	70	71
F1083 *Cook*	ASN	70	70	71
F1084 *McCandless*	ASN	70	71	71
F1085 *Donald B. Beary*	ASN	70	71	72
F1086 *Brewton*	ASN	70	71	72
F1087 *Kirk*	ASN	70	71	72
F1088 *Barbey*	ASN	71	71	72
F1089 *Jesse L. Brown*	ASN	71	72	73
F1090 *Ainsworth*	ASN	71	72	73
F1091 *Miller*	ASN	71	72	73
F1092 *Thomas C. Hart*	ASN	71	72	73
F1093 *Cappodanno*	ASN	71	72	73
F1094 *Pharris*	ASN	72	72	74
F1095 *Truett*	ASN	72	73	74
F1096 *Valdez*	ASN	72	73	74
F1097 *Moinester*	ASN	72	73	74

Displacement: 3,010 tons standard; 4,080 tons full load
Dimensions: 133.5m×14.3m×7.7m

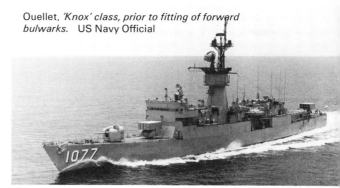

Ouellet, 'Knox' class, prior to fitting of forward bulwarks. US Navy Official

Armament:
Two quadruple Harpoon SSMs launchers
One eight-celled Sea Sparrow SAM launcher
One eight-celled ASROC launcher
One 5in (127mm) gun
Four fixed AS torpedo tubes
Machinery:
One geared steam turbine, 35,000shp
One shaft
Speed: 27kts
Aircraft: One LAMPS helicopter with hangar

Though much criticised for their lack of speed and manoeuvrability, this extensive class are excellent ASW platforms. Their AS punch is derived from a LAMPS helicopter, able to deploy both sensors and weapons, an ASROC 'pepperbox' forward and four fixed Mk 32 torpedo tubes, sited under cover in the superstructure. For their extensive range, they originally lacked capability in other directions. Point defence was added through the installation of a Sea Sparrow launcher right aft (*Downes*, only, has a NATO Sea Sparrow installation with a lighter launcher and distinctive Mk 91 'binocular' director). Somewhat inexplicably, considering the ships' prime role, some were modified to fire Harpoon or Standard missiles from cells of the ASROC launcher, the latter missile, indeed, requiring two cells to be converted to fire one round. This practice has probably ceased with the more general adoption of the quadruple Harpoon mounting.

The profile of the 'Knox' is dominated by the massive conical tower which encloses the uptakes from both boilers and supports the electronics. Though the hangar aft was configured originally to house the abortive DASH (Drone AS helicopter) it was later increased in

height and given a telescoping after end to accommodate a LAMPS (Light Airborne Multi-Purpose System) helicopter.

The primary sensor of the 'Knox' is the SQS-26 sonar, mounted in a bow dome of homeric proportions. Even though this attachment is partially flooded to achieve near neutral buoyancy, it causes the ships to be particularly wet forward and, they are, therefore, being fitted with spray chines and bow bulwarks to increase freeboard. In addition, all were fitted with a VDS, streamed through an aperture in the transom. This is being replaced by the new SQS-35 towed array known as TACTAS (Tactical Towed Array Sonar System), a series of passive sonars towed well astern to be clear of ship-induced noise.

Bronstein Frigate   USA

	Builders	LD	L	C
FF1037 Bronstein	ASN	61	62	63
FF1038 McCloy	ASN	61	62	63

Displacement: 2,350 tons standard; 2,650 tons full load
Dimensions: 113.3m × 12.3m × 7m
Armament:
Two 3in (76mm) guns (1 × 2)
One eight-celled ASROC launcher
Two triple AS torpedo tubes
Machinery:
One geared steam turbine, 20,000shp
One shaft
Speed: 25kts

Though bearing a superficial resemblance to the 'Garcias' and 'Brookes' that followed them, the two 'Bronsteins' can be easily recognised by a more compact superstructure and distinctive drop in level aft. They were intended for evaluation as new style ocean escorts, breaking away from the previous trend in destroyer escorts. The latter were really cut-down destroyers and the newcomers echoed the trends in Europe toward a more capacious frigate approach, long and with high freeboard for greater weatherliness.

Since the introduction of previous AS escorts, the US navy had adopted the low-frequency SQS-26 sonar for maximum range in deep water. This equipment had to be housed forward as low frequencies demand large transducer arrays, far too large for keel-mounted arrangements and the resulting fine forward end, with its strongly-raked bow, was introduced. To capitalise on the longer submarine detection ranges, possible with the new gear, two new stand-off weapons were introduced, the ASROC and the DASH helicopter. Of these, the former proved a great success, firing a half-ton solid fuelled rocket on a ballistic trajectory out to 10km with a payload of a Mark 46 torpedo or a nuclear depth charge, either of which would be released over the position computed to best intercept a submerged target. Unfortunately, the DASH had to be abandoned. The concept of a pilotless helicopter, controlled out to horizon range by the ship with a brace of AS torpedoes to be released on command, was a good one but, in practice, the aircraft proved to have a mind of its own.

As evaluated, the 'Bronsteins' established the need for a higher speed and a larger calibre main armament, both rectified in subsequent classes. A second twin 3-inch mounting on the quarterdeck was removed in favour of a cable drum and winch for an early version of a towed array.

Neither ship has been really updated and still lack even LAMPS facilities but were certainly successful in that their line of development can clearly be followed down to the 'Perrys'.

Bronstein; *note wash produced by bow sonar dome.*
Mike Lennon

Ohio. US Navy Official

Ohio Nuclear-powered ballistic missile submarine   *USA*

	Builders	LD	L	C
SSBN726 *Ohio*	GDG	76	79	81
SSBN727 *Michigan*	GDG	77	80	81
SSBN728 *Florida*	GDG	77	81	83
SSBN729 *Georgia*	GDG	79	81	84
SSBN730 *Rhode Island*	GDG	81	82	84
SSBN731 *Alabama*	GDG	81	83	85
SSBN732 —	GDG	—	—	85
SSBN733 —	GDG	—	—	—
SSBN734 —	GDG	—	—	—
SSBN735-740 Proposed				

Displacement: 16,600 tons surfaced; 18,700 tons submerged
Dimensions: 170.7m × 12.8m × 10.8m
Armament:
24 Trident C4 SLBMs
Four 21in (533mm) torpedo tubes
Machinery:
One PWC reactor
Two sets geared steam turbines, 60,000shp
One shaft
Speed: 22kts submerged

Monstrous though these boats are, their claim to being 'the largest ever' was rapidly eclipsed by the Soviet 'Typhoons'. That vessels of this size can operate at all is due to the range of their missiles, initially the 4,500-mile C-4 Trident with an almost certain later conversion to the D-5, capable of 6,000 miles. The submarines can, therefore, remain fairly close to home waters and still range their targets while keeping within a secure 'citadel' area. With a hull diameter of 12.8m, the 10.4m C-4 (interchangeable with the Poseidon C-3) would be contained within the hull but the D-5, some 3.5m longer, necessitates the launch tubes protruding upward into a hump-backed casing. With a launch weight exceeding 57 tonnes, these weapons are reported to have about two dozen separate vehicles in their MIRV heads, capable of saturating a defence system. The 'Ohios' are the first SSBNs to carry 24 such weapons, which not only gets more of them to sea but which is a simple matter in a hull whose enormous length was dictated by the required diameter.

Set well forward because of the amidships-mounted launch tubes and the need for the hydroplanes to be effective, the fin appears very small. So large is the hull that there are four decks forward, over the battery space. With a large sonar sphere set right in the bows, the defensive battery of four torpedo tubes is little forward of the fin. The large reactor and steam plant are located aft of amidships and develop nearly four times the power of that in earlier SSBNs.

Great delays have been experienced in the production of these vessels, hardly surprising, considering the enormous jump in size. Once built, however, they are planned to last for nearly a decade between re-corings and be capable of alternating 70-day periods with 25-day recreation and refit periods.

Lafayette Nuclear-powered ballistic missile submarine   *USA*

	Builders	LD	L	C	Poseidon Con	Trident Con
SSBN616 *Lafayette*	GDG	61	62	63	74	—
SSBN617 *Alexander Hamilton*	GDG	61	62	63	75	—
SSBN619 *Andrew Jackson*	MID	61	62	63	75	—
SSBN620 *John Adams*	PDN	61	63	64	75	—
SSBN622 *James Monroe*	NNS	61	62	63	77	—
SSBN623 *Nathan Hale*	GDG	61	63	63	75	—
SSBN624 *Woodrow Wilson*	MID	61	63	63	75	—
SSBN625 *Henry Clay*	NNS	61	62	64	77	—
SSBN626 *Daniel Webster*	GDG	61	63	64	77	—
SSBN627 *James Madison*	NNS	62	63	64	70	81

Woodrow Wilson, *'Lafayette' class SSBN.*
US Navy Official

	Builders	LD	L	C	Poseidon Con	Trident Con
SSBN628 *Tecumseh*	GDG	62	63	64	71	—
SSBN629 *Daniel Boone*	MID	62	63	64	70	80
SSBN630 *John C. Calhoun*	NNS	62	63	64	71	80
SSBN631 *Ulysses S. Grant*	GDG	62	63	64	70	—
SSBN632 *von Steuben*	NNS	62	63	64	70	81
SSBN633 *Casimir Pulaski*	GDG	63	64	64	71	82
SSBN634 *Stonewall Jackson*	MID	62	63	64	71	81
SSBN635 *Sam Rayburn*	NNS	62	63	64	71	—
SSBN636 *Nathanael Greene*	PND	62	64	64	71	—
SSBN640 *Benjamin Franklin*	GDG	63	64	65	72	81
SSBN641 *Simon Bolivar*	NNS	63	64	65	72	80
SSBN642 *Kamehameha*	MID	63	65	65	72	—
SSBN643 *George Bancroft*	GDG	63	65	66	72	81
SSBN644 *Lewis and Clark*	NNS	63	64	65	72	—
SSBN645 *James K. Polk*	GDG	63	65	66	72	—
SSBN654 *George C. Marshall*	NNS	64	65	66	73	—
SSBN655 *Henry L. Stimpson*	GDG	64	65	66	73	80
SSBN656 *George Washington Carver*	NNS	64	65	66	73	—
SSBN657 *Francis Scott Key*	GDG	64	66	66	73	78
SSBN658 *Mariano G. Vallejo*	MID	64	65	66	73	80
SSBN659 *Will Rogers*	GDG	65	66	67	74	—

Displacement: 7,250 tons surfaced; 8,250 tons submerged
Dimensions: 129.5m × 10.1m × 9.6m
Armament:
Sixteen Poseidon C-3 SLBMs
Four 21in (533mm) torpedo tubes (all forward)
Machinery:
One PWC reactor
Two sets geared steam turbines, 15,000shp
One shaft
Speed: 20/30kts

Developed directly from the earlier 'Ethan Allens', this extensive class is about 4.5m longer to allow subsequent updating of electronics. Though of a size with the British 'Resolutions', the comparison stops there for they have been fitted with the 1,500 mile A-2 Polaris and the remainder the 2,500-mile A-3 version (that still is deployed by the British boats). Five of the A-2 boats

were converted to the A-3 before SSBN627 tests fired the first Poseidon C-3 in 1970. This scarcely three years after the class was completed, yet by 1974, all were deploying the Poseidon, a slightly larger missile than the A-3, of about the same range but equipped with up to 14 MIRVS. The extra length enabled the fire control to be changed from the Mark 84 to the more capable Mark 88. Four years later saw SSBN657 acting as trials ship for the Trident C-4 (otherwise Trident I), a 4,000-mile version of the same size as the C-3.

A first programme of 12 conversions to the C-4 was completed in 1981 and a further 12 are planned. By this time the oldest hulls in the class will have passed 20 years of age.

Officially, boats from SSBN640 onward are of a separate class, but differences are confined mainly to improvements in machinery sound insulation. It is rather hard to believe that they can manage a submerged 30kts on the 'official' power of about 15,000shp.

Los Angeles   Nuclear-powered attack submarine   *USA*

	Builders	LD	L	C
SSN688 *Los Angeles*	NNS	72	74	76
SSN689 *Baton Rouge*	NNS	72	75	77
SSN690 *Philadelphia*	GDG	72	74	77
SSN691 *Memphis*	NNS	73	76	77
SSN692 *Omaha*	GDG	73	76	78
SSN693 *Cincinnati*	NNS	74	77	78
SSN694 *Groton*	GDG	73	76	78
SSN695 *Birmingham*	NNS	75	77	78
SSN696 *New York City*	GDG	73	77	79
SSN697 *Indianapolis*	GDG	74	77	80
SSN698 *Bremerton*	GDG	76	78	81
SSN699 *Jacksonville*	GDG	76	78	81
SSN700 *Dallas*	GDG	76	79	81
SSN701 *la Jolla*	GDG	76	79	81
SSN702 *Phoenix*	GDG	77	79	81
SSN703 *Boston*	GDG	78	80	81
SSN704 *Baltimore*	GDG	79	80	82
SSN705 *City of Corpus Christi*	GDG	79	81	82
SSN706 *Albuquerque*	GDG	79	81	82
SSN707 *Portsmouth*	GDG	80	82	83
SSN708 *Minneapolis/St Paul*	—	80	82	83
SSN709 *Hyman G. Rickover*	—	81	82	84
SSN710 *Olympia*	—	81	83	84
SSN711 *San Francisco*	NNS	77	79	81
SSN712 *Atlanta*	NNS	78	80	81
SSN713 *Houston*	NNS	79	81	82
SSN714 *Norfolk*	NNS	79	81	82
SSN715 *Buffalo*	NNS	80	82	83
SSN716 *Salt Lake City*	NNS	80	82	83
SSN717 —	—	81	82	84
SSN718 —	—	81	83	84
SSN719 —	GDG	81	83	84
SSN720 —	GDG	82	83	85
SSN721 —	NNS	—	—	86
SSN722 —	NSS	—	—	87
SSN723 —	NNS	—	—	87

SSN724-6 authorised
SSN727-743 planned

Displacement: 6,000 tons surfaced (standard); 6,900 tons submerged
Dimensions: 109.7m × 10.1m × 9.9m
Armament: Four 21in (533mm) torpedo tubes
Machinery:
One PWC reactor
Two sets geared steam turbines, 30,000+shp
One shaft
Speed: 'Over 30kts' submerged

As part of the current 5-year programme to expand the strength of the US Navy, the SSN-strength (counting 'Skipjacks' and later craft) has been increased from 90 to 100 boats.

With the projected FA-SSN Los Angeles replacement having been abandoned, this additional strength will be made up of '688s' which are not only large and expensive but produced by only two yards.

The origin of the class lay in the threat posed by the Soviet 'Victors' but, where the latter have been improved from the 'Victor Is' (which began to commission in 1967, when the 688 design was being formulated) to the current 'Victor IIIs' without any great increases in dimensions or crew (about 90), the 688 is about 8m longer than the largest of the Soviets, has a standard crew of about 127 (a factor that restricts

Los Angeles.   US Navy Official

patrol endurance) and has only four torpedo tubes. Even though these can launch a variety of weapons, storage must be a problem and the weapon mix, to a total of about 26, will likely be a function of ship's mission.

Research for the class was carried out partially in the 'one-off' *Glenard P. Lipscomb* (SSN685); much of a size, this submarine evaluated a quieter turbo-electric drive, a system often favoured by the US Navy as it does not require gearboxes. Even so, the 688's reverted to a more conventional final drive and, with a likely speed well in excess of that given officially (in spite of admitted steam turbine problems) they are likely to be noisy in one important high-speed role, that of escorting the navy's planned 15 carrier groups.

The bow is devoted to housing the large sphere of the BQQ-5 which pushes the torpedo tubes well aft, beyond the forward ballast tanks. Developed from the earlier BQQ-2, the large sonar suite comprises the BQS-6 active component in the sphere and the BQR-7 in a conformal passive array around the bows, and is associated with the nuclear-tipped Subroc which can be launched from the tubes and is effective out to 25 miles.

Against surface ships the submarine can launch torpedoes (about 20 miles), the encapsulated Harpoon (60 miles) and, later, Tomahawk (at least 300 miles). The latter weapon, a cruise missile, can also be used against land based targets. A towed sonar can be used well distant from 'own noise' and taking into account thermal and saline ducting.

Fully computerised fire controls complete a formidable fighting machine but, as they cost for instance about a fifth of a CVN, it must be wondered if they can really be allowed to grow further or whether the development of a smaller, and probably less-capable, alternative should be pursued.

Seahorse, 'Sturgeon' class.   Mike Lennon

Sturgeon   Nuclear-powered attack submarine   *USA*

	Builders	LD	L	C
SSN637 *Sturgeon*	GDG	63	66	67
SSN638 *Whale*	GDG	64	66	68
SSN639 *Tautog*	ISP	64	67	68
SSN646 *Grayling*	PND	64	67	69
SSN647 *Pogy*	ISP	64	67	71
SSN648 *Aspro*	ISP	64	67	69
SSN649 *Sunfish*	GDG	65	66	69
SSN650 *Pargo*	GDG	64	66	68
SSN651 *Queenfish*	NNS	64	66	66
SSN652 *Puffer*	ISP	65	68	69
SSN653 *Ray*	NNS	65	66	67
SSN660 *Sand Lance*	PND	65	69	71
SSN661 *Lapon*	NNS	65	66	67
SSN662 *Gurnard*	MID	64	67	68
SSN663 *Hammerhead*	NNS	65	67	68
SSN664 *Sea Devil*	NSS	66	67	69
SSN665 *Guitarro*	MID	65	68	72
SSN666 *Hawkbill*	MID	66	69	71
SSN667 *Bergall*	GDG	66	68	69
SSN668 *Spadefish*	NNS	66	68	69
SSN669 *Seahorse*	GDG	66	68	69
SSN670 *Finback*	NNS	67	68	70
SSN672 *Pintado*	MID	67	69	71
SSN673 *Flying Fish*	GDG	67	69	70
SSN674 *Trepang*	GDG	67	69	70
SSN675 *Bluefish*	GDG	68	70	71
SSN676 *Billfish*	GDG	68	70	71
SSN677 *Drum*	MID	68	70	72
SSN678 *Archerfish*	GDG	69	71	71
SSN679 *Silversides*	GDG	69	71	72
SSN680 *William H. Bates*				
(ex-*Redfish*)	ISP	69	71	73
SSN681 *Batfish*	GDG	70	71	72
SSN682 *Tunny*	ISP	70	72	74
SSN683 *Parche*	ISP	70	73	74
SSN684 *Cavalla*	GDG	70	72	73
SSN686 *L. Mendel Rivers*	NNS	71	73	75
SSN687 *Richard B. Russell*	NNS	71	74	75

Displacement: 3,650 tons surfaced; 4,650 tons submerged
Dimensions: 89m × 9.6m × 8.8m
Armament: Four 21in (533mm) torpedo tubes
Machinery:
One PWC reactor

Two sets geared steam turbines, 15,000shp
One shaft
Speed: 20/30kts

Stretched versions of the immediately preceding 'Threshers', the 'Sturgeons' use the same power plant. Externally, the later boats can be recognised through a much higher fin, which actually makes them appear smaller than they are. The last nine boats of the class are 3m longer still, to incorporate improved electronics that were to be fitted in the next group, the 688s, the first of which was laid down within three months of the last 'Sturgeon'.

An interesting shift of policy is evident in the 688 programme being shared between only two yards. Up to and including the 'Sturgeons', it was obviously believed that the expertise in building nuclear boats should be spread widely, six for instance (including two naval dockyards) being involved with the 'Sturgeons'. That policy presented some difficulty is evident from the wide disparity in building times. *Pogy* took seven years to build with Ingalls having to take over the contract from New York Shipbuilding. General Dynamics produced the *Pargo* in 3½ years while Newport News managed the *Ray* in barely a week over two years. With the San Francisco Naval Yard at Mare Island taking nearly seven years also to build the *Guitarro*, which was flooded whilst fitting out, perhaps it is scarcely surprising that some rationalisation was inevitable. Like all current US attack submarines, the 'Sturgeons' carry only four torpedo tubes, sited well back because of the bow sonars. Again, they carry a variety of torpedoes, including the big Mark 48, Subroc and encapsulated Harpoon for use against surface ships. Though a feature probably not confined to this class, the fin-mounted foreplanes can be rotated to provide cutting edges for the penetration in thin ice areas (polynyas) in an ice pack. Such regions provide cover for the lurking SSBN and the SSN has to be able to operate there also, being assisted by the BQS-8 directional sonar, a device capable of detecting and charting irregularities in the underside of ice with a discrimination that makes it useful also to warn against moored mines.

160

Tinosa, 'Permit' class.   Mike Lennon

Permit   Nuclear-powered attack submarine   *USA*

	Builders	LD	L	C
SSN594 *Permit*	MID	59	61	62
SSN595 *Plunger* (ex-*Pollack*) -	MID	60	61	62
SSN596 *Barb* (ex-*Pollack*),				
(ex-*Plunger*)	ISP	59	62	63
SSN603 *Pollack* (ex-*Barb*)	NYS	60	62	64
SSN604 *Haddo*	NYS	60	62	64
SSN605 *Jack*	PND	60	63	67
SSN606 *Tinosa*	PND	59	61	64
SSN607 *Dace*	ISP	60	62	64
SSN612 *Guardfish*	NYS	61	65	66
SSN613 *Flasher*	GDG	61	63	66
SSN614 *Greenling*	GDG	61	64	67
SSN615 *Gato*	GDG	61	64	68
SSN621 *Haddock*	ISP	61	66	67

Displacement: 3,750/3,800 tons standard; 4,300/ 4,600 tons submerged
Dimensions: 85/89.5m × 9.6m × 4m
Armament: Four 21in (533mm) torpedo tubes
Machinery:
One PWC reactor
Two geared steam turbines, 15,000shp
One shaft
Speed: 20+/30+kts
Loss: Thresher (SSN593), April 1963

With the limited length and extreme 'highspeed' shape of the 'Skipjacks' causing all manner of design problems, the follow-on class was made larger and fuller of line. Unfortunately, the class was ony four-strong when the nameship, *Thresher* (SSN593), went missing with all hands. The results of this were to rename the class after the next-in-line, *Permit*, and to enlarge later units to incorporate further safety features. Those modified, SSN613 to 615, can be identified by rather loftier fins.

This class marks the transition point of the nuclear attack boat from being a largely experimental phenomenon to a warship in its own right, a confidence reflected in the extended series built. They were able to dive more deeply than earlier boats and were the first equipped with the new Subroc, a two-ton nuclear tipped weapon which, fired from a torpedo tube, will surface and ignite a rocket engine, thence proceeding on a ballistic trajectory of up to 30 miles, to explode over the computed position of the submerged submarine target. As it is of no use deploying a long-ranged weapon without the means of detecting and tracking a target at similar range, the class was also equipped with the new BQQ-2 sonar suite, whose active component, the BQS-6 has its transducers contained in a sphere of nearly 5 metres diameter, the passive elements of the BQR-7 being 'wrapped around' in a conformal bow array. In spite of their age, they have still sufficient life to warrant up-grading the sonars to the latest BQQ-5 in recent refits.

One unit, *Jack* (SSN 605) was built with contra rotating propellers which, by reducing loading on the blades, also reduced noise. Propulsive efficiency was also improved but neither parameter to the extent that justified the extra complexity and the experiment was not repeated.

Skipjack   Nuclear-powered attack submarine   *USA*

	Builders	LD	L	C
SSN585 *Skipjack*	GDG	56	58	59
SSN588 *Scamp*	MID	59	60	61
SSN590 *Sculpin*	ISP	58	60	61
SSN591 *Shark*	NSS	58	60	61
SSN592 *Snook*	ISP	58	60	61

Displacement: 3,075 tons surfaced; 3,510 tons submerged
Dimensions: 76.7m × 9.6m × 8.8m
Armament: Six 21in (533mm) torpedo tubes (all forward)
Machinery:
One PWC reactor
Two sets geared steam turbines, 15,000shp
One shaft

Sculpin, 'Skipjack' class.   US Navy Official

Speed: 20/30+kts
Loss: Scorpion (SSN589) May 1968

In 1953 was commissioned the *Albacore* (AGSS569) which was a landmark in submarine development, designed, as she was, to test ideas on perfect underwater hullforms, unencumbered solids of revolution driven by a large-diameter propeller set abaft the control surfaces which, themselves, could be of vertical or diagonal cruciform configuration. (Serious students may wish to check details of the British 'R' class of 1917). Other features evaluated by *Albacore* were divebrakes, a control flap on the fin's trailing edge and contrarotating propellers; not all of these proved to be of immediate use but all were geared to a three-dimensional approach to submarine operation with high speeds requiring more exact control in order to work within a safe band of submergence.

The high speed underwater hull, wedded to nuclear propulsion for virtually unlimited endurance, had tremendous promise and came together for the first time in the 'Skipjacks', though the class was delayed somewhat by the over-riding priority of the Polaris programme. This demanded not only resources but even the first-of-class herself, the *Scorpion* being commandeered and stretched, becoming the first American SSBN, the *George Washington*. A further *Scorpion* (SSN589) was built to replace her, but was lost with all hands in 1968.

Experience has shown the boats to be a little too extreme in their quest for speed and efficiency. At a time when stern-mounted tubes were usual, the fine tail precluded their fitting, six tubes being set right forward. These, however, occupy the space taken in current boats by a large sonar suite, so the electronics, so vital to a successful SSK (hunter-killer) design, are somewhat deficient, coupled with a depth limitation on the hull and an inability to deploy Subroc.

Their machinery was very successful, however, providing the basic design for most subsequent boats. A feature was the pair of small 'get-you-home' electric motors which could be clutched into the single shaft drive and powered from either batteries or diesel generators.

Skate   Nuclear-powered attack submarine   *USA*

	Builders	LD	L	C
SSN578 *Skate*	GDG	55	57	57
SSN579 *Swordfish*	PND	56	57	58
SSN583 *Sargo*	MID	56	57	58
SSN584 *Seadragon*	PND	56	58	59

Displacement: 2,550 tons surfaced; 2,850 tons submerged
Dimensions: 81.5m × 7.6m × 6.5m
Armament: Eight 21in (533mm) torpedo tubes (six forward, two aft)
Machinery:
One PWC reactor
Two sets geared steam turbines, 15,000shp
Twin shafts
Speed: 18/22kts

Diminutives of the pioneer *Nautilus*, the 'Skates' were the first full class of SSN, using two types of modified *Nautilus* reactor but inheriting the same basic 'Guppy'-type hull which, though clean, retained a bulky casing and, worse, a twin-screw drive. They were, in fact, interim boats, 'classic' type layouts with an advanced propulsion system. In the earlier days of their lives they proved over and over again the potential of the nuclear submarine, performing submerged voyages of previously unheard-of distances and to previously inaccessible zones such as beneath the high lattitudes of the Arctic ice cap. Though all still active with the US Pacific Fleet, their use must now be greatly restricted as, by modern standards, they are slow, noisy, lack modern electronics and are unable to deploy the latest weaponry.

Seadragon has been decommissioned but not yet stricken.

Sargo, 'Skate' class.   US Navy Official

Ethan Allen   Nuclear-powered attack submarine   *USA*

	Builders	LD	L	C
SSN608 *Ethan Allen*	GDG	59	60	61
SSN609 *Sam Houston*	NNS	59	61	62
SSN610 *Thomas A. Edison*	GDG	60	61	62
SSN611 *John Marshall*	NNS	60	61	62
SSN618 *Thomas Jefferson*	NNS	61	62	63

Displacement: 6,600 tons surfaced; 7,900 tons submerged
Dimensions: 125.1m × 10.1m × 9.5m
Armament: Four 21in (533mm) torpedo tubes (all forward)
Machinery:
One PWC reactor
Two sets geared steam turbines, 15,000shp
One Shaft
Speed: 20/28kts

As the second class of SSBNs, the US Navy, the 'Ethan Allens' were designed for the job, as opposed to the 'Washingtons', which were stop-gap boats, improvised from a stretched 'Skipjack' hull. Built to deploy the earliest A2 version of the Polaris SLBM, they were all subsequently modified to take the A3. They were not considered worth a further update to the Poseidon, in view of their age, depth limitations and the imminence of the Trident. By terms of the SALT agreements, all five have been re-rated SSNs, their launch tubes plugged and fire control removed. It has been announced that they will act as SSNs until the end of the decade, but this would seem unrealistic as, coupled with a size that eclipses even the over-large 688s, they lack speed, depth and modern attack sensors. Their only possible use has to be as spare hulls that can reasonably be fitted as Poseidon carriers in an emergency.

The five 'Washingtons' were also A3 conversions but are now paying-off, also as a result of SALT, although they had serious limitations in performance when it is remembered that their missiles' range was only 2,500 miles.

Sam Houston, *'Ethan Allen' class.*   US Navy Official

Barbel   Patrol submarine   *USA*

	Builders	LD	L	C
SS580 *Barbel*	PND	56	58	59
SS581 *Blueback*	ISP	57	59	59
SS582 *Bonefish*	NYS	57	58	59

Displacement: 2,150 tons surfaced; 2,900 tons submerged
Dimensions: 66.8m × 8.8m × 8.5m

Bonefish, *'Barbel' class.*   US Navy Official

Armament:
Six 21in (533mm) torpedo tubes (all forward)
Machinery:
Three diesel generators
Two electric motors, 3,200shp
One shaft
Speed: 15/21kts

Constructed at the same time as the 'Skipjacks' the 'Barbels' were also designed close to the principles established by the 'Albacore' equipments. As high-speed conventionals of an ocean-going size, they have seemed well ahead of their time, their nearest equivalent being the Dutch 'Zwaardfis' and, possibly the Japanese 'Uzushio' classes, both of which were laid down more than a decade later. By American diesel-electric boat standard, they are quite small and were the first to be propelled by a single, large-diameter propeller and fin-mounted planes (though these were removed from an earlier bow position). As in the 'Skip-jacks', the fine run aft precluded the fitting of the time-honoured after torpedo tube and a battery of six bow tubes had to suffice. In appearance, the 'Barbels' look like small nuclear boats but can be distinguished on the surface by the tell-tale diesel exhaust aft.

With the Rickover 'all-nuclear' school seemingly still all-powerful in the US submarine world, the conventional boat will be a memory when the 'Barbels' are shortly withdrawn from service. Many would point out the cost-effectiveness and extreme silence of the conventional boat and draw attention to its obvious place as complementary to the 'nuclears' rather than supplanted by them. In the long-range, two-ocean US fleet of today, however, no plans would seem to exist to exploit the stealthy 'in-fighting' equipment qualities of the patrol submarine. Fortunately, as in the case of the long-neglected mine countermeasures department, it can be shown that these plans are not immutable.

One Off Submarines   *USA*

During the 30-odd years of American nuclear submarine development, half-a-dozen 'specials' have been built for the purpose of evaluation and experiment.

Most recent and important of these is the *Glenard P. Lipscomb* (SSN685 — 5,820/6,500 tons, completed 1974) whose primary function is to investigate the possibilities of using turbo-electric drive in the cause of silence. Nuclear plant is designed to produce heat which is used, via a heat-exchanger, to raise steam from a conventional boiler. This steam drives a turbine but, where this machinery is usually geared down to drive the propeller shaft, it drives alternators in the *Lipscomb*, the power from these being rectified to turn dc motors with very fine speed control and directly coupled to the shaft. With the gearing removed, a primary source of noise has gone but the extra machinery, while, apparently, developing lower power demanded a hull even longer than that of the 688s, which have reverted to the more orthodox layout. In other respects, *Lipscomb* is an 'ordinary' SSN.

Another example of the use of this machinery was in the *Tullibee* (SSN597 — 2,320/2,640 tons, completed 1960). This submarine was an early attempt to build a small and agile AS submarine but, like the *Lipscomb*, had a disappointingly low speed. No doubt this was because of the tight control on the size of the boat which, even so, turned out at twice the totally inadequate displacement target. The designed silence of the boat was to be matched by advanced detection techniques, the bow sonar being an innovation and the three domes of the PUFFS passive ranging sonar (BQG-4) being prominent. With its pronounced dislike for small submarines, the USN abandoned the *Tullibee* design for the more capable (and larger) 'Permits'.

Another aspect of noise reduction was addressed in the *Narwhal* (SSN671 — 4,450/5,350 tons, completed 1969); that of the large circulating pumps of the reactor. Heat from the reactor is removed by water pumped around the pressurised primary circuit of the heat exchanger. To reduce noise in this stage, the whole layout was redesigned to use natural convection to the utmost. As the arrangement does not appear to have been used in subsequent classes it has, apparently, been only a qualified success with, probably, pumps of smaller capacity still being necessary to achieve the flow rate required. In all other respects, *Narwhal* is a fully-capable SSN, basically a stretched 'Sturgeon'.

An earlier attempt to tackle this problem was in the American's second nuclear submarine, *Seawolf* (SSN575 — 3,770/4,200 tons, completed 1957). Commissioned about $2\frac{1}{2}$ years after the prototype *Nautilus* (now a museum ship) she was designed to evaluate the merits of using a sodium-potassium (NaK) alloy which, liquid at lowish temperatures, promised excellent heat transfer properties in comparison with water. Unfortunately, the alloy proved too corrosive for easy containment and pressurised-water cooling was substituted after barely two years.

With her early hull form and low power, *Seawolf* is now restricted to research tasks only and can expect to be paid off soon.

In the *Triton* (SSN586 — 5,950/6,680 tons, completed 1959), the US Navy completed a purpose-designed radar picket boat. The ring of pickets stationed far ahead of an operation to give early warning of enemy movements was a feature of WW2 and proved very vulnerable to attack. Like the Soviet 'Whiskey' 'Canvas Bags' the *Triton* was designed to overcome this handicap of exposed pickets for the purpose of accurate targeting but her usefulness was overtaken by improved methods of radar surveillance. She is unique among SSNs in having a higher surfaced speed than submerged, the necessary 34,000shp being raised by two reactors that, in turn, demanded a 136m hull, unsurpassed in size until the advent of the Soviet 'Delta IIs'. She saw less than 10 years of service before being laid up, in which state she remains.

Finally there is the *Halibut* (SSN587 — 3,850/5,000 tons, completed 1960). Unique in the US Navy as being categorised SSGN, she was designed to carry a couple of the planned 1,000-mile Regulus II missiles, but,

164

when this weapon was cancelled, she was completed around five of the earlier Regulus Is, with about half the range. The humped forebody is a legacy of this arrangement, which lasted only about five years and, with Regulus I also being discarded, the *Halibut* changed to a 'conventional' SSN. Lacking a role, she was refitting for research into the operation of Deep Submergence Rescue Vehicles (DSRVs), a function that continued until 1976, since when she has been laid-up.

Also worth mention is the *Grayback* (SS574 —

2,650/3,650 tons, completed 1958), the last of four conventionally-propelled submarines also designed for Regulus II deployment. With the end of this programme, the missile arrangements were stripped and the capacious, pressure-tight stowage retained for submarine transportation use. Not only equipment but troops or clandestine operators with their craft can be housed. Although the submarine is old, therefore, she retains a useful capacity for the unorthodox, where refined offensive potential is not required.

Blue Ridge Amphibious command ship USA

	Builders	LD	L	C
LCC19 *Blue Ridge*	PND	67	69	70
LCC20 *Mount Whitney*	NNS	69	70	71

Displacement: 19,300 tons full load
Dimensions: 188.5m×25.3m×8.5m
Armament:
Two eight-celled Sea Sparrow point defence SAM launchers
Four 3in (76mm) guns (2×2)
Machinery:
One set geared steam turbines, 22,000shp
Single shaft
Speed: 22kts

Mount Whitney, *'Blue Ridge' class.* Mike Lennon

Even early examples of amphibious landings in WW2 showed the requirement for specialist command ships that could accommodate the staff and communications necessary to prevent a complex operation from disintegrating. Earlier ships, notably the 15-strong 'Mount McKinley' class, were conversions from mercantile hulls, but the two 'Blue Ridges' are purpose-built on hulls derived from the 'Iwo Jimas'. Despite the compact bridge block being mounted on the centreline, a strong carrier-like aura remains, the vast expanses of open weather deck being occupied for the most part by light masts bearing an array of communications antennas. Deck area is increased still further amidships by sponsons, which serve also as boat stowage. There is

no funnel, the ships' two boilers exhausting through ducts in the square structure abaft the bridge.

Means of gathering, processing and distributing data is comprehensive. Satellite communications antennas top the solid tower aft, shared with what look like ECM and ESM pods.

Although only point defence SAMs are fitted, a full SPS48 three-dimensional air search system is attached, together with TACAN. Three separate data systems are aboard, the usual NTDS allowing data-sharing between ships, together with two specialised suites for use in amphibious work and intelligence processing. The ships' complements of about 700 men are doubled when the full command complements are aboard.

Tarawa Amphibious assault ship USA

	Builders	LD	L	C
LHA1 *Tarawa*	ISP	71	73	76
LHA2 *Saipan*	ISP	72	74	77
LHA3 *Belleau Wood*	ISP	73	77	78
LHA4 *Nassau*	ISP	73	78	79
LHA5 *Pelileu* (ex-*Da Nang*)	ISP	76	78	80

Displacement: 39,300 tons full load
Dimensions: 250m×32.5m×8.5m (Width over flight-deck 36m)
Armament:
Two Sea Sparrow point defence SAM launchers
Three 5in (127mm) guns (3×1)
Machinery:
Two sets geared steam turbines, 70,000shp

Twin shafts
Speed: 24kts
Aircraft: About 20 heavy helicopters or 26 medium helicopters or mix of these and V/STOL aircraft.

Though these are large ships, their proportions give an impression, from a distance, of something much smaller. Very ambitious in concept, they exceeded planned budgets by a degree that enforced curtailment of the planned nine units to only five. In one hull they seek to combine the qualities of an 'Iwo Jima' class LPH and an 'Austin' class LPD with a large cargo capacity besides. They carry a reinforced Marine battalion, their armour, transport and fire support, together with the means of landing and supporting them. Only

the after end of the space below the near full-length flightdeck is devoted to helicopter garaging. Forward of this are stores and ordnance spaces, connected to the flightdeck by small elevators. Serving the hangar are a portside and centreline elevator set over the large sterngate. The length of the docking space is rather less than that of an LSD but far wider, so that capacity exists for four 41m LCU's compared to the LSD's maximum of three. The airspace under the guillotine-type stern gate is not generous and a heavy swell could cause undocking problems, possibly eased by use of a large, forward-mounted side-thrust unit. All vehicle decks are connected by ramp to the docking well.

Nassau, 'Tarawa' class.   Mike Lennon

Armament is on a light, defensive scale, with two Sea Sparrow point-defence launchers, one forward of the large island and one on the port quarter, and three single 5in 54s at the other three corners.

Besides helicopters, V/STOL aircraft can be operated. Electronics are comprehensive, including a Mark 86 Fire Control system, a carrier control approach radar (an aft-looking SPN-35 beneath a large radome) and, despite the lack of an area-defence SAM system, an SPS 42 three-dimensional set.

Iwo Jima   Amphibious assault ship   USA

	Builders	LD	L	C
LPH 2 *Iwo Jima*	PSD	59	60	61
LPH 3 *Okinawa*	PND	60	61	62
LPH 7 *Guadalcanal*	PND	61	63	63
LPH 9 *Guam*	PND	62	64	65
LHP10 *Tripoli*	ISP	64	65	66
LPH11 *New Orleans*	PND	66	68	68
LPH12 *Inchon*	ISP	68	69	70

Displacement: 17,600 tons standard; 18,250 tons full load
Dimensions: 180m×25.6m×7.9m (Width over flight-deck 31.9m)
Armament:
Two Sea Sparrow point defence SAM launchers
Four 3in (76mm) guns (2×2)
Machinery:
One geared steam turbine set, 22,000shp
One Shaft
Speed: 21kts
Aircraft: Eleven heavy or 20 medium helicopters

Though looking like carriers, the 'Iwo Jimas' were designed from the outset as the means of transporting over 2,000 troops and putting them ashore by helicopter only. This seems to have been a somewhat unnecessary constraint as *Inchon* (only) is equipped with a brace of LCVPs under heavy davits, allowing her to off-load vehicles over the beach.

Very much utility ships in concept they follow the earlier escort carriers in their single-screw propulsion. A full-length hangar is connected to the flightdeck by two deck-edge elevators, but lack of facilities for fixed-wing aircraft has resulted in a characteristic round forward end to the flightdeck. Their drawback, like that of earlier British commando carriers, is an inability to carry the embarked Marines' heavy vehicles and armour.

Guam operated for some years as an interim Sea Control Ship (SCS), an Elmo Zumwalt project to provide an inexpensive means of giving air superiority in a local zone, such as a landing beach or a group of ships. In

Guadalcanal, 'Iwo Jima' class.   Mike Lennon

this role, she became the first ship to thoroughly evaluate V/STOL in squadron strength at sea. Though proved sound, the project competed unsuccessfully for funds in competition with the larger naval lobbies, and was shelved indefinitely, though the design forms the basis for the new Spanish carrier *Principe de Asturias*.

Commencing FY 1984 is a projected replacement class, a 40,000 ton general-purpose assault ship (LHD). The size of this would seem ambitious and faces obvious dangers from political axes.

Austin   Amphibious transport dock

USA

	Builders	LD	L	C
LPD 4 *Austin*	NYD	63	64	65
LPD 5 *Ogden*	NYD	63	64	65
LPD 6 *Duluth*	NYD	63	65	65
LPD 7 *Cleveland*	ISP	64	66	67
LPD 8 *Dubuque*	ISP	65	66	67
LPD 9 *Denver*	LSC	64	65	68
LPD10 *Juneau*	LSC	65	66	69
AGF11 *Coronado*	LSC	65	66	70
LPD12 *Shreveport*	LSC	65	66	70
LPD13 *Nashville*	LSC	66	67	70
LPD14 *Trenton*	LSC	66	68	71
LPD15 *Ponce*	LSC	66	70	71

Displacement: 10,000 tons standard; 16,700 tons full
Dimensions: 173.6m×30m×7.1m
Armament: Two 3in (76mm) guns (1×2)
Machinery:
Two sets geared steam turbines 24,000shp
Twin shafts
Speed: 21kts

The 'Raleighs' were limited to a class of three and stretched by nearly 15m to the 'Austin'. Extra space has been devoted to more cargo capacity, particularly vehicular, and fewer troops are carried, pointing to an evening-out of priorities. In appearance, there is little to distinguish them from the earlier class although LPD7-13 have capacity for a flag officer and staff, in order to act as command ships. Externally, this shows as the extra row of windows of the command bridge in the bridgefront.

With an increased ability to operate large helicopters (up to half-a-dozen CH46 Sea Knights may be allocated) a telescopic hangar has been added between the stacks, for maintenance rather than stowage, and the masthead, unlike those of the LSDs, is adorned with the beehive antenna of TACAN.

Though the latest of class was completed as late as 1971 (indeed LDP16 was cancelled at the onset of the LHA programme) the armament is still of outdated 3in 50s. Recent experience has shown that amphibious transport ships can be caught by airstrikes outside an adequate screen and the ensuing loss is expensive, both in life and materiel. The 3in 50 is of little use against a modern aircraft, let alone an incoming SSM; it is not heavy enough for shore bombardment and, if it needs to be used against a surface warship, the latter will already have sunk the LPD anyway. It is high time to identify the primary threat, which is from the air, and commence a retrofit programme of suitable point-defence missiles and a CIWS.

Juneau, *'Austin' class*. US Navy Official

Raleigh   Amphibious transport dock

USA

	Builders	LD	L	C
LPD1 *Raleigh*	NYD	60	62	62
LPD2 *Vancouver*	NYD	60	62	63
AGF3 (ex-LPD3) *La Salle*	NYD	62	63	64

Displacement: 8,050 tons standard; 13,800 tons full load
Dimensions: 158.7m×30.5m×6.5m
Armament: Six 3in (76mm) guns (3×2)

Raleigh. Mike Lennon

Machinery:
Two sets geared steam turbines, 24,000shp
Twin shafts
Speed: 20kts

Predating the 'Anchorage' class as they do, the 'Raleighs' do not represent an evolution from the LSD but an alternative type of ship. The emphasis is upon a balanced capability, so the docking well is smaller (having capacity for three 17m LCM6s nose-to-tail, alongside a larger LCU), the extra space so released being devoted to three times as many troops, over 1,100, together with their vehicles. Internal ramps connect the vehicle decks not only to the 'beach' in the docking well but also the permanent helicopter deck and, through side ports, to any available dock apron. In essence, the LPD combines the merits of the LSD with the Amphibious Transport (LPA) and the Amphibious Cargo Ship (LKA). The LPAs were C-2 and C-4 cargo conversions which, while being able to carry up to 1,400 troops, were rather restricted in their means for putting them ashore as landing craft carried were limited in size by davit and derrick capacities. Most have now been deleted. LKAs still thrive, however, reinforced by the five 'Charlestons' which combine a useful cargo deadweight of about 8,000 tons with accommodation for about 330 troops, but with the same landing craft limitations.

In appearance, the LPDs present a bulkier appearance than the LSDs, due to the larger super-structure. The helicopter deck aft is more solid and permanently spans the dock; though marked out for two heavy helicopters, the ship has no hangar facilities. Only one large crane is fitted.

La Salle has been modified to include extra accommodation for duties as a Miscellaneous Command Ship (AGF), mainly for deployment on the Indian Ocean and the Gulf. The establishment of the Rapid Deployment Force in the area may well make her redundant in the role.

Scheduled for FY 1987 is a new class, designated at present LPDX.

Whidbey Island   Landing ship (Dock)   *USA*

	Builders	LD	L	C
LSD41 *Whidbey Island*	LSC	—	—	—
LSD42	LSC	—	—	—
LSD43	—	—	—	—
LSD44	—	—	—	—
LSD45	—	—	—	—
LSD46	—	—	—	—
LSD47–51 projected				

Displacement: 11,000 tons standard; 15,750 tons full load
Dimensions: 185.3m × 25.5m × 6m
Armament: Two Vulcan/Phalanx CIWS
Machinery:
Four diesels, 36,000shp
Twin shafts
Speed: 23kts

Whidbey Island, *artist's impression.* US Navy Official

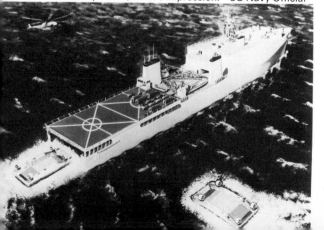

Something of a political football, this class was designed to replace the 'Thomastons', which will then be 30 years of age. As they are simple ships, based heavily on the 'Anchorage' class (themselves already into their second decade) they were cancelled by the Carter Administration as being technically unadvanced. The 'Reaganavy' view, however, is that what is needed is hulls, and the LSD41 programme was re-instated.

Considerably larger than the ships they replace, the LSD41s will have a docking well some 15m longer and configured for the operation of either 21 of the LCM6s in a seven-by-three stowage or four of the new 27m LACVs (40kts) (amphibious air cushion vehicles) which look like enlarged versions of the experimental JEFF-A.

A new departure for the class is diesel propulsion. Much neglected by the Americans, the marine diesel is enjoying a new popularity due to its economy and compactness. In this case, four medium-speed Pielsticks, built under licence in the US, power a pair of shafts. Two machinery spaces are used, as in earlier practice, the starboard diesels being in the forward compartment. What appears to be a third diminutive stack atop the superstructure, presumably exhausts the auxiliaries. Shaft horsepower has had to be almost doubled to improve sustained sea speed by something like three knots.

The large, open upper deck is a substantial affair capable of handling not only V/STOL aircraft but also the CH-53E Super Stallion helicopter which, at a maximum take off weight of about 31 tons, is well over half as heavy again as the CH-53D assault version.

Pensacola, *'Anchorage' class.* Mike Lennon

Anchorage   Landing ship (Dock)   *USA*

	Builders	LD	L	C
LSD36 *Anchorage*	ISP	67	68	69
LSD37 *Portland*	GDQ	67	69	70
LSD38 *Pensacola*	GDQ	69	70	71
LSD39 *Mount Vernon*	GDQ	70	71	72
LSD40 *Fort Fisher*	GDQ	70	72	72

Displacement: 8,600 tons standard; 13,700 tons full load
Dimensions: 168.6m×25.6m×5.7m
Armament: Six 3in (76mm) guns (3×2)
Machinery:
Two sets geared steam turbines, 24,000shp
Twin shafts
Speed: 21kts

These are little more than enlarged versions of the 'Thomastons' and, having a similar power plant, are rather slower, just fast enough to conform to the 20kts sustained speed of which amphibious units have to be capable. In appearance they differ by virtue of a higher freeboard, having a full deck more over the greater part of their length. Amidships, between the two cranes is a large gap in the deck, a bridge spanning the space between the after spar deck and the superstructure. Unlike the LPDs, the LSDs accommodate only 300-400 troops, so there is less emphasis internally on the free movement of vehicles, such of which that are carried usually being stowed topsides. This means that the two 50-ton cranes are vital for loading the landing craft carried in the well (three LCUs) or off-loading the deck stowed LCM. Small craft, such as LCVPs, are carried under davits.

The thin, pole mast of the earlier class has been replaced by a widely-braced tripod bearing basic air and surface search antennas. Again six 3in 50s comprise the total armament which, for such vulnerable ships, having a couple of decades still to run, should be updated.

Thomaston   Landing ship (Dock)   *USA*

	Builders	LD	L	C
LSD28 *Thomaston*	ISP	52	54	54
LSD29 *Plymouth Rock*	ISP	53	54	54
LSD30 *Fort Snelling*	ISP	53	54	55
LSD31 *Point Defiance*	ISP	53	54	55
LSD32 *Spiegel Grove*	ISP	54	55	56
LSD33 *Alamo*	ISP	54	56	56
LSD34 *Hermitage*	ISP	55	56	56
LSD35 *Monticello*	ISP	55	56	57

Displacement: 6,900 tons standard; 11,800 tons full load
Dimensions: 155.5m×25.6m×5.8m
Armament: Six 3in (76mm) guns (3×2)
Machinery:
Two sets geared steam turbines, 24,000shp
Twin shafts
Speed: 22kts

Plymouth Rock, *'Thomaston' class.* Mike Lennon

Now distinctly long in the tooth, the eight 'Thomastons', were a great improvement on the pioneer 'Casa Grande' class that preceded them. Built to high standards beyond the exigencies of war, they all had steam turbine propulsion and a hull of more weatherly aspect. The layout was — and has since remained — unchanged, demonstrating the sound basic idea of a self-propelled floating deck with a ship at the forward end and sterngate at the other. As the docking well is about 120m in length, it extends well forward beneath the superstructure, which bridges it. Abaft the superstructure the well is spanned by a light, removable spar deck which can be used for helicopter operations, stowage of transport and stores, or removed altogether to allow loads of high air draught to be floated-in and transported.

This type introduced the staggered funnels consequent upon separate machinery spaces. Two cranes of 50-ton capacity are fitted, one on either side. Now armed with only three twin 3in 50s these ships would be very vulnerable to any sort of attack but are unlikely to be updated as they will be replaced by the new LSD41 series.

Newport Tank landing ship   USA

	Builders	LD	L	C
LST1179 Newport	PND	66	68	69
LST1180 Manitowoc	PND	67	69	70
LST1181 Sumter	PND	67	69	70
LST1182 Fresno	NSD	67	68	69
LST1183 Peoria	NSD	68	68	70
LST1184 Frederick	NSD	68	69	70
LST1185 Schenectady	NSD	68	69	70
LST1186 Cayuga	NSD	68	69	70
LST1187 Tuscaloosa	NSD	68	69	70
LST1188 Saginaw	NSD	69	70	71
LST1189 San Bernardino	NSD	69	70	71
LST1190 Boulder	NSD	69	70	71
LST1191 Racine	NSD	69	70	71
LST1192 Spartanburg County	NSD	70	70	71
LST1193 Fairfax County	NSD	70	70	71
LST1194 La Moure County	NSD	70	71	71
LST1195 Barbour County	NSD	70	71	71
LST1196 Harlan County	NSD	70	71	72
LST1197 Barnstable County	NSD	70	71	72
LST1198 Bristol County	NSD	71	71	72

Displacement: 8,400 tons full load
Dimensions: 159.2m×21.3m×5.3m (171.5m max length)
Armament: Four 3in (76mm) guns (2×2)
Machinery:
Six diesels 16,200bhp
Twin shafts
Speed: 20kts

Very different in concept to all earlier LSTs, the 'Newports' unique arrangement resulted from a requirement for a 20kt minimum speed for amphibious task groups. 'Classic' LSTs with their blunt forward lines are not the most sea-kindly of ships and need to reduce speed in any sort of head sea to avoid damage to the bowdoors. In the 'Newports', the hull has been lengthened and the bow ramp transformed into a movable bridge stowed on the weatherdeck forward and slung over the bows by means of a pair of horns. Where earlier LSTs needed to bridge only a small gap by virtue of discharging from tank deck level, the Newports need a ramp nearly 35m in length to achieve an acceptable gradient; the penalty in topweight of ramp and horns is about 50 tons and the space consumed, considerable. The tank deck can be loaded or discharged through a stern door in the wide transom, connecting also with the weather deck via an internal ramp. A through driveway passes through the superstructure, connecting forward deck to after. Supported on edge alongside the after hull are floating pontoons which can be used either as motorised ferries or connected in train to form a bridge over larger water gaps. The ships have carried on the flexible six-diesel machinery fit of earlier LSTs but, being split into two machinery spaces, require two stacks.

That on the port side is further forward and larger in section, probably exhausting the auxiliaries in addition.

Like trawlers and tugs, LSTs are designed with a larger draught aft than forward, in this case 5.3 and 3.5m respectively enabling them to beach more easily.

Two or three of the 'County' class LSTs of the earlier 135m engines-aft type are still operated but the majority have been transferred abroad.

Spartanburg Co, 'Newport' class; note bow ramp being brought forward through open clamshell doors and raft sections secured to after hull. Mike Lennon

Pegasus   Hydrofoil   *USA*

	Builders	Completed
PHM1 *Pegasus*	BMS	77
PHM2 *Hercules*	BMS	82
PHM3 *Taurus*	BMS	81
PHM4 *Aquila*	BMS	81
PHM5 *Aries*	BMS	82
PHM6 *Gemini*	BMS	82

Displacement: 231 tons full load
Dimensions: 40.5m × 8.6m × 2.3m (over hull)
Armament:
Two quadruple Harpoon SSM launchers
One 76mm gun
Machinery:
Foilborne — One 17,000shp gas turbine driving water-jets
Hullborne — Two diesels (1,600shp total) driving waterjets
Speed 45/12kts

Taurus, *'Pegasus' class. SSM launchers are dummies.*
US Navy Official

The chequered career of the 'Pegasus' class PHMs shows the ambivalence of American attitudes to small warships: though they have little application in the USN it is felt that some expertise in their design and construction should be kept, if only to encourage export orders. NATO's southern flank in the Mediterranean, meanwhile, is one that offers potential to this type of craft owing to comparatively short passages and a multiplicity of maritime choke points. Boeing was encouraged by a favourable NATO response to propose a multi-national hydrofoil but, in the event, only West Germany and Italy pledged full support. The design was based heavily on the earlier 22.7m 'Tucumcari' with an inverted-T forward foil and a full-width after foil. Both are fitted with flaps which are electro-hydraulically actuated for height, pitch and roll control as well as course change. To avoid the complications of flexible propeller drives, waterjet propulsion is used, the jets exiting through the transom.

Italy pulled out of the agreement in favour of the much-smaller home-built 'Sparviero' class, followed by West Germany whose projected Exocet-armed Type 162 has been abandoned for conventional FACs. The US programme looked like ending at the prototype, *Pegasus*, but was eventually funded for a class of six, compared with the 30 originally planned.

At a foilborne speed of 39kts, the range is claimed to be over 1,200 miles which would seem to be under calm conditions and, though this could be extended by refuelling underweigh this latter evolution would rarely be possible except for uncontested passages. The eight Harpoons, nevertheless, represent a very heavy punch for such a small craft and are backed by ESM and a US-built version of HSA's WM28 fire control, which also controls the 76mm gun. Though topweight margins allow for a pair of 20mm canon forward of the gasturbine exhaust, these would be in a deafening and hot environment and be unlikely to cope with an aerial attack from astern.

Avenger   Mine countermeasures ship   *USA*

MCM1 *Avenger*
Displacement: 1,040 tons full load
Dimensions: 64m × 13.5m × 3.3m
Armament: Light automatic weapons
Machinery:
Four diesels
Twin shafts
Speed: 14kts

Compared with the 'big-gun' aviation, carrier and submarine departments, mine countermeasures had enjoyed the status of a naval Cinderella in recent years, despite the lessons of Haiphong and Suez, the undoubted expertise of the Soviets and the qualified achievements of the helicopter-towed minesweeping sled. Compared with European fleets — which themselves, to be sure, have little to be complacent about — the US navy is disastrously under-equipped to meet a well-planned mining offensive, whose effects today would equal those of the German 'Happy Time' submarine campaign of 1942. To supplement the aging and diminishing fleet of MSOs, plans have been abroad for some considerable time but were over-ambitious, and easy to defeat politically, looking as they were for 1,650ton, gas turbine-propelled ships nearly 81m in length. Now these have been trimmed to the provisional data listed above, a programme of about 15 ships will be undertaken, the lead ship undergoing a

'Avenger' class MCM, artist's impression.
US Navy Official

couple of years of evaluation first. How this single vessel can prove her capabilities with the newly-designed deep team sweeps in not clear, but the requirement to deal with deep-laid anti-submarine mines is of high importance and, together with a hull capable of ocean passages, has largely dictated the size of the ship. Other types of mine can also be countered. An interesting feature is a centre 'moon-pool' for lowering advanced minehunting sonars. Departures from the earlier proposals include diesel propulsion in place of the gas turbines and the deletion of a VERTREP area.

The 'Avengers' have a wood-planked hull on laminated wood-framed construction. Like the Royal Navy, the USN is considering a smaller and less-capable minehunter to complement the larger MCMs. Provisionally termed MSH, it would be of about 45m and of about 450 tons displacement.

MSO Minesweeper   *USA*

	Completed		Completed
MSO427 *Constant*	54	MSO440 *Exploit*	54
MSO428 *Dash*	53	MSO441 *Exultant**	54
MSO429 *Detector*	54	MSO442 *Fearless**	54
MSO430 *Direct*	54	MSO443 *Fidelity**	55
MSO431 *Dominant*	54	MSO446 *Fortify**	54
MSO433 *Engage**	54	MSO448 *Illusive**	53
MSO437 *Enhance**	55	MSO449 *Impervious**	54
MSO438 *Esteem**	55	MSO455 *Implicit*	54
MSO439 *Excel*	55	MSO456 *Inflict**	54

Esteem, *'MSO' class.* Mike Lennon

	Completed
MSO464 *Pluck*	54
MSO488 *Conquest**	55
MSO489 *Gallant*	55
MSO490 *Leader**	55
MSO492 *Pledge*	56
MSO509 *Adroit*	57
MSO511 *Affray*	58

Displacement: 620 tons standard; 740 tons full load
Dimensions: 52.5m×10.9×4.3m
Armament: Not armed at present
Machinery:
Two/four diesels, 2,300bhp
Twin shafts
Speed: 14kts

The Americans, as well as the Europeans, were warned from Korean War experience of the enemy potential for mine-laying and, on both sides of the Atlantic, large minesweeper programmes were initiated, with the USN building both MSOs and MSCs. All the latter have now been either transferred to other flags or discarded, but the MSOs have soldiered on, all but a handful now run by the Naval Reserve. Of the 100 planned hulls, only 65 were actually built for the USN together with three more for other NATO fleets; these, together with 40 others, have gone foreign or been discarded, leaving 25 remaining under the Old Glory.

The hulls are timber planked on laminated-timber framing, with aluminium superstructure. All machinery, and propulsion gear is of non-magnetic metal construction. All were to have been updated in the late 1960s, with new electronics and gear, including main diesels. Due to spiralling costs, however, only 13 (12 remainder marked*) were so rebuilt in full, the remaining receiving varying degrees of facelift on opportunity. MSO509 and 511 belong to improved sub-group, known as the 'Acme' class. MSO428-430 are slated for disposal.

Charleston   Amphibious cargo ship   *USA*

	Builders	Completed
LKA113 *Charleston*	NND	68
LKA114 *Durham*	NND	69
LKA115 *Mobile*	NND	69
LKA116 *St Louis*	NND	69
LKA117 *El Paso*	NND	70

Displacement: 18,600 tons full load
Dimensions: 175.4m×19m×7.8m
Armament: Six 3in guns (3×2)

Machinery:
One set geared steam turbines, 19,500shp
Single shaft
Speed: 20kts

The function of this type of ship is to carry the vast amount of dry cargo necessary to sustain an amphibious operation. They can off-load this 'over the beach' by means of nine LCM 6s carried on deck, and transferred to and from the water by a pair of 75-ton Stülcken heavy-lift derricks. In any exposed seaway this could be a limiting factor. About 255 fully-equipped troops can also be accommodated.

Sacramento   Fast combat support ship   *USA*

	Builders	Completed
AOE1 *Sacramento*	PSD	64
AOE2 *Camden*	NYS	67
AOE3 *Seattle*	PSD	69
AOE4 *Detroit*	PSD	70

Displacement: 53,000 tons full load

Dimensions: 241.7m×32.6m×12m
Armament:
One Sea Sparrow point defence SAM system
Four/eight 3in guns (2/4×2)
Machinery:
Two sets geared steam turbines, 100,000shp
Twin shafts

Sacramento.   US Navy Official

Speed: 26kts
Aircraft: Two large helicopters with hangar

Though superficially similar to the 'Wichitas', the 'Sacramentos' are much larger, due primarily to greatly increased machinery power. Their tank capacity is about the same and the dry cargo capacity increased by less than 800 tons. Nevertheless, this has shifted their emphasis sufficiently for an AOE categorisation. Very expensive ships, the initial programme was cut from five to four, but the establishment of the Navy's proposed fighting groups will enforce the need for more and a pair each of AOE and AOR are planned.

Wichita   Replenishment oiler   *USA*

	Builders	Completed
AOR1 *Wichita*	GDQ	69
AOR2 *Milwaukee*	GDQ	69
AOR3 *Kansas City*	GDQ	70
AOR4 *Savannah*	GDQ	70
AOR5 *Wabash*	GDQ	71
AOR6 *Kalamazoo*	GDQ	73
AOR7 *Roanoke*	NSD	76

Displacement: 37,400 tons full load
Dimensions: 201m×29.3m×10.3m
Armament: Four 3in guns (2×2)

Machinery:
Two sets geared steam turbines, 32,000shp
Twin shafts
Speed: 20kts
Aircraft: Two large helicopters with hangar

Primarily oilers, with a tank capacity half as large again as the 'Cimarrons', the 'Wichitas' can also ship about 1,200 tons of ammunition and stores, which can be transferred rapidly whilst underway . The high value of these ships is underlined by plans to fit them with two CIWS and a Sea Sparrow point defence system as well as the usual Chaffroc launchers.

Kilauea   Ammunition ship   *USA*

	Builders	Completed
AE26 *Kilauea*	CDQ	68
AE27 *Butte*	GDQ	68
AE28 *Santa Barbara*	BSS	70
AE29 *Mount Hood*	BSS	71
AE32 *Flint*	ISP	71
AE33 *Shasta*	ISP	72
AE34 *Mount Baker*	ISP	72
AE35 *Kiska*	ISP	72

Displacement: 18,000 tons full load

Dimensions: 172m×24.7m×8.5m
Armament: Up to four 3in guns (2×2)
Machinery:
One set geared steam turbines, 22,000shp
Single shaft
Speed: 20kts
Aircraft: Two large helicopters with hangar

Specialised ammunition carriers with good speed. Equipped with high-speed transfer equipment for underweigh replenishment.

Kilauea. Mike Lennon

Suribachi   Ammunition ship

USA

	Builders	Completed
AE21 *Suribachi*	BSS	56
AE22 *Mauna Kea*	BSS	57
AE23 *Nitro*	BSS	59
AE24 *Pyro*	BSS	59
AE25 *Haleakala*	BSS	59

Displacement: 10,000 tons standard; 15,700 tons full load

Dimensions: 156m×21.9m×8.8m
Armament: Four 3in guns (2×2)
Machinery:
One set geared steam turbines, 16,000shp
Single shaft
Speed: 18kts

'Mariner'-type hulls. Modernised to handle all types of surface ship missiles and ammunition in underway replenishment.

Mars   Combat stores ship

USA

	Builders	Completed
AFS1 *Mars*	NSD	63
AFS2 *Sylvania*	NSD	64
AFS2 *Niagara Falls*	NSD	67
AFS4 *White Plains*	NSD	68
AFS5 *Concord*	NSD	68
AFS6 *San Diego*	NSD	69
AFS7 *San José*	NSD	·70

Displacement: 16,200 tons full load
Dimensions: 177m×24m×7.3m

Armament: Four 3in guns (2×2)
Machinery:
One set geared steam turbines, 22,000shp
Single shaft
Speed: 20kts
Aircraft: Two heavy helicopters with hangar

Capacity of about 4,000 tons of dry stores, one third of which may be refrigerated. One set of double-sided, self-tensioning transfer-at-sea cargo gear at each of five holds. Machinery amidships.

Cimarron   Oiler

USA

	Builders	Completed
AD177 *Cimarron*	ASN	81
AD178 *Monongahela*	ASN	81
AD179 *Merrimack*	ASN	81
AD180 *Willamette*	ASN	82
AD186 *Platte*	ASN	83

Displacement: 27,500 tons full load
Dimensions: 180.5m×26.8×10.8m
Armament: CIWS planned

Machinery:
One set geared steam turbines, 24,000shp
Single shaft
Speed: 20kts

Engines aft-ships with all-tankage capacity, ie no dry stores. Stowage sufficient to refuel two task groups of one carrier and full escort of six/eight destroyers. Up to 20 more, to be civilian-manned, and designated the AO187 (or 'Henry J. Kaiser') class, are projected FY 1982-87. Three stretched WW2-vintage tankers ('Ashtabula' class) are also naval manned.

Monongahela, *'Cimarron' class.*   Mike Lennon

Neosho   Oiler   *USA*

	Builders	Completed
AO143 *Neosho*	BSQ	54
AO144 *Mississinewa*	NYS	55
AO145 *Hassayampa*	NYS	55
AO146 *Kawishiwi*	NYS	55
AO147 *Truckee*	NYS	55
AO148 *Ponchatoula*	NYS	56

Displacement: 11,500 tons light; 38,000 tons full load
Dimensions: 199.5m × 26.3m × 10.8m

Armament: Not usually armed
Machinery:
Two sets geared steam turbines, 28,000shp
Twin shafts
Speed: 20kts

Of a size with the Royal Navy's 'O' class tankers but fitted with an early type of underweigh replenishment gear. They are civilian-manned as are seven other tankers of WW2 vintage. About 24 freighting tankers (AOT) are also operated.

Yellowstone   Destroyer tender   *USA*

	Builders	LD	L	C
AD37 *Samuel Gompers*	PSD	64	66	67
AD38 *Puget Sound*	PSD	65	66	68
AD41 *Yellowstone*	NSD	77	79	80
AD42 *Acadia*	NSD	78	79	81
AD43 *Cape Cod*	NSD	79	80	82
AD44 *Shenandoah*	NSD	80	81	83

Displacement: 20,500 tons full load
Dimensions: 194m × 25.9m × 7m

Armament:
One 5in (127mm gun) can be fitted
Two 40mm guns (2 × 1)
One eight-celled NATO Sea Sparrow point defence SAM system planned
Machinery:
One set geared steam turbines, 20,000shp
Single shaft
Speed: 18kts

Designed for the repair and general servicing of the latest types of destroyer in forward areas. Can handle nuclear-powered and/or guided missile ships. Reportedly able to support up to six destroyers simultaneously. Built on hull common with that of 'L. Y. Spear' class Submarine Tenders.
Two further units planned.

Dixie   Destroyer tender   *USA*

	Builders	LD	L	C
AD14 *Dixie*	NYS	37	39	40
AD15 *Prairie*	NYS	38	39	40
AD17 *Piedmont*	TSC	41	42	44
AD18 *Sierra*	TSC	41	43	44
AD19 *Yosemite*	TSC	42	43	44

Machinery:
Two sets geared steam turbines, 12,000shp
Twin shafts
Speed: 17kts

Displacement: 9,500 tons standard; 17,600 tons full load
Dimensions: 161.8m × 22.3m × 8m
Armament: None at present

Very old ships, modernised only to the extent that they can handle older classes of conventional destroyer. Failing an emergency, their remaining life is likely to be limited, their decommissioning commencing with *Dixie* in 1982.
AD17 *Piedmont* transferred to Turkey in 1982.

Dixon, *'LY Spear' class.*   US Navy Official

Simon Lake and L.Y. Spear   Submarine tender   *USA*

	Builders	LD	L	C
AS33 *Simon Lake*	PSD	63	64	64
AS34 *Canopus*	ISP	64	65	65
AS36 *L. Y. Spear*	GDQ	66	67	70
AS37 *Dixon*	GDQ	67	70	71
AS39 *Emory S. Land*	LSC	76	77	79
AS40 *Frank Cable*	LSC	76	77	80
AS41 *McKee*	LSC	78	80	81

Displacement: 13,800 tons standard, 23,000 tons full load
Dimensions: 194m × 25.9m × 7m
Armament:
Two 40mm guns (2 × 1)

One eight-celled NATO Sea Sparrow point defence SAM system planned
Machinery:
One set geared steam turbines, 20,000shp
Single shaft
Speed: 18kts

Though varying only marginally in external detail, these seven ships are fitted out differently to the extent where they form three distinct groups, viz: AS33-34 can service up to three SSBNs simultaneously, including work on Poseidon C3 SLBMs, AS36-37 can service up to four attack submarines at a time while AS39-41 are fitted particularly to handle 'Los Angeles' class (SSN688) attack submarines. Very similar to 'Yellowstone' class Destroyer Tenders.

177

Hunley Submarine tender

	Builders	LD	L	C
AS31 *Hunley*	NNS	60	61	62
AS32 *Holland*	ISP	62	63	63

Machinery:
Six diesels 15,000bhp
Single shaft
Speed: 19kts

Displacement: 10,500 tons standard; 19,000 tons full load
Dimensions: 182.5m × 25.3m × 8.3m
Armament: Not normally carried

Postwar-designed specifically for refit and support of SSBNs and have been modernised to handle Poseidon C3 boats. Their machinery-amidships layout was apparently not suited to servicing large submarines, for the Simon Lakes that followed-on immediately, changed to engines-aft, leaving a large working area amidships, a layout adopted for all subsequent ASs and ADs.

Fulton Submarine tender

USA

	Builders	LD	L	C
AS11 *Fulton*	MID	34	40	41
AS12 *Sperry*	MSO	40	41	42
AS17 *Nereus*	MID	44	45	45
AS18 *Orion*	MSO	41	42	43
AS19 *Proteus*	MSO	41	42	44

Machinery:
Diesel electric, 11,000hp
Twin shafts
Speed: 15kts

Displacement: 9,750 tons standard; 16,750 tons full load
Dimensions: 161.8m × 22.3m × 8m
Armament: Not normally armed

Generally similar to the 'Dixie' class ADs but vary in their propulsion system. Now very elderly though modernised to service nuclear-powered attack submarines. *Proteus* underwent a pilot conversion in 1959 to bring her up to Polaris SSBN standards. Very thorough rebuild which included the insertion of an extra 13m centre section (19,200 tons full load displacement). Remainder not rebuilt, it being more cost-effective to build new ships.

Sperry was stricken in 1982 but retained to provide spares for remaining vessels.

United States Coastguard

Though normally operating as a department of the USS Treasury, the USCG can, when so directed by the President, work in conjunction with the regular navy. Usually acting as a seagoing law-enforcement service, it is responsible also for the maintenance of navigational facilities, lifesaving and certain oceano-graphical functions. As many of its larger vessels are useful in a naval 'blue-water' capacity, they are listed briefly.

(1) 'Hamilton' class High Endurance Cutters

WHEC715 *Hamilton*
WHEC716 *Dallas*
WHEC717 *Mellon*
WHEC718 *Chase*
WHEC719 *Boutwell*
WHEC720 *Sherman*
WHEC721 *Gallatin*
WHEC722 *Morgenthau*
WHEC723 *Rush*
WHEC724 *Munro*
WHEC725 *Jarvis*
WHEC726 *Midgett*

3,050 ton ships completed 1967-72, they have a hangar and helicopter, sonar and AS torpedo tubes. A 5in gun and a pair of 40mm are carried, with full fire control and search/surveillance radars. CODOG pro-pulsion for 29kts with a useful 14,000-mile range on diesels alone. The prewar 'Campbell' class WHECs are now being discarded.

(2) 'Bear' class Medium Endurance Cutters

WMEC901 *Bear*
WMEC902 *Tampa*
WMEC903 *Harriet Lane*
WMEC904 *Northland*
WMEC905 *Spencer*
WMEC906 *Seneca*
WMEC907 *Escanaba*
WMEC908 *Tahoma*
WMEC909-901 ordered. WMEC 911-913 approved

First of a class completed in 1982. They are 1,780-ton ships closer to regular warships than any previous cutters, with a towed array and hull sonar backed up by a LAMPS helicopter and full facilities. A 76mm gun with the HSA-derived Mk 92 fire control is fitted. Topweight allocations can cater also for CIWS and 'some' Harpoon SSMs. Diesel propulsion for 19kts. Class of 25 planned.

(3) 'Reliance' class Medium Endurance Cutters

WMEC615 *Reliance*
WMEC616 *Diligence*
WMEC617 *Vigilant*
WMEC618 *Active*
WMEC619 *Confidence*
WMEC620 *Resolute*
WMEC621 *Valiant*
WMEC622 *Courageous*
WMEC623 *Steadfast*
WMEC624 *Dauntless*
WMEC625 *Venturous*
WMEC626 *Dependable*
WMEC627 *Vigorous*
WMEC628 *Durable*
WMEC629 *Decisive*
WMEC630 *Alert*

Completed 1964-9, these 1,000-tonners are diesel-propelled for 16kts. Though only 64m in length, they are capable of operating a Sea King helicopter, though no hangar facilities are provided. An open 3in mounting is sited forward. The USCG operates also six large icebreakers with powers ranging from 10,000 to 60,000shp and about 80 large patrol craft.

List of Shipbuilding Yards

AA	At. et. Ch. Auroux, Arcachon, France	EBG	Electric Boat Company, Groton, Mass, USA (Now GDE)
ACB	At. et. Ch. de Bretagne, France		
ACG	At. et. Ch. de la Gironde, Bordeaux, France	ENB	Empresa Nacional Bazan, el Ferrol, Spain
ACN	At. et. Ch. de Nantes, Nantes, France	EVC	Estaleiros Navais de Viana do Castelo E.P., Portugal
AF	Aarhus Drydock Co, Aarhus, Denmark		
AGW	AG 'Weser', Bremen, West Germany		
AL	Ansaldo SpA, Livorno, Italy	FSB	Federal Shipbuilding, Kearny, New Jersey, USA
AMV	Akers Mek. Verksted A/S, Oslo, Norway		
AMW	Avondale Marine Ways, Inc, New Orleans, Louisiana, USA	FSG	Fairfield Shipbuilding Co Ltd, Govan, UK
		FVF	Fredrikshavn Vaerft A/S, Fredrikshavn, Denmark
ARL	Abeking und Rasmussen, Lemwerder, West Germany		
		FWL	Flenderwerft AG, Lübeck-Siems, West Germany
AS	Alinavi SpA, La Spezia, Italy		
ASG	Alexander Stephen & Sons Ltd, Glasgow, UK		
ASN	Avondale Shipyard Inc, Westwego, La, USA	GDG	General Dynamics (Electric Boat Div), Groton, Conn, USA
AV	Aalborg Vaerft A/S, Aalborg, Denmark		
		GDQ	General Dynamics Corporation, Quincy, Mass, USA
BDS	Burrard Drydock Co Ltd, Vancouver BC, Canada		
		GI	Golcuk Naval Yard, Izmit, Turkey
BIW	Bath Iron Works, Bath, Maine, USA	GN	v.d. Giessen-de Noord, Alblasserdam, Netherlands
BM/BSM	Batservis Verft A/S, Mandal, Norway		
BMM	Breda Marghera, Maestre, Venezia, Italy	GSB	Gulf Shipbuilding Corporation, Chickasaw, Alabama, USA
BMS	Boeing Marine Systems, Seattle, Wa, USA		
BMV	Bergens Mekaniske Verksteder A/S, Bergen, Norway	GSE	General Shipbuilding & Eng. Works, Boston, Mass, USA
BND	Brest Naval Dockyard, Brest, France	GSW	Gebr. Schürenstedt, Schiffswerft AG, Bardenfleth, West Germany
BNY	Boston Navy Yard, Boston, Mass, USA		
BSB	Burmester Schiffswerft, Bremen, West Germany	GVG	Gotaverken AB, Goteberg, Sweden
BSF	Bethlehem Steel Corporation, San Francisco, Cal, USA	HCS	H. C. Stülcken, Sohn, Hamburg, West Germany
BSP	Bethlehem Steel Corporation, San Pedro, Cal, USA	HDC	HM Dockyard, Chatham, UK
		HDD	HM Dockyard, Devonport, UK
		HDP	HM Dockyard, Portsmouth, UK
BSQ	Bethlehem Steel Corporation, Quincy, Mass, USA	HDW	Howaldtswerke-Deutsche Werft AG, Hamburg, West Germany
BSS	Bethlehem Steel Corporation, Staten Island, NY, USA	HJM	Helsingor Verft, Elsinore, Denmark
BT	Boelwerf, Temse, Antwerp, Belgium	HLH	Hawthorn Leslie, Hebburn, UK
BVH	Blohm und Voss AG, Hamburg, West Germany	HMC	HM Dockyard, Chatham, UK
BVV	Bremer Vulkan, Bremen-Vegesack, West Germany	HMV	Haugesund Mekaniske Verksted A/S, Haugesund, Norway
		HRA	Hall, Russell & Co, Ltd, Aberdeen, UK
CDA	Chantiers de l'Atlantique, St Nazaire, France	HRL	Henry Robb Ltd, Leith, UK
CH	Cockerill NV, Hoboken, Belgium	HSL	Halifax Shipyards Ltd, Halifax, Nova Scotia, Canada
CLB	Cammell Laird Shipbuilders Ltd, Birkenhead, UK	HSS	Hellenic Shipyard Co, Skaramanga, Greece
CMN	Chantiers Méchaniques de Normandie, Cherbourg, France	HV	State Dockyard, Horten, Norway
		HVH	Horten Verft A/S, Horten, Norway
CND	Cherbourg Naval Dockyard, Cherbourg, France	HWB	Harland & Wolff Shipbuilding Co, Ltd, Belfast, UK
CNR	Cantieri Navali Reuniti, Riva Trigoso, Italy		
CSC	Consolidated Steel Corporation, Orange, Texas, USA	IC	Italcantieri, Castellamare di Stabia, Italy
CVM	Canadian Vickers Limited, Montreal, Canada	IM	Italcantieri, Monfalcone, Italy
		IMS	Intermarine SpA, Sarzana, La Spezia, Italy
DN	Dubigeon-Normandie SA, Nantes, France	ISP	Ingalls Shipbuilding, Pascagoula, Miss, USA
DSC	Defoe Shipbuilding Co, Bay City, Michigan, USA		
		JBC	John Brown Shipbuilding, Clydebank, UK
DSL	Davie Shipbuilding Ltd, Levis, Quebec, Canada	JSW	J. Samuel White, Cowes, UK
		JTW	John I. Thornycroft, Woolston, UK (Now VT)

KMdeS	Kon. Mij. 'de Schelde', Vlissingen, Netherlands
KMV	Kockums Varv AB, Malmo, Sweden
KR	Krögerwerft Rendsburg GmbH, Rendsberg, West Germany
KV	Karlskronavarvet AB, Karlskrona, Sweden
LL	LISNAVE, Lisbon, Portugal
LND	Lorient Naval Dockyard, Lorient, France
LSC	Lockheed Shipbuilding & Construction Co, Seattle, Wa, USA
LV	Lürssen Werft GmbH, Bremen, West Germany
MID	Mare Island Naval Yard, Vallejo, Cal, USA
MIS	Marine Industrie Ltee, Sorel, Quebec, Canada
MKB	Mjellem & Karlsen A/S, Bergen, Norway
MSB	Manitowoc Shipbuilding Co, Manitowoc, Wisconsin, USA
MSO	Moore Shipbuilding & Drydock Co, Oakland, Cal, USA
N	Normand et Cie, Le Havre, France
NNS	Newport News Shipbuilding & Drydock Co, Newport News, Va, USA
NR	Werft Nobiskrug, Rendsburg, West Germany
NS	Nakskov Skibsvaerft, A/S, Nakskov, Denmark
NSD	National Steel Shipbuilding Co, San Diego, Cal, USA
NSM	Nederlandsche Dok en Sch. Mij., Amsterdam, Netherlands
NV	Nylands Verksted, Oslo, Norway
NWH	Norderwerft GmbH, Hamburg, West Germany
NYD	New York Naval Yard, NY, USA
NYS	New York Shipbuilding Corporation, NY, USA
PLK	Paul Lindenau Schiffswerft GmbH, Kiel, West Germany
PND	Philadelphia Naval Yard, Pa, USA
PNY	Portsmouth Naval Yard, Kittery, Maine, USA
PSB	Puget Sound Bridge & Drydock Company, Ltd, Seattle, Wa, USA
PSD	Puget Sound Naval Yard, Seattle, USA
RDK	Royal Dockyard, Copenhagen, Denmark
RDM	Rotterdamsche Droogdok Mij., Rotterdam, Netherlands
RNE	Rheinstahl-Nordseewerke AG, Emden, West Germany
RWB	Rolandwerft, Bremen, West Germany
SFD	San Francisco Naval Yard, Ca, USA
SHH	Swan Hunter Ltd, Hebburn, UK
SHW	Swan Hunter Shipbuilders Ltd, Wallsend, UK
SJD	St. John Shipbuilding & Drydock Co, St John NB, Canada
SLG	Scott-Lithgow Shipbuilding, Greenock, UK
SM	At. et. Ch. de la Seine Maritime, le Havre, France
SND	Royal Dockyard, Stockholm, Sweden
SSG	Scott's Shipbuilding Co, Ltd, Greenock, UK
SV	Svendborg Vaerft, Svendborg, Denmark
SWH	Schliekerwerft AG, Hamburg, West Germany
SWT	Schlichting-Werft GmbH, Lübeck-Travemünde, West Germany
TNE	Thyssen Nordseewerke, GmbH, Emden, West Germany
TPS	Todd-Pacific Shipyards, Seattle, Washington, USA
TSC	Tampa Shipbuilding Co, Tampa, Florida, USA
TSP	Todd Shipyard Corporation, San Pedro, Cal, USA
TSS	Todd Shipyard Corporation, Seattle, Wa, USA
VAN	See VSN
VCD	Verolme Cork Dockyard, Cork, Eire
VDS	Verolme Dock and Shipbuilding Co, Rotterdam, Netherlands
VMD	Victoria Mchy Depot, Victoria BC, Canada
VSB	Vickers Shipbuilding Ltd, Barrow-in-Furness, UK
VSN	Vickers Shipbuilding Ltd, Newcastle, UK
VT	Vosper Thornycroft, Portchester & Woolston, UK
VTW	See VT
WF	Wilton-Fijenoord BV, Rotterdam, Netherlands
WMA	Westermoen A/S, Mandal, Norway
YE	Yarrows Ltd, Esquimalt, Victoria BC, Canada
YSG	Yarrow (Shipbuilders) Ltd, Glasgow, UK

Pennant Numbers

Note: Only characters *not* in parentheses appear on the ship

Type	No.	Name
(MCM)	1	Avenger (US)
(FFG)	1	Brooke
(PHM)	1	Pegasus
(LPD)	1	Raleigh
(LHA)	1	Tarawa
(D)	01	Aetos
(A)	FS1	Mars
(A)	OE1	Sacramento
(A)	OR1	Wichita
	P(C)O1	Lazaga
	RO1	Dedalo
	SO1	Porpoise
	VO1	Skanor
(DDG)	2	Charles F. Adams
(PHM)	2	Hercules
(LPH)	2	Iwo Jima
(FFG)	2	Ramsey
(LHA)	2	Saipan
(LPD)	2	Vancouver
(A)	FS2	Sylvania
(A)	OE2	Camden
(A)	OR2	Milwaukee
	MO2	Alvsborg
	P(C)O2	Alcedo
	VO2	Smyge
(LHA)	3	Belleau Wood
(DDG)	3	John King
(AGF)	3	la Salle
(LPH)	3	Okinawa
(FFG)	3	Schofield
(PHM)	3	Taurus
(A)	FS3	Niagara Falls
(A)	OE3	Seattle
(A)	OR3	Kansas City
	MO3	Visborg
	P(C)O3	Cadarso
	VO3	Arild
(PHM)	4	Aquila
(LPD)	4	Austin
(DDG)	4	Lawrence
(LHA)	4	Nassau
(FFG)	4	Talbot
(A)	FS4	White Plains
(A)	OE4	Detroit
(A)	OR4	Savannah
	MO4	Carlskrona
	P(C)O4	Villamil
	VO4	Viken
(PHM)	5	Aries
(DDG)	5	Claude V. Ricketts
(LPD)	5	Ogden
(LHA)	5	Peleliu
(FFG)	5	Richard L. Page
(A)	FS5	Concord
(A)	OR5	Wabash
	P(C)O5	Bonifaz
	RO5	Invincible
	VO5	Oregrund
(DDG)	6	Barney
(LPD)	6	Duluth
(PHM)	6	Gemini
(FFG)	6	Julius A. Furer
(D)	06	Aspis
(A)	FS6	San Diego
(A)	OR6	Kalamazoo
	P(C)O6	Recalde
	RO6	Illustrious
	VO6	Slite
(S07)		Sealion
(LPD)	7	Cleveland
(LPH)	7	Guadalcanal
(DDG)	7	Henry B. Wilson
(FFG)	7	Oliver Hazard Perry
(A)	FS7	San Jose
	KO7	Challenger
(A)	OR7	Roanoke
	VO7	Sandhamn
		Walrus
(S08)		
(LPD)	8	Dubuque
(DDG)	8	Lynde McCormick
(FFG)	8	McInerney
	KO8	Engadine
	VO8	Lysekil
(S09)		Oberon
(LPD)	9	Denver
(LPH)	9	Guam
(CGN)	9	Long Beach
(FFG)	9	Wadsworth
	R09	Ark Royal
	V09	Marstrand
(S10)		Odin
(FFG)	10	Duncan
(LPD)	10	Juneau
(DDG)	10	Sampson
(LPH)	10	Tripoli
	F10	Aurora
	L10	Fearless
	V10	Lister
(S11)		Orpheus
(FFG)	11	Clark
(AGF)	11	Coronado
(LPH)	11	New Orleans
(DDG)	11	Sellers
	L11	Intrepid
	P(C)11	Barcelo
	R11	Principe de Asturias
	R11	Stockholm
(A)	S11	Fulton
	V11	Torhamn
(S12)		Olympus
(FFG)	12	George Philip
(CVS)	12	Hornet
(LPH)	12	Inchon
(DDG)	12	Robinson
(LPD)	12	Shreveport
	F12	Achilles
	P(C)12	Laya
	R12	Hermes
	R12	Malmo
(A)	S12	Sperry
	V12	Dalaro
(S13)		Osiris
(DDG)	13	Hoel
(LDP)	13	Nashville
FFG	13	Samuel Eliot Morison
	P(C)13	Javier Quiroga
(S14)		Onslaught
(DDG)	14	Buchanan
(FFG)	14	Sides
(LPD)	14	Trenton
(A)	D14	Dixie
	P14	Antiploiarhos Aninnos
	P(C)14	Ordonez
		Otter
(S15)		
(DDG)	15	Berkeley
(FFG)	15	Estocin
(LPD)	15	Ponce
(A)	D15	Prairie
	F15	Euryalus
	P(C)15	Acevedo
	P15	Ipoploiarhos Arliotis
		Oracle
(S16)		
(FFG)	16	Clifton Sprague
(DDG)	16	Joseph Strauss
(CG)	16	Leahy
(AVT)	16	Lexington
(D)	16	Velos
	F16	Diomede
	P(C)16	Candido Perez
	P16	Ipoploiarhos Betsis
		Ocelot
(S17)		
(DDG)	17	Conyngham
(CG)	17	Harry E. Yarnell
(A)	D17	Piedmont
	P17	Ipoploiarhos Batsis
(A)	S17	Nereus
		Otus
(S18)		
(DDG)	18	Semmes
(CG)	18	Worden
(A)	D18	Sierra
	D18	Antrim (Br)
	F18	Galatea
	J18	Halland
(A)	S18	Orion
		Opossum
(S19)		
(LCC)	19	Blue Ridge
(CG)	19	Dale
(FFG)	19	John A. Moore
(DDG)	19	Tatnall
(A)	D19	Yosemite
	D19	Glamorgan
	J19	Smaland
(A)	S19	Proteus
(S20)		Opportune
(FFG)	20	Antrim
(CVS)	20	Bennington
(DDG)	20	Goldsborough
(LCC)	20	Mount Whitney
(CG)	20	Richmond K. Turner
	D20	Fife (Br)
	P20	Antiploiarhos Laskos
	P20	Deirdre
		Onyx
(S21)		
(DDG)	21	Cochrane
(FFG)	21	Flatley
(CG)	21	Gridley
(D21)		Lepanto
(A)	E21	Suribachi
	M21	Jucar
	N21	Abdiel
	P21	Emer
	P21	Plotarhis Blessas
	R21	Goteborg
		Resolution
(S22)		
(DDG)	22	Benjamin Stoddert
(CG)	22	England
(FFG)	22	Fahrion
(A)	E22	Mauna Kea
	M22	Ebro
	P22	Aoife
	P22	Ipoploiarhos Mikonios
	R22	Galve
		Repulse
(S23)		
(CG)	23	Halsey
(FFG)	23	Lewis B. Pullen
(DDG)	23	Richard E. Byrd
	D23	Almirante Valdes
	D23	Bristol
(A)	E23	Nitro
	J23	Halsingland
	M23	Duero
	P23	Aisling
	P23	Ipopoiarhos Troupakis
	R23	Kalmar
(FFG)	24	Jack Williams
(CG)	24	Reeves
(DDG)	24	Waddell
	D24	Alcata Galiano
(A)	E24	Pyro
	M24	Tajo
	P24	Simeoforos Kavalondis
	R24	Sundsvall
(CGN)	25	Bainbridge
(FFG)	25	Copeland
	D25	Jorge Juan
(A)	E25	Haleakala
	M25	Genil
	P25	Antiploiarhos Kostakos
	R25	Halsingborg
		Renown
(S26)		
(CG)	26	Belknap
(FFG)	26	Gallery
(A)	E26	Kilauea
	M26	Odiel
	P26	Ipoploiarhos Deyiannis
	R26	Harnösund
		Revenge
(S27)		
(CG)	27	Josephine Daniels
(FFG)	27	Mahlon S. Tisdale
(A)	E27	Butte
	P27	Simeoforos Zenos
(FFG)	28	Boone
(LSD)	28	Thomaston
(D)	28	Thyella
(CG)	28	Wainwright
(A)	E28	Santa Barbara
	F28	Cleopatra
	P28	Simeoforos Simitzopoulos
(CG)	29	Jouett
(LSD)	29	Plymouth Rock
(FFG)	29	Stephen W. Groves
(A)	E29	Mount Hood
	M29	Brecon
	P29	Simeoforos Starakis
(LSD)	30	Fort Snelling

Type	Pennant	Name
(CG)	30	Horne
(FFG)	30	Reid
	M30	Ledbury
(CVA)	31	Bonne Homme Richard
(DDG)	31	Decatur
(D)	31	Ierax
(LSD)	31	Point Defiance
(FFG)	31	Stark
(CG)	31	Sterett
	F31	Descubierta
	L31	Galicia
	M31	Cattistock
	S31	Almirante Garcia de los Reyes
(A)	S31	Hunley
(FFG)	32	John L. Hall
(DDG)	32	John Paul Jones
(LSD)	32	Spiegel Grove
(CG)	32	William H. Standley
(A)	E32	Flint
	F32	Diana (Sp)
	M32	Cottesmore
(A)	S32	Holland
	S32	Isaac Peral
(SLD)	33	Alamo
(CG)	33	Fox
(FFG)	33	Jarrett
(DDG)	33	Parsons
(A)	E33	Shasta
	F33	Infanta Elena
	M33	Brocklesby
(A)	S33	Simon Lake
(FFG)	34	Aubrey Fitch
(CG)	34	Biddle
(LSD)	34	Hermitage
(CG)	34	Oriskany
(DDG)	34	Somers
(A)	E34	Mount Baker
	F34	Infanta Cristina
	M34	Middleton
(A)	S34	Canopus
	S34	Cosme Garcia
(LSD)	35	Monticello
(CGN)	35	Truxtun
(A)	E35	Kiska
	F35	Cazadora
	S35	Narciso Monturiol
(LSD)	36	Anchorage
(CGN)	36	California
(FFG)	36	Underwood
	F36	Vencedora
(A)	S36	L. Y. Spear
(FFG)	37	Crommelin
(DDG)	37	Farragut
(LSD)	37	Portland
(CGN)	37	South Carolina
(A)	D37	Samuel Gompers
	F37	Centinela
	M37	Chiddingfold
(A)	S37	Dixon
(FFG)	38	Curts
(DDG)	38	Luce
(LSD)	38	Pensacola
(CVS)	38	Shangri-la
(CGN)	38	Virginia
(A)	D38	Puget Sound
	F38	Arethusa
	F38	Serviola
(FFG)	39	Doyle
(DDG)	39	MacDonough
(LSD)	39	Mount Vernon
(CGN)	39	Texas
	F39	Naiad
(A)	S39	Emery S. Land
(DDG)	40	Coontz
(LSD)	40	Fort Fisher
(FFG)	40	Halyburton
(CGN)	40	Mississippi
	F40	Sirius
(A)	S40	Frank Cable
(CGN)	41	Arkansas
(DDG)	41	King
(FFG)	41	McClusky
(CV)	41	Midway
(LSD)	41	Whidbey Island
(A)	D41	Yellowstone
	M41	Guadalete
(S)	S41	McKee
(FFG)	42	Klakring
(DDG)	42	Mahan
(D)	42	Kimon
(A)	D42	Acadia
	D42	Roger de Lauria
	F42	Phoebe
	M42	Guadalmedina
(CV)	43	Coral Sea
(DDG)	43	Dahlgren
(A)	D43	Cape Cod
	D43	Marques de la Ensenada
	F43	Torquay
	M43	Guadalquivir
(DDG)	44	William V. Pratt
(A)	D44	Shenandoah
	M44	Guadiana
(FFG)	45	Dewart
(DDG)	45	Dewey
	F45	Minerva
(S46)		Churchill
(DDG)	46	Preble
(FFG)	46	Rentz
(FFG)	47	Nicholas
(CG)	47	Ticonderoga
	F47	Danae
(S48)		Conqueror
(FFG)	48	Vandergrift
(CG)	48	Yorktown
(FFG)	49	Robert G. Bradley
(S50)		Courageous
	P50	Hesperos
	M51	Nalon
	P51	Kataigis
(FFG)	52	Carr
	F52	Juno
	M52	Ulla
	N52	Vidar (No)
	P52	Kentauros
	M53	Mino
	N53	Vale (No)
	P53	Kyklon
(D)	54	Leon
	A54	Isar
	M54	Turia
	P43	Lelaps
	A55	Lahn
	M55	Sil
	P55	Skorpios
(D)	56	Lonchi
	A56	Lech
	F56	Argonaut
	P56	Tyfon
	F57	Andromeda
	M57	Arkö
	A58	Rhein
	F58	Hermione
	M58	Sparö
(CV)	59	Forrestal
	A59	Deutschland
	M59	Karlsö
(CV)	60	Saratoga
	F60	Jupiter
	M60	Iggö
(CV)	61	Ranger
	A61	Elbe
(BB)	61	Iowa
	D61	Churruca
	M61	Styrsö
	PA61	Atrevida
	S61	Delfin (Sp)
(CV)	62	Independence
(BB)	62	New Jersey
	D62	Gravina
	M62	Skaftö
	PA62	Princesa
	S62	Tonina
(CV)	63	Kitty Hawk
(BB)	63	Missouri
(D)	63	Navarinon
	A63	Main
	D63	Mendez Nuñez
	M63	Aspö
	S63	Marsope
(CV)	64	Constellation
(BB)	64	Wisconsin
	D64	Langara
	M64	Hasslö
	PA64	Nautilus
	S64	Narval (Sp)
(CVN)	65	Enterprise
(D)	65	Nearchos
	A65	Saar
	D65	Blas de Lezo
	M65	Vinö
	PA65	Villa de Bilbao
(CV)	66	America
	A66	Neckar
	M66	Vallö
(CV)	67	John F. Kennedy
(D)	67	Panthir
	A67	Mosel
	M67	Namdö
(CVN)	68	Chester W. Nimitz
	A68	Werra
	M68	Blidö
(CVN)	69	Dwight D. Eisenhower
	A69	Donau
(CVN)	70	Carl Vinson
	F70	Apollo
(CVN)	71	Theodore Roosevelt
	F71	Baleares
	F71	Scylla
	M71	Landsort
	S71	Galerna
(CVN)	72	Abraham Lincoln
	72	Ojibwa
	F72	Andalucia
	F72	Ariadne
	M72	Arholma
	S72	Scirocco
(CVN)	73	George Washington
	73	Onondaga
	F73	Cataluña
	M73	Koster
	S73	Mistral
	74	Okanagan
	F74	Asturias
	M74	Kullen
	S74	Tramontana
	F75	Charybdis
	F75	Estremadura
	M75	Vinga
	M76	Ven
	N80	Falster
	F81	Navarra
	N81	Fyn
	F82	Murcia
	N82	Moen
	F83	Leon
	N83	Sjaelland
(D)	85	Sfendoni
	D86	Birmingham
	D87	Newcastle
	D88	Glasgow
	F88	Broadsword
	D89	Exeter
	F89	Battleaxe
	D90	Southampton
	F90	Brilliant
	D91	Nottingham
	F91	Brazen
	D92	Liverpool
	F92	Boxer
	F93	Beaver
	F94	London
	D95	Manchester
	F95	Brave
	D96	Gloucester
	D97	Edinburgh
	R97	Jeanne d'Arc
	R98	York
	R98	Clemenceau
	R99	Foch
	F101	Yarmouth
(S102)		Valiant
	F103	Lowestoft
(S103)		Warspite
	F104	Dido
(S104)		Sceptre
(S105)		Spartan
	F106	Brighton
(S106)		Splendid
	F107	Rothesay
(S107)		Trafalgar
	D108	Cardiff
	F108	Londonderry
(S108)		Sovereign
	F109	Leander
	S109	Superb
	N110	Nusret
	S110	Glavkos
	S111	Nereus
	S112	Triton
(LKA)	113	Charleston
	F113	Falmouth
	S113	Proteus
(LKA)	114	Durham
	F114	Ajax
	S114	Papanikolis
(LKA)	115	Mobile
	F115	Berwick
	S115	Katsonis
(LKA)	116	St Louis
	S116	Poseidon
(LKA)	117	El Paso
	F117	Ashanti
	S117	Amphitrite
	F118	Okeanos
	F119	Eskimo
	S119	Pontos
	T121	Spica (Sw)
	A122	Olwen
	F122	Gurkha
	T122	Sirius
	A123	Olna
	T123	Capella

	A124	Olmeda		P199	Pigassos		M316	Vosso
	F124	Zulu		S199	U20		S316	Kinn
	T124	Castor (Sw)		P200	Toxotis		M317	Glomma
	F125	Mohawk		M202	Atalanti		S317	Kya
	T125	Vega		M205	Antiopi		S318	Kobben
(S126)		Swiftsure		206	Saguenay		S319	Kunna
	F126	Plymouth		M206	Faedra	(S320)		Narhvalen
	T126	Virgo		207	Skeena		W320	Nordkapp
	F127	Penelope		F207	Bremen		P321	Denizkusu
	F129	Rhyl		F208	Niedersachsen	(S321)		Nordkaperen
	F131	Nubian		F209	Rheinland-Pfalz		W321	Senja
	T131	Norrköping	(D)	210	Themistocles		P322	Atmaca
	T132	Nynäshamn		F210	Emden (new)		W322	Andenes
	F133	Tartar		M210	Thalia		P323	Sahin
	T133	Norrtälje	(D)	211	Miaoulis		P324	Kartal
(CA)	134	Des Moines		F211	Köln (new)		P325	Meltem
	T134	Varberg		M211	Alkyon	(S326)		Delfinen
	T135	Västeras	(D)	212	Kanaris		P326	Pelikan
	T136	Västervik		F212	Karlsruhe (new)	(S327)		Spaekhuggeren
	T137	Umea	(D)	213	Kountouriotis		P327	Albatros (Tu)
	T138	Pitea		M213	Klio		P328	Simsek
(CA)	139	Salem	(D)	214	Sachtouris	(S329)		Springeren
	T139	Lulea		M214	Avra		P329	Kasirga
	T140	Halmsted	(D)	215	Tompazis		P330	Firtina
	T141	Strömstad	(D)	216	Apostolis		M331	Tista
	T142	Ystad	(D)	217	Kriezis		P331	Tufan
(A)	0143	Neosho		F220	Köln		M332	Kyina
(A)	0144	Mississinewa		F221	Emden		P332	Kiliç
(A)	0145	Hassayampa		F222	Augsburg		P333	Mizrak
(A)	0146	Kawishiwi		F223	Karlsruhe		S333	Ikinci Inönö
(A)	0147	Truckee		F224	Lübeck		M334	Ulta
(A)	0148	Ponchatoula		F225	Braunschweig		P334	Yildiz
	P150	Jägaren		229	Ottawa		P335	Kalkan
	P151	Hugin		230	Margaree		S335	Burak Reis
	P152	Munin		233	Fraser		P336	Karayel
	L153	Navkratoussa		234	Assiniboine		S336	Murat Reis
	P153	Magne		235	Chaudiere		S337	Orus Reis
	P154	Mode		236	Gatineau		P338	Yildirim
	P155	Vale (Sw)		P239	Peacock		S338	Ulu Ali Reis
	P156	Vidar (Sw)		M240	Pleias		S339	Dumlupinar
	P157	Mjolner		M241	Kichli		D340	Istanbul
	P158	Mysing		M242	Kissa		F340	Beskytteren
	P159	Karparen		M246	Aigli		P340	Dogan
	P160	Vaktaren		M247	Dafni		S340	Cerbe
	P161	Snapphanan		M248	Aedon		D341	Izmir
	P162	Spejaren		M254	Niovi		P341	Marti
	P163	Styrbjorn		256	St Croix		S341	Canakkale
	S163	Albacora		257	Restigouche		P342	Tayfin
	P164	Starkodder		258	Kootenay		S342	Turgut Reis
	S164	Barracuda		P258	Leeds Castle		D343	Iskenderun
	P165	Tordon		259	Terra Nova		P343	Volkan
	S165	Delfin (Po)		260	Columbia		S343	Piri Reis
	P166	Tirfing		261	Mackenzie		D344	Içel
	F169	Amazon		262	Saskatchewan		S345	Prevese
	S170	U21		263	Yukon		S346	Borinci Inönü
	A171	Endurance		264	Qu'appelle		D347	Antitepe
	F171	Active		265	Annapolis		S347	Atilay
	S171	U22		P265	Dumbarton Castle		D348	Savashtepe
	F172	Ambuscade		266	Nipigon		F348	Hvidbjornen
	S172	U23		A268	Green Rover		S348	Saldiray
	F173	Arrow		A269	Grey Rover		D349	Kiliç Ali Pasa
	S173	U24		A270	Blue Rover		F349	Vaedderen
	F174	Alacrity		A271	Gold Rover		S349	Batiray
	S174	U25		A273	Black Rover		D350	Piyale Pasa
	S175	U26		P277	Anglesey		F350	Ingolf
	S176	U27		P278	Alderney		S350	Yildiray
(A)	0177	Cimarron	(DD)	280	Iroquois		D351	M. Fevzi Çakmak
	S177	U28	(DD)	281	Huron		F351	Fylla
(A)	0178	Monongahela	(DD)	282	Athabaskan		D352	Gayret
	S178	U29	(DD)	283	Algonquin		F352	Peder Skram
(A)	0179	Merrimack		P295	Jersey		D353	Adatepe
	S179	U30		P297	Guernsey		F353	Herluf Trolle
(A)	0180	Willamette		P298	Shetland		D354	Koçatepe
	S180	U1		P299	Orkney		F354	Niels Juel
	D181	Hamburg		F300	Oslo		D355	Tinaztepe
	S181	U2		S300	Ula		F355	Olfert Fischer
	D182	Schleswig-Holstein		P300	Lindisfarne		D356	Zafer
	D183	Bayern		F301	Bergen		F356	Peter Tordenskjold
	D184	Hessen		S301	Utsira		DM357	Muavanet
	D185	Lütjens		F302	Trondheim		D358	Berk
	F185	Avenger (Br)		S302	Utstein		D359	Peyk
	D186	Mölders		F303	Stavanger		A385	Fort Grange
(A)	0186	Platte		S303	Utvaer		A386	Fort Austin
	D187	Rommel		F304	Narvik		M401	São Roque
	S188	U9		S304	Uthang		M402	Ribeira Grande
	S189	U10		S305	Sklinna		M403	Lagoa
	S190	U11		S306	Skolpen		M404	Rosario
	S191	U12		S307	Stadt		P420	Sparviero
	S192	U13		S308	Stord		P421	Nibbio
	S193	U14		S309	Svenner		P422	Falcone
	S194	U15		F310	Sleipner		P423	Astore
	S195	U16		F311	Aeger		P424	Grifone
	S196	U17		M311	Sauda		P425	Gheppio
	P196	Andromeda		M312	Sira		P426	Condor
	P197	Kastor		M313	Tana	(MSO)	427	Constant
	S197	U18		M314	Alta	(MSO)	428	Dash
	P198	Kyknos		M315	Ogna	(MSO)	429	Detector
	S198	U19		S315	Kaura	(MSO)	430	Direct

	Pennant	Name	Code
(MSO)	431	Dominant	
(MSO)	433	Engage	
(MSO)	437	Enhance	
(MSO)	438	Esteem	
(MSO)	439	Excel	
(MSO)	440	Exploit	(C)
(MSO)	441	Exultant	
(MSO)	442	Fearless (US)	
(MSO)	443	Fidelity	(R)
(MSO)	446	Fortify	
(MSO)	448	Illusive	
(MSO)	449	Impervious	(C)
(F)	450	Elli	
(F)	451	Limnos	
(MSO)	455	Implicit	(C)
(MSO)	456	Inflict	
(MSO)	464	Pluck	
(MSO)	488	Conquest	
(MSO)	489	Gallant	
(MSO)	490	Leader	
(MSO)	492	Pledge	
(MSO)	509	Adroit	
(MSO)	511	Affray	
	F471	Antonio Enes	
	F472	Almirante Pereira da Silva	
	F473	Almirante Gago Coutinho	
	F474	Almirante Magalhães Correa	
	F475	João Coutinho	
	F476	Jacinto Candido	
	F477	General Pereira d'Eca	(SS574)
	F480	Comandante João Belo	
	F481	Comandante Hermenegildo Capelo	(SSN575)
	F482	Comandante Roberto Ivens	
	F483	Comandante Sacadura Cabral	
	F484	Augusto de Castilho	
	F485	Honorio Barreto	
	F486	Baptista de Andrada	
	F487	João Roby	(SSN578)
	F488	Afonso Cerqueira	
	F489	Oliveira E. Carmo	(SSN579)
(S)	502	Gianfranco Gazzana Priaroggia	
(S)	505	Attilio Bagnolini	(SS581)
(S)	506	Enrico Toti	
	M507	Seymen	(SS582)
	508	Provider	(SSN583)
	M508	Selçuk	(SSN584)
	509	Protecteur	(SSN585)
	M509	Seyhan	(SSN586)
	510	Preserver	(SSN587)
	M510	Samsun	(SSN588)
	P510	Soloven	(SSN590)
	M511	Sinop	(SSN591)
	P511	Soridderen	(SSN592)
	M512	Surmene	
	P512	Sobjornen	(SSN594)
(S)	513	Enrico Dandalo	
	M513	Seddulbahir	(SSN595)
	P513	Sohesten	
(S)	514	Lazzaro Mocenigo	(SSN596)
	M514	Silifke	
	P514	Sohunden	(SSN597)
(S)	515	Livio Piomarta	(S601)
	M515	Saros	(S602)
	P515	Soulven	
(S)	516	Romeo Romei	(SSN603)
	M516	Sigaçik	
	M517	Sapanca	(SSN604)
(S)	518	Nazario Sauro	(SSN605)
	M518	Sariyer	(SSN606)
(S)	519	Fecia di Cossato	(SSN607)
(S)	520	Leonardo di Vinci	
	M520	Karamursel	(SSN608)
(S)	521	Guglielmo Marconi	(SSN609)
	M521	Kerempe	
	M522	Kilimli	(S610)
	M523	Kozlu	(SSN610)
	M524	Kusadasi	
	M525	Kemer	(S611)
	M530	Trabzon	(SSN611)
	M531	Terme	
	M532	Tirebolu	
	M533	Tekirdag	(S612)
	F540	Pietro de Cristofaro	(SSN612)
	P540	Bille	
	F541	Umberto Grosso	(S613)
	P541	Bredal	(SSN613)
	F542	Aquila	(S614)
	P542	Hammer	(SSN614)
	F543	Albatros (It)	(S615)
	P543	Huitfeld	(SSN615)
	F544	Alcione	(WMEC615)
	P544	Kreiger	
	F545	Airone	(SSBN616)
	P545	Norby	(WMEC616)

F546	Licio Visintini
P546	Rodsteen
P547	Sehested
P548	Suenson
P549	Willemoes
550	Vittorio Veneto
D550	Ardito
F550	Salvatore Todaro
551	Giuseppe Garibaldi
D551	Audace
F551	Canopo
553	Andrea Doria
F553	Castore
F554	Centauro
554	Caio Duilio
F555	Cigno
D558	Impetuoso
D559	Indomito
F564	Lupo
F565	Sagittario
F566	Perseo
F567	Orsa
D570	Impavido
F570	Maestrale
D571	Intrepido
F571	Grecale
M571	Aarsund
F572	Libeccio
F573	Scirocco
M573	Egernsund
	Grayback
F574	Aliseo
M574	Gronsund
	Seawolf
F575	Euro
M575	Guldborgsund
F576	Espero
M576	Omosund
F577	Zefiro
M577	Ulvsund
	Skate
M578	Vilsund
	Swordfish
A579	Cezaryirli Gazi Hasan Pasa
F580	Alpino
	Blueback
F581	Carabiniere
	Bonefish
	Sargo
	Seadragon
	Skipjack
	Triton
	Halibut
	Scamp
	Sculpin
	Shark
	Snook
F593	Carlo Bergamini
	Permit
F594	Virgilio Fasan
	Plunger
F595	Carlo Margottini
	Barb
F596	Luigi Rizzo
	Tullibee
	Rubis
	Saphir
D602	Suffren
	Pollack
D603	Duquesne
	Haddo
	Jack
	Tinosa
	Dace
A607	Meuse
	Ethan Allen
	Sam Houston
D609	Aconit
	le Foudroyant
	Thomas A. Edison
D610	Tourville
	le Redoutable
	John Marshall
C611	Colbert
D611	Duguay-Trouin
	le Terrible
	Guardfish
D612	de Grasse
	l'Indomptable
	Flasher
	le Tonnant
	Greenling
	l'Inflexible
	Gato
	Reliance
A615	Loire
	Lafayette
	Diligence

(SSBN617)		Alexander Hamilton
(WMEC617)		Vigilant
	A617	Garonne
(SSN618)		Thomas Jefferson
(WMEC618)		Active
	A618	Rance
(SSBN619)		Andrew Jackson
(WMEC619)		Confidence
(SSBN620)		John Adams
(WMEC620)		Resolute
	S620	Agosta
(SSN621)		Haddock
(WMEC621)		Valiant
	A621	Rhin
	S621	Bévéziers
(SSBN622)		James Monroe
(WMEC621)		Courageous
	A622	Rhône
	D622	Kersaint
	S622	la Praya
(SSBN623)		Nathan Hall
(WMEC623)		Steadfast
	S623	Ouessant
(SSBN624)		Woodrow Wilson
(WMEC624)		Dauntless
(SSBN625)		Henry Clay
(WMEC625)		Venturous
	D625	Dupetit Thouars
(SSBN626)		Daniel Webster
(WMEC626)		Dependable
(SSBN627)		James Madison
(WMEC627)		Vigorous
	D627	Maille Brézé
(SSBN628)		Tecumseh
(WMEC628)		Durable
	D628	Vauquelin
(SSBN629)		Daniel Boone
(WMEC629)		Decisive
	A629	Durance
	D629	d'Estrees
(SSBN630)		John C. Calhoun
(WMEC630)		Alert
	D630	du Chayla
(SSBN 631)		Ulysses S. Grant
	D631	Casabianca
	S631	Narval
(SSBN632)		von Steuben
	D632	Guépratte
	S632	Marsouin
(SSBN633)		Casimir Pulaski
	D633	Duperré
	S633	Dauphin
(SSBN634)		Stonewall Jackson
	S634	Requin
(SSBN635)		Sam Rayburn
(SSBN636)		Nathanael Greene
	S636	Argonaute
(SSN637)		Sturgeon
	S637	Espadon
(SSN638)		Whale
	D638	la Galissonnière
	S638	Morse
(SSN639)		Tautog
	S639	Amazone
(SSBN640)		Benjamin Franklin
	D640	Georges Leygues
	S640	Ariane
(SSBN641)		Simon Bolivar
	D641	Duplex
	M641	Eridan
(SSBN642)		Kamehameha
	D642	Montcalm
	M642	Cassiopée
	S642	Diane
(SSBN643)		George Bancroft
	D643	Jean de Vienne
	S643	Doris
(SSBN644)		Lewis & Clark
(SSBN645)		James K. Polk
	S645	Flore
(SSN646)		Grayling
	S646	Galatée
(SSN647)		Pogy
(SSN648)		Aspro
	S648	Junon
(SSN649)		Sunfish
	S649	Venus
(SSN650)		Pargo
	S650	Psyché
(SSN651)		Queenfish
	S651	Sirène
(SSN652)		Puffer
(SSN653)		Ray
(SSBN654)		George C. Marshal
(SSBN655)		Henry L. Stimson
(SSBN656)		George Washington
		Carver

Designation	Name
(SSBN657)	Francis Scott Key
(SSBN658)	Mariano G. Vallejo
(SSBN659)	Will Rogers
(SSN660)	Sand Lance
(SSN661)	Lapon
(SSN662)	Gurnard
(SSN663)	Hammerhead
(SSN664)	Sea Devil
(SSN665)	Guitarro
(SSN666)	Hawkbill
(SSN667)	Bergall
(SSN668)	Spadefish
(SSN669)	Seahorse
(SSN670)	Finback
P670	Trident
(SSN671)	Narwhal
P671	Glaive
(SSN672)	Pintado
P672	Epée
(SSN673)	Flying Fish
P673	Pertuisane
(SSN674)	Trepang
(SSN675)	Bluefish
(SSN676)	Billfish
(SSN677)	Drum
(SSN678)	Archerfish
(SSN679)	Silversides
(SSN680)	William H. Bates
(SSN681)	Batfish
(SSN682)	Tunny
(SSN683)	Parche
(SSN684)	Cavalla
(SSN685)	Glenard P. Lipscomb
(SSN686)	L. Mendell Rivers
(SSN687)	Richard B. Russell
(SSN688)	Los Angeles
(SSN689)	Baton Rouge
(SSN690)	Philadelphia
(SSN691)	Memphis
(SSN692)	Omaha
(SSN693)	Cincinnati
(SSN694)	Groton
(SSN695)	Birmingham
(SSN696)	New York City
(SSN697)	Indianapolis
(SSN698)	Bremerton
(SSN699)	Jacksonville
(SSN700)	Dallas
(SSN701)	la Jolla
(SSN702)	Phoenix
(SSN703)	Boston
(SSN704)	Baltimore
(SSN705)	City of Corpus Christi
(SSN706)	Albuquerque
(SSN707)	Portsmouth
(SSN711)	San Francisco
(SSN712)	Atlanta
(SSN713)	Houston
M712	Cybèle
M713	Calliope
(SSN714)	Norfolk
M714	Clio
(SSN715)	Buffalo
M715	Circé
(WHEC715)	Hamilton
(SSN716)	Salt Lake City
(WHEC716)	Hamilton
M716	Ceres
(WHEC716)	Dallas
(WHEC717)	Mellon
(WHEC718)	Chase
(WHEC719)	Boutwell
(WHEC720)	Sherman
(WHEC721)	Gallatin
(WHEC722)	Morgenthau
(WHEC723)	Rush
(WHEC724)	Munro
(WHEC725)	Jarvis
F725	Victor Schoelcher
(SSBN726)	Ohio
(WHEC726)	Midgett
F726	Commandant Bory
(SSBN727)	Michigan
F727	Amiral Charner
(SSBN728)	Florida
F728	Doudart de Lagrée
(SSBN729)	Georgia
F729	Balny
(SSBN730)	Rhode Island
(SSBN731)	Alabama
F733	Commandant Rivière
F740	Commandant Bourdais
F748	Protet
F749	Enseigne de Vaisseau Henry
F781	d'Estienne d'Orves
F782	Amyot de 'Inville
F783	Drogou

Number	Name	Type
F784	Detroyat	
F785	Jean Moulin	
F786	Quartier Maître Anquetil	
F787	Commandant de Pimodan	
F788	Second Maître le Bihan	
F789	Lt de Vaisseau le Henaff	
F790	Lt de Vaisseau Lavallée	
F791	Commandant l'Herminier	
F792	Premier Maître l'Her	
F793	Commandant Blaison	
F794	Enseigne de Vaisseau Jacoubet	
F795	Commandant Ducuing	
F801	Tromp	
F802	van Speijk	
F803	van Galen	
S802	Walrus	
S803	Zeeleeuw	
F804	Tjerk Hiddes	
S804	Potvis	
F805	van Nes	
S805	Tonijn	
F806	de Ruyter	
S806	Zwaardvis	
F807	Kortenaer	
S807	Tijgerhaai	
F808	Callenburgh	
S808	Dolfijn	
F809	van Kinsbergen	
S809	Zeehond	
F810	Banckert	
F811	Piet Heyn	
F812	Pieter Florisz	
F813	Witte de With	
F814	Isaac Sweers	
F815	Evertsen	
F816	Abraham Crijnssen	
F817	Wolf	
F818	Fret	
F819	Hermelijn	
F820	Vos	
F821	Panter	
F822	Jaguar	
F823	Philips van Almonde	
F824	Bloys van Treslong	
F825	Jan van Brakel	
F826	Willem van der Zaan	
A832	Zuiderkruis	
A835	Poolster	
Y849	Stier	
M851	Delfzijl	
M850	Alkmaar	
M852	Dordrecht	
M853	Haarlem	
M854	Harlingen	
M855	Hellevoetsluis	
M856	Maassluis	
M857	Makkum	
M858	Middelburg	
M859	Scheveningen	
M860	Schiedam	
M861	Urk	
M862	Zierikzee	
M863	Vlaardingen	
M864	Willemstad	
	Bear	(WMEC901)
	Tampa	(WMEC902)
M902	J. E. van Haverbeke	
	Harriet Lane	(WMEC903)
M903	A. F. Dufour	
	Northland	(WMEC904)
M904	de Brouwer	
	Spencer	(WMEC905)
	Seneca	(WMEC906)
M906	Breydel	
	Escanaba	(WMEC907)
M907	Artevelde	
	Tahoma	(WMEC908)
M908	G. Truffaut	
M909	F. Bovesse	
F910	Wielingen	
F911	Westdiep	
F912	Wandelaar	
F913	Westhinder	
M928	Stavelot	
M930	Rochefort	
931	Forrest Sherman	(DD)
M932	Nieuwpoort	
M933	Koksijde	
933	Barry	(DD)
M934	Verviers	
M935	Veurne	
937	Davis	(DD)
938	Jonas Ingram	(DD)
940	Manley	(DD)
941	du Pont	(DD)
942	Bigelow	(DD)
943	Blandy	(DD)

Type	Number	Name
(DD)	944	Mullinnix
(DD)	945	Hull
(DD)	946	Edson
(DD)	948	Morton
(DD)	950	Richard S. Edwards
(DD)	951	Turner Joy
	A960	Godetia
	P960	Storm
	A961	Blink
	P961	Zinnia
(DD)	963	Spruance
	P963	Skjold
(DD)	964	Paul F. Foster
	P964	Trygg
(DD)	965	Kinkaid
	P965	Kjekk
(DD)	966	Hewitt
	P966	Djerv
(DD)	967	Elliott
	P967	Skudd
(DD)	968	Arthur W. Radford
	P968	Arg
(DD)	969	Peterson
	P969	Steil
(DD)	970	Caron
	P970	Brann
(DD)	971	David R. Ray
	P971	Tross
(DD)	972	Oldendorf
	P972	Hvass
(DD)	973	John Young
	P973	Traust
(DD)	974	Comte de Grasse
	P974	Brott
(DD)	975	O'Brien
	P975	Odd
(DD)	976	Merrill
	P976	Pil
(DD)	977	Briscoe
	P977	Brask
(DD)	978	Stump
	P978	Rokk
(DD)	979	Conolly
	P979	Gnist
(DD)	980	Moosbrugger
	P980	Snogg
(DD)	981	John Hancock
	P981	Rapp
(DD)	982	Nicholson
	P982	Snar
(DD)	983	John Rodgers
	P983	Rask
(DD)	984	Leftwich
	P984	Kvikk
(DD)	985	Cushing
	P985	Kjapp
(DD)	986	Harry W. Hill
	P986	Hauk
(DD)	987	O'Bannon
	P987	Orn
(DD)	988	Thorn
	P988	Terne
(DD)	989	Deyo
	P989	Tjeld
(DD)	990	Ingersoll
	P990	Skarv
(DD)	991	Fife (US)
	P991	Teist
(DD)	992	Fletcher
	P992	Jo
	P993	Lom
	P994	Stegg
	P995	Falk
	P996	Ravn
(DD)	997	Hayler
	P997	Gribb
	P998	Geir
	P999	Erle
(FF)	1037	Bronstein
(FF)	1038	McCloy
(FF)	1040	Garcia
(FF)	1041	Bradley
(FF)	1043	Edward McDonnell
(FF)	1044	Brumby
(FF)	1045	Davidson
(FF)	1047	Voge
(FF)	1048	Sample
(FF)	1049	Koelsch
(FF)	1050	Albert David
	M1051	Castor
(FF)	1051	O'Callahan
(FF)	1052	Knox
(FF)	1053	Roark
(FF)	1054	Gray
	M1054	Pollux
(FF)	1055	Hepburn
	M1055	Sirius
(FF)	1056	Connole

	M1056	Rigel	(FF)	1098	Glover	M5525	Palma
(FF)	1057	Rathburne		M1103	Alfriston	M5527	Sandalo
	M1057	Regulus		M1109	Bickington	M5531	Agave
(FF)	1058	Meyercord		M1110	Bildeston	M5532	Alloro
	M1058	Mars		M1113	Brereton	M5533	Edera
(FF)	1059	W. S. Sims		M1114	Brinton	M5535	Gelsomino
	M1059	Spica (Ge)		M1115	Bronington	M5536	Giaggiolo
(FF)	1060	Lang		M1116	Wilton	M5538	Loto
	M1060	Skorpion		M1124	Crichton	M5540	Timo
(FF)	1061	Patterson		M1125	Cuxton	M5541	Trifoglio
(FF)	1062	Whipple		M1133	Bossington	M5542	Vischio
	M1062	Schütze		M1140	Gavington	P6052	Thetis
(FF)	1063	Reasoner		M1141	Glasserton	P6053	Hermes (Ge)
	M1063	Waage		M1146	Hodgeston	P6054	Najade
(FF)	1064	Lockwood		M1147	Hubberston	P6055	Triton
	M1064	Deneb		M1151	Iveston	P6056	Theseus
(FF)	1065	Stein		M1153	Kedleston	P6092	Zobel
	M1065	Jupiter (Ge)		M1154	Kellington	P6093	Wiesel
(FF)	1066	Marvin Shields		M1157	Kirkliston	P6094	Dachs
(FF)	1067	Francis Hammond		M1158	Laleston	P6095	Hermelin
	M1067	Altair		M1165	Maxton	P6096	Nerz
(FF)	1068	Vreeland		M1166	Nurton	P6097	Puma
(FF)	1069	Bagley		M1173	Pollington	P6098	Gepard
	M1069	Wega		M1180	Shavington	P6099	Hyäne
(FF)	1070	Downes	(LST)	1179	Newport	P6100	Frettchen
	M1070	Göttingen	(LST)	1180	Manitowoc	P6101	Ozelot
(FF)	1071	Badger	(LST)	1181	Sumter	P6111	Albatros (Ge)
	M1071	Koblenz		M1181	Sheraton	P6112	Falke
(FF)	1072	Blakeley	(LST)	1182	Fresno	P6113	Geier
	M1072	Lindau	(LST)	1183	Peoria	P6114	Bussard
(FF)	1073	Robert E. Peary	(LST)	1184	Frederick	P6115	Sperber
	M1073	Schleswig	(LST)	1185	Schenectady	P6116	Greif
(FF)	1074	Harold Holt	(LST)	1186	Cayuga	P6117	Kondor
	M1074	Tübingen	(LST)	1187	Tuscaloosa	P6118	Seeadler
(FF)	1075	Trippe		M1187	Upton	P6119	Habicht
	M1075	Wetzlar	(LST)	1188	Saginaw	P6120	Kormoron
(FF)	1076	Fanning		M1188	Walkerton	P6121	Gepard (new)
	M1076	Paderborn	(LST)	1189	San Bernardino	P6122	Puma (new)
(FF)	1077	Ouellet	(LST)	1190	Boulder	P6123	Hermelin (new)
	M1077	Weilheim	(LST)	1191	Racine	P6124	Nerz (new)
(FF)	1078	Joseph Hewel	(LST)	1192	Spartanburg County	P6125	Zobel (new)
	M1078	Cuxhaven	(LST)	1193	Fairfax County	P6126	Frettchen (new)
(FF)	1079	Bowen	(LST)	1194	la Moure County	P6127	Dachs (new)
	M1079	Düren	(LST)	1195	Barbour County	P6128	Ozelot (new)
(FF)	1080	Paul	(LST)	1196	Harlan County	P6129	Wiesel (new)
	M1080	Marburg		M1195	Wotton	P6130	Hyäne (new)
(FF)	1081	Aylwin	(LST)	1196	Harlan County	P6141	Tiger
	M1081	Konstanz	(LST)	1197	Barnstable County	P6142	Iltis
(FF)	1082	Elmer Montgomery	(LST)	1198	Bristol County	P6143	Luchs
	M1082	Wolfsburg		M1200	Soberton	P6144	Marder
(DD)	1083	Cook		M1204	Stubbington	P6145	Leopard
	M1083	Ulm		M1208	Lewiston	P6146	Fuchs
(FF)	1084	McCandless		M1216	Crofton	P6147	Jaguar
	M1084	Flensburg		L3004	Sir Bedivere	P6148	Löwe
(FF)	1085	Donald B. Beary		L3027	Sir Geraint	P6149	Wolf
	M1085	Minden		L3029	Sir Lancelot	P6150	Panther (Ge)
(FF)	1086	Brewton		L3036	Sir Percivale	P6151	Häher
	M1086	Fulda		A5327	Stromboli	P6152	Storch
(FF)	1087	Kirk		A5329	Vesuvio	P6153	Pelikan
	M1087	Volkingen		M5430	Salmone	P6154	Elster
(FF)	1088	Barbey		M5431	Storione	P6155	Elk
(FF)	1089	Jesse L. Brown		M5432	Sgombro	P6156	Dommel
(FF)	1090	Ainsworth		M5433	Squalo	P6157	Weih
	M1090	Perseus		M5504	Castagno	P6158	Pinguin
(FF)	1091	Miller		M5505	Cedro	P6159	Reiher
(FF)	1092	Thomas C. Hart		M5508	Frassino	P6160	Kranich
	M1092	Pluto		M5509	Gelso	L9003	Argens
(FF)	1093	Cappodanno		M5510	Larice	L9004	Bidassoa
	M1093	Neptune (Ge)		M5511	Noce	L9007	Trieux
(FF)	1094	Pharris		M5512	Olmo	L9008	Dives
	M1094	Widder		M5516	Platano	L9009	Blavet
(FF)	1095	Truett		M5517	Quercia	L9021	Ouragan
	M1095	Herkules		M5519	Mandorlo	L9022	Orage
(FF)	1096	Valdez		M5521	Bambu	L9030	Champlain
	M1096	Fische		M5522	Ebano	L9031	Francis Garnier
(FF)	1097	Moinester		M5523	Mango		
	M1097	Gemma		M5524	Mogano		

Index

188

Addenda

UK

New, single-role MCMVs to be named *Blackwater, Carron, Dovey, Helford, Helmsdale, Humber, Itchen,* and *Waveney. Waveney* launched September 1983.

New 'Brecon' class MCMVs to be named *Atherstone* and *Bicester.*

Type 22 *Boxer* (F92) commissioned October 1983.

Last three (Batch 3) Type 22s to be named *London, Coventry* and *Sheffield.*

New Type 23s reported to be 'Daring' class.

Narwhal has been sunk as a target; *Porpoise* will be used for the same.

Antrim sold to Chile and renamed *O'Higgins.*

Canada

New frigates to be named *Calgary, Halifax, Regina, Toronto, Vancouver* and *Ville de Quebec.*

France

First of two new 33,000 tonne nuclear aircraft carriers to be named *Charles de Gaulle.*

Four FACs to be called *Chacal, Guepard, Lion* and *Tigre.*

Italy

'Lerici' class minesweepers *Gaeta* to *Viareggio* have been numbered in sequence M5554 to M5559.

Netherlands

MCMV *Delfzijl* commissioned August 1983.

MCMVs *Haarlam* and *Harlingen* launched May 1983.

MCMV *Middelburg* commenced July 1983.

USA

SSN706, *Albuquerque,* commissioned May 1983.

SSN710 to be named *Augusta.*

SSN709 to be named *Hyman G. Rickover.*

SSN750 to be named *Newport News.*

SSBN728, *Florida,* commissioned June 1983.

SSBN732 to be named *Connecticut.*

SSBN733 to be named *Montana.*

FFG55 to be named *Elrod.*

FFG56 to be named *Simpson.*

FFG57 to be named *Reuben James.*